W9-CQR-132

Practical
Food Microbiology and Technology
Second Edition

other Avi books

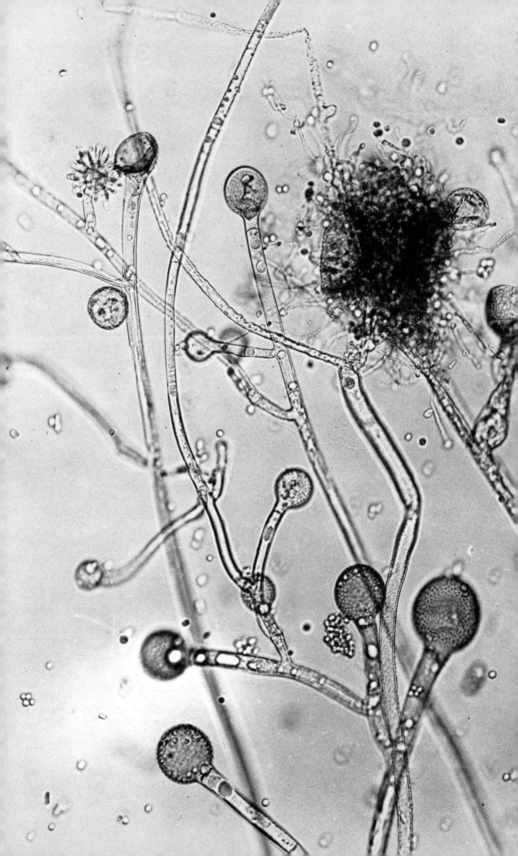

Practical
Food Microbiology
And Technology
Second Edition

by HARRY H. WEISER, Ph.D. *(Deceased)*

Former Professor of Microbiology
Ohio State University
Columbus, Ohio

GEORGE J. MOUNTNEY, Ph.D.

Former Professor, Departments of
Poultry Science and Home Economics,
Ohio Agricultural Research and
Development Center and Ohio State
University, Columbus, Ohio

Presently Research Management
Specialist (Food Science)
USDA, Cooperative State Research
Service, Washington, D. C.

WILBUR A. GOULD, Ph.D.

Professor, Food Processing and
Technology, Department of Horticulture,
Ohio State University, Columbus, Ohio
and Agricultural Research and Development
Center, Wooster, Ohio

WESTPORT, CONNECTICUT
THE AVI PUBLISHING COMPANY, INC.
1971

Printed in the United States of America
By Mack Printing Company, Easton, Pennsylvania

Preface to Second Edition

An attempt has been made in the Second Edition to bring the original manuscript up-to-date and to reorganize segments of the First Edition of the book. New tables and the latest laboratory methods for isolating and culturing microorganisms of importance to the food industry also have been added.

The authors wish to thank the following for reviewing portions of the revised book and for making many helpful suggestions: Dr. A. W. Anderson, Oregon State University; Dr. Nancy Bigley, Ohio State University; Dr. Gene Geisman, Ohio State University; Dr. Herbert O. Hultin, University of Massachusetts; Dr. Maynard A. Joslyn, University of California, Berkeley; Dr. Lloyd L. Kempe, University of Michigan; Dr. James J. Jezeski, University of Minnesota; Dr. John T. R. Nickerson, Massachusetts Institute of Technology; Dr. Herbert Ockerman, Ohio State University; Dr. Z. John Ordal, University of Illinois; Dr. Carl S. Pederson, New York State Agricultural Experiment Station; Dr. Andrew Peng, Ohio State University; and Dr. Fred Stephens, Ohio State University.

The assistance of Mrs. Carol Day, Miss Marie Francis, and Miss Becky Gould is also acknowledged with thanks.

July 1970   H. H. WEISER
                                               G. J. MOUNTNEY
                                               W. A. GOULD

Preface to the First Edition

The interrelationships between food microbiology and food technology are very intricate. Micro-organisms associated with foods may be classified as desirable and undesirable. In fact micro-organisms are excellent biochemists and many of their reactions are beneficial and even indispensable in certain foods.

It is assumed that students in food microbiology and food technology have had basic courses in microbiology and chemistry. Therefore, they should be familiar with morphology, biochemical behavior and control measures that may govern the activity of desirable and undesirable micro-organisms associated with foods.

The purpose of this book is to emphasize a few basic concepts that are related to some of the biochemical changes induced by micro-organisms from a practical viewpoint in processing certain foods.

Obviously the composition of foods will influence the kind and nature of biochemical changes caused by micro-organisms in food.

Food spoilage is discussed from a food technologist's viewpoint, with emphasis on appropriate control measures. Food additives, including antibiotics are stressed because they are legally used in some cases while in other instances they may be detrimental. The role of radiation in food technology is explained and discussed.

Food poisoning is emphasized because it is on the increase in spite of the sanitary measures taken at the present time.

A discussion on sources and treatment of water supplies is stressed. The food industry is a large consumer of water which must be potable in order to produce a good food product and eliminate public health hazards resulting from a contaminated water supply.

New advances in methods and research activities will no doubt be published before this book is printed. Nevertheless the basic general principles discussed here will still apply to the field of food microbiology and technology processes.

No attempt has been made to list microbial standards for raw and processed foods. This information is readily available from various sources. Moreover, microbial standards are constantly changing due to new technological developments in the food industry. Also there are many differences in viewpoints among food technologists, biochemists, food microbiologists and sanitarians as to specific standards for various food products.

The author is grateful for the advice and encouragement so generously given by his associates in the preparation of the subject matter, especially Doctors A. R. Winter, Poultry Science; Wilbur Gould, Horticulture Products; F. E. Deatherage, Agricultural Biochemistry; W. F. Gray, Botany and Plant Pathology; J. M. Birkeland and G. W. Malaney, Microbiology; and Robert Angelotti, Robert A. Taft, Environmental Center, Food Division, Cincinnati, Ohio. The aid of Dr. G. M. Dack, Director, Food Research Institute, University of Chicago, Chicago, Illinois, is also acknowledged.

The author is particularly indebted to Dr. George Mountney for his assistance in reading proof and making many helpful suggestions.

H. H. Weiser

March, 1962   *Columbus, Ohio*

Contents

CHAPTER 1

Introduction: Food and Man

GENERAL ASPECT OF FOOD

Man is the only species in the animal kingdom that seeks to adjust his environment to his own personal needs. It has been a constant struggle through the ages for man to keep up with the constant changes in the environment in which he lives. Technological development has raised him from a cave man existence to a high standard of living in which he has more leisure, works less and enjoys life according to his own dictates.

Food is one of the governing factors which forces man to adjust to his surroundings. His ability to obtain food is closely related to fertility of the soil, climate, and ultimate sources of food supply.

Insects, micro-organisms, and other animals compete with him for the available food supply. For example, many organisms are undesirable from the public health standpoint and for the role they play in bringing about the spoilage of many foods, thus rendering them inedible for human consumption. Thus far, man, through technological developments, has been able to increase or at least hold his own food supplies stable in competition with other organisms for food. The development of insecticides, fungicides, germicides, and other chemicals has enabled him to maintain a balance between himself and other living organisms.

Many kinds of living organisms are highly desirable for the part they play in creating, preserving, and processing certain kinds of food, for example, the honey bee not only produces honey but also pollinates the flowers of many fruit trees.

Man has been able to utilize many animals as a source of food for himself; therefore, a balance between man and food animals has been carefully controlled. Many other animals are not used for human food, and, naturally, a problem is presented in their control. Fortunately, through scientific developments, the animal called man has been successful in reducing the populations of these animals in the competition for survival.

Food is the ever dominant concern of the human race; it is one of the first things demanded after birth, and throughout life it is essential for health and happiness.

Lin Yutang in his book, "The Importance of Living," gives us food

1

for thought: "That revolutions, peace, war, patriotism, international understanding, our daily life and the whole human social structure are influenced by food." Perhaps this is why men refuse to work, soldiers refuse to fight, prima donnas refuse to sing and senators refuse to debate without food.

Historical Food Supply

Prehistoric man and other animals consumed their food in the raw state. Later in the evolution of man he began to cook his food. Wandering tribes and animals usually found food in abundance in the natural state; when it was less abundant they simply moved to new sources. When the natural supply of food was plentiful, there was very little trouble in the animal kingdom. However, when the potential supply was less abundant, then competition and warfare resulted. Our forefathers practiced this art and we see parallels to this struggle among wild animals that live in thick woodlands. In the course of man's development, he and animals learned to store foods for future use. For instance, squirrels store nuts in season for winter use. Man learned to preserve certain foods very early by drying, souring, and later by cooking food. Moreover, nature has endowed many kinds of birds with an instinct to migrate during certain seasons, primarily for mating and also in search of an abundant food supply. Snakes and bears undergo a process of annual hibernation. During this period, animal metabolic activity is low. No food is consumed but life is sustained by utilizing a reserve deposit of fat in the body.

Sources of Our Food Supply

It has been estimated that there are two billion acres of farm land in the world today devoted to the production of food for human consumption. This does not include the acreage used for growing sugar, potatoes, and cereals. However, one billion acres of tropical, subtropical and arid lands now untilled could be used if irrigation and fertilizers were available. There are over 300 million acres in the temperate zone in the same category.

The population of the world is increasing at the rate of about 40–50 million a year and more food must be obtained. Soil erosion and improper farming practices have done much to deplete the soil of its fertility. However, steps are being taken to reduce these practices to a minimum. High fertility levels of the soil can be maintained while at the same time increasing the crop yield. Nitrogen-fixing bacteria are playing an important role in keeping soil fertility up to a high level. The use of commercial fertilizer and good farm practices will go a long way in supplying an ever-increasing food supply.

Practically all of our food is derived from animal and vegetable sources from land and sea. Processes are being developed for making waste products usable for food, for example, the conversion of wood cellulose to digestible carbohydrates. For animals, German farm chemists have been pioneers in the field of animal feeds for many years. It has been stated that 60 per cent of forest products are wasted in the form of sawdust and branches after the logs suitable for lumber have been removed from the tree. It has been estimated that 600 lbs. of sugar can be obtained from one ton of wood.

Moreover, man is not able to make edible food out of air and water as the plant does in the processes of photosynthesis. Our food supply in the future may be substantially increased if the proteins of grass can be transformed into beefsteak more efficiently than by comparable processes used by the beef or dairy cow today.

A variety of algae called Chlorella has been investigated as a source of edible protein. Something like 45 tons of algae protein can be produced annually on one acre of soil. With such a yield of food, one can see great possibilities of an increased food supply grown on a few acres of land. One pound of algae protein is comparable to two large pork chops and to one-half pound of butter in nutritive value.

General Biological Characteristics for Food

Food is a perishable product and is subject to attack by micro-organisms. If it were not subject to biochemical changes, it would not be suitable for energy production in man. These changes may be desirable or undesirable from an economical, nutritional, and public health standpoint depending upon the kind of micro-organisms present which are in turn determined by environmental factors.

These biochemical activities are brought about in many complicated yet interrelated processes by enzymes. All living tissues possess enzyme systems which are endogenous and are just as much a part of the tissue as other constituents that make up the cell. These enzymes are, as a rule, not destroyed after the product reaches maturity but may continue to function long after or even during the storage of the food product. For example, everyone is familiar with what happens when an apple is peeled. The removal of the outer skin exposes the meat of the apple to atmospheric oxygen and, within a short time, the apple will turn brown indicating that a biochemical change has taken place. The change is brought about by enzymes.

Then too, micro-organisms also possess complex enzyme systems.

This is important because as organisms grow in various foods, enzymes are liberated in the food and they in turn can bring about profound changes in the product very much in the same way as the inherent enzymes. In other words, [enzymes, whether they are inherent or secreted by micro-organisms, produce significant changes in food.] Many examples will be discussed in succeeding pages to emphasize the importance of these biochemical changes in different foods.

Functions of Food for the Living Cell

Perhaps we are beginning to get some concept of food. It might be in order to ask this question: what is the purpose of food? The physiologist says we eat food because: (1) it gives energy to sustain life, (2) it promotes growth, (3) it repairs damaged and worn out tissues, (4) it makes reproduction possible, and (5) the consumption of food provides a unique psychological or esthetic effect. In other words, there is a great deal of pleasure and satisfaction in tasting and consuming well prepared food.

FOOD AND MICRO-ORGANISMS

The activity of inherent enzymes present in foods may be stimulated by man in his efforts to process or preserve food. In frozen and dehydrated foods, enzymes, unless inactivated, will ultimately bring about off-flavors, off-odors, and off-color. One basic principle in food processing and preservation is to inactivate or destroy the inherent enzymes present. This can be done by heating, which not only destroys the enzymes but eliminates undesirable micro-organisms./ These organisms, like any living cell, produce enzymes and they in turn can play an important role in the quality of the food product.

During processing and preserving food, changes take place in concentrations of the constituents, also a change in pH may occur. These variables may be conducive to enzyme activity. Moreover, the addition of certain ingredients to the food during the processing may be important. For example, salt may inhibit many micro-organisms, but at the same time permit halophilic bacteria to grow and produce undesirable changes in the food. Another illustration is a case in which butterscotch flavored starch puddings failed to set when cooled. It was found that one ingredient of the flavor was made from Mexican materials. This product showed a positive diastase action which partially liquefied the pudding starch during cooking.

Nature can be very uncooperative at times as evidenced by the way she has placed amino acids and aldehydes in contact with each other in food products. This condition may be desirable in some products

Maillard rxns

and undesirable in others. On the favorable side, a variety of breakfast foods owe their satisfying flavors to a chemical rearrangement of these constituents. Many times a new breakfast food can be developed by controlling the time, temperature, and moisture relationship. Then if sugar is added reactions occur which may destroy the moisture relationship.

Sugars in general parallel the reactivity of amino acids in foods. Carbohydrates having a free aldehyde or ketone group naturally react more rapidly than those which first have to be hydrolyzed or broken down to release these groups.

In processing certain foods, if the temperature is increased the number of molecules of water in proportion to the number of molecules of amino acids increases. This is because an amino acid has served as a catalyst which brings about a reaction causing dehydration of carbohydrates in the foodstuff.

Unfortunately objectionable changes sometimes occur due to this complex combination of factors. If these variables are not carefully controlled, certain obvious changes occur in the food product such as: (1) darkening of the product, (2) development of a bitter flavor, and (3) unpleasant odor.

To suppress undesirable flavors or induce desirable flavors in food products, the food technologist recognizes the basic constituents in the product and by altering their natural relationships he can determine to a large extent the quality of the food product.

Micro-organisms in Foods

Without a basic knowledge of microbiology man cannot comprehend the significance and importance of micro-organisms in the biological world. Micro-organisms are widely distributed in nature wherever favorable environmental factors are present for their growth. Usually food supply, temperature, and moisture are the main factors that determine the growth of micro-organisms. No food product after it reaches maturity, commonly referred to as "ripeness," is free of organisms. However, there is a marked difference in the microbial content of foods. Hickory nuts, pecans, and other shell products are protected by a semi-impermeable shell which offers the maximum protection to the nut meats against biological activity. But in the course of time these products will undergo slow biochemical changes which alter their natural flavor. In contrast, fresh raw milk is a highly perishable product and sours in a short time in a warm temperature.

Bacteria, molds, and yeasts constitute a large group of micro-organisms. Obviously their presence in food is widespread. Their competition with man and other animals can be quite significant in a food supply. Micro-organisms derive their energy and other metabolic activities from food exactly as man does. They may cause significant biochemical changes in food. Fortunately a few of these changes are desirable, such as the transformation of fluid raw milk into cheese, or the production of sauerkraut from raw cabbage. These examples are but a few used in the food industry. Industrial uses of the products from various types of fermentations are well known.

Recently micro-organisms have been used to assay for certain vitamins and amino acids in food products. The microbiologist does not understand all of the complex biochemical changes that may take place in food during the natural fermentation process. However, he does know that the chemical and physical composition of the food is markedly changed as compared to the raw product. Food microbiologists and biochemists have found many challenging research problems in the field of food processing and food microbiology. The production of biological acidity is a very complex problem since many intermediate products are formed, and they in turn may determine very largely the type of end products that may be formed during the fermentation process. The organic acids thus formed may serve as a food preservative. Actually these acids may inhibit or destroy many kinds of organisms, which may render the food product inedible. Hence, biological acidity is one of nature's ways of preserving food from further microbiological activity.

Sauerkraut is an excellent example of self-preservation by the production of acids by micro-organisms, and in addition the formation of various "esters" which contribute to its characteristic flavor.

Again bacteria, molds, and yeasts may be highly undesirable in foods by causing food spoilage. A more complete discussion will be given elsewhere. There is the ever present group of organisms that may be dangerous to public health. Certain food-borne diseases have been recognized in which man, other animals, and insects may contaminate the food and make it potentially dangerous for human consumption. Moreover, there are other organisms which, when present in certain foods, may grow and liberate an exotoxin which causes food poisoning in man.

Classification of Micro-organisms Found in or on Foods

Perhaps a broad classification of organisms in foods may be based on their ability to attack the various constituents in foods. All micro-organisms found in food may be classified into aerobes and anaerobes.

Nearly all foods contain carbohydrates which vary from simple monosaccharides to complex polysaccharides such as starch. Not all organisms can attack the various carbohydrates. Starch is very difficult to break down by organisms, although a few micro-organisms called "starch splitters" are capable of attacking it. Monosaccharides and disaccharides are readily attacked by a large group of organisms. Most fruits are rich in monosaccharides, hence a spontaneous fermentation takes place with the production of acids and gases. Milk contains lactose, a disaccharide, which undergoes lactic acid fermentation very quickly. The production of acids by acid forming organisms is very common in foods rich in carbohydrates. As a rule molds and yeasts are not active in the production of biological acidity in foods.

Foods rich in proteins also undergo biochemical changes. As a rule the protein molecule is more complex than the carbohydrate, hence is much more difficult to break down. Certain bacteria and molds which are capable of attacking the protein molecule are called "protein digesters." Protein digesting organisms, like any living cell, possess a complex enzyme system and through specific enzymes the protein is broken down to amino acids. This form of protein is simple enough for the living cell to utilize it as a source of energy. Several end products such as acids, gases, and protein degradation products are formed during the protein digestion process. Some of these products are desirable as in cheese ripening.

Many foods contain fats although the composition of the fat will vary markedly with different foods. Fats are composed of glycerol and fatty acids. Vegetable fats as a rule contain members of the higher fatty acid series such as stearic and others. Such fats do not undergo decomposition as readily as the animal fatty acid series. Butter, for example, becomes rancid very quickly due to the formation of large amounts of butyric acid, a member of the lower fatty acid series.

In general fats are not attacked by micro-organisms as readily as the carbohydrates and proteins in foods. In cheese ripening the breakdown of the milk fat is a part of the desirable changes involved in the ripening.

Man's Control of Micro-organisms

Man, through his understanding of food chemistry and food microbiology, is now able in a considerable measure to control the micro-organisms present in foods for the encouragement and improvement of desirable changes and for the suppression of undesirable and deteriorative effects caused by micro-organisms. Table 1 shows the organisms which cause spoilage in some important foods.

TABLE 1

SPOILAGE ORGANISMS OF IMPORTANT FOODS

Class of Food Products	Genera Dominating When Spoilage Occurs During Standard Conditions of Storage
Milk and milk products	*Streptococcus, Lactobacillus, Microbacterium,* Gram-negative rods,[1] *Bacillus*
Fresh meat	Gram-negative rods,[1] *Micrococcus, Cladosporium, Thamnidium*
Poultry	Gram-negative rods,[1] *Micrococcus*
Sausage, bacon ham, etc.	*Micrococcus, Lactobacillus, Streptococcus, Debaromyces, Penicillium*
Whale meat	*Streptococcus, Clostridium,* Gram-negative rods[1]
Fish, shrimp	Gram-negative rods,[1] *Micrococcus*
Shellfish	Gram-negative rods,[1] *Micrococcus*
Eggs	*Pseudomonas, Cladosporium, Penicillium, Sporotrichum*
Vegetables	Gram-negative rods,[1] *Lactobacillus Bacillus*
Fruits and Juices	*Acetobacter, Lactobacillus Saccharomyces, Torulopsis Botrytis, Penicillium, Rhizopus*
Cereal grains	*Aspergillus, Fusarium, Monilia, Penicillium, Rhizopus*
Bread	*Bacillus, Aspergillus, Endomyces, Neurospora, Rhizopus*

[1]This includes, particularly, strains of *Achromobacter, Pseudomonas* and *Flavobacterium,* with exclusion of the coli-aerogenes group.

CHAPTER 2

Composition of Foods

The microbiology of foods is a comprehensive subject and is concerned not only with spoilage but also with beneficial changes in food brought about by micro-organisms. Spoilage may be injurious to health when such food is eaten. Changes in physical appearance, flavor, and odor in spoiled foods compared with normal food are very difficult to evaluate. One group of people selects certain kinds of cheese because of their peculiar fine flavors and odors, while others would consider such products spoiled. Individuals have not learned to perceive the changes that affect the nutritive values in foods that may be important to health. Food may contain traces of arsenical sprays or salts of other heavy metals which are detrimental but which cannot be detected by taste.

Our discussion of food spoilage will be confined largely to changes in the food due to micro-organisms and to certain enzymes. Let us consider some of the factors associated with spoilage and also with some desirable biochemical changes. Obviously these changes will depend very largely on the composition of the foods.

Foods are made up of carbohydrates, proteins, fats, minerals, water, vitamins, hormones, nucleotides,[1] and other unnamed constituents often called "growth factors," as well as a complex endogenous enzyme system. There is evidence to indicate that the fertility of the soil affects the composition and nutritive value of the food. However, more study and confirmation is necessary before any definite conclusions can be drawn regarding soil fertility and human nutrition.

In considering the general composition of foods, a few examples will serve to show how the constituents may vary in different foods by altering the composition by processing and handling. In addition, the stage of maturity, climatic conditions, and other factors such as inherent acidity may vary widely in different foods. Moreover, a food product such as butter is mainly fat; meat, on the other hand, has a high protein content and fruits of various kinds have appreciable amounts of carbohydrates. Obviously, one would not expect the

---

[1] Nucleotides are components of the bacterial cell which absorb ultraviolet light and by means of this property help to distinguish between Gram-positive and Gram-negative organisms.

same biochemical changes to take place in butter as in meat because the composition differs very widely in these two products. Some foods are protected by a tough hard shell or outer coating. Nuts have been known to keep in a natural state for a long time but if one removes the shell, changes will be evident in a relatively short time unless some provision is made to protect the product.

Many foods are produced over a wide range of geographical and climatic conditions. Often large volumes of fresh foods are produced within a relatively short time and cannot be consumed as rapidly as the food becomes available. Hence, much of our food must be preserved for future use when the product is less available. Preservation involves a knowledge of food technology as well as the many biochemical changes that usually take place in the food during the processing and storage of the product. Certainly micro-organisms play an important role in determining the quality of the food from the nutritional and public health standpoint.

Foods may be classified according to their inherent acidity. Many fruits are acid in character while vegetables as a rule are low in acid. The acid content of a food determines the activity of many micro-organisms. Molds and yeast can tolerate fairly high degrees of acidity; that is one reason why these organisms are usually found on fruits about to undergo spoilage. Molds can tolerate severe acid conditions and in addition may actually utilize the acid as a source of energy for themselves. Bacteria on the other hand, cannot survive in a highly acid environment. Although they may produce many organic acids, their ability to tolerate the biological acid is markedly limited. There are exceptions in many food fermentations where the so-called acid tolerant bacteria may survive for a long time. A more detailed discussion will be presented elsewhere.

CARBOHYDRATES

By definition carbohydrates contain carbon, hydrogen, and oxygen. The name carbohydrate is based on the assumption that members of this group contain carbon united with hydrogen and oxygen in the same ratio as these elements are present in water, namely 2:1. Chemically simple carbohydrates are aldehydes or ketone derivatives of polyhydric alcohols. The structural formulas shown in Table 1A illustrate this relationship.

General classification of carbohydrates:

1. Monosaccharides   1.   Bioses   Aldose
     $C_6H_{12}O_6$ 2.   Trioses   Aldoses
                                          Ketoses

	3. Tetroses	Aldoses Ketoses

	4. Pentoses	Aldose
		  xylose
		  arabinose
		Ketoses
		  ribose
		  arabinose

	5. Hexoses	Aldoses
		  glucose
		  mannose
		  galactose
		Ketose
		  fructose

2. Disaccharides $C_{12}H_{22}O_{11}$

✓Reducing — Maltose (glucose + glucose)
Lactose (glucose + galactose)

✓Non-reducing — Sucrose (glucose + fructose)
Trisaccharides — Raffinose (glucose + galactose)
Tetrasaccharides — Stachyose, derived from 2 mols. Galactose + d-glucose + fructose

Dextrins — Amylodextrin—derived from d-glucose
Erythrodextrin—derived from d-glucose
Achrodextrin—derived from d-glucose

3. Polysaccharides $(C_6H_{10}O_5)_n$

Starch—derived from d-glucose
Glycogen—derived from d-glucose
Cellulose—derived from d-glucose
Hemicelluloses—derived from d-glucose
Inulin—derived from fructose

4. Compound Carbohydrates

Glucosides
Tannins
Pectic Compounds
Gums and Mucilages

Sugars as they naturally occur in foods are not concentrated enough to affect microbial activities. Sugars are sometimes added to food products to accelerate the growth of organisms, for instance the addition of sucrose or lactose to fermenting cabbage will help the desirable organisms to produce acetic and lactic acids more rapidly. Both of these acids are associated with good sauerkraut fermentation. Concentrations of from 1 to 10 per cent of certain sugars added to foods under selected conditions will accelerate the growth of microorganisms. It is generally thought necessary to have approximately 65 and 80 per cent sugar to inhibit the growth of bacteria and mold, re-

TABLE 1A

SIMPLE SUGARS

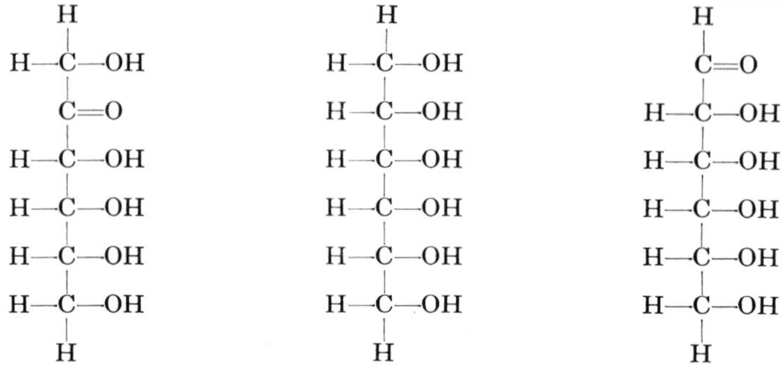

H	H	H
H—C—OH	H—C—OH	C=O
C=O	H—C—OH	H—C—OH
H—C—OH	H—C—OH	H—C—OH
H—C—OH	H—C—OH	H—C—OH
H—C—OH	H—C—OH	H—C—OH
H—C—OH	H—C—OH	H—C—OH
H	H	H
Carbohydrate, a Ketose	Hexahydric alcohol	Carbohydrate, an aldose

spectively.⌉ Some bacteria, including certain molds and yeasts, can tolerate a greater concentration of sugar than others. These are called saccharolytic organisms.

The application of concentrated sugar solutions in food preservation will be discussed in more detail later.

Foods rich in carbohydrates are easily attacked by certain kinds of micro-organisms because carbohydrate is easier to utilize than proteins and fats. ⌊Acids and gases are the main products of carbohydrate fermentation,⌋ although many intermediate products are also formed in appreciable amounts. Many organisms are selective in their action on specific sugars as shown by the following examples:

Organism	Dextrose	Lactose	Sucrose
Staphylococcus aureus	Acid	Acid	Acid
Aerobacter aerogenes	Acid and gas	Acid and gas	Acid and gas
Alcaligenes faecalis	No acid or gas	No acid or gas	No acid or gas

Certain bacteria can utilize starch as a source of energy and form substances resembling gums. Perhaps this is one way in which these organisms protect themselves against excessive acid production. This is the situation in the case of ropy bread. Some of the starch in the bread is hydrolyzed by Bacillus mesentericus into a gum. This material has the consistency of unbaked bread. The sugar is not converted into acid, thus it does not inhibit the growth of the causative organism. The proteins, as well as the starch, are attacked with resulting foul odors and unattractive appearance of the bread.

Lactic acid is one of the principal acids found in fermentation processes, such as the souring of milk or in sauerkraut. The amount of acid may become so high in the food that it inhibits the organisms responsible for its formation. It may interfere with the growth of even the acid-tolerant bacteria. The production of acid will depend upon the types of organisms present, the kind of food, and the sugar content. A pH range between 3.0 and 4.3 will usually stop the growth of bacteria. However, some organisms can tolerate relatively high concentrations of sugar. Such organisms are called saccharolytic.

The inherent acidity of many foods retards the growth of certain micro-organisms. For instance, the acidity of fruit juices acts as a preservative in some cases. Biological acids develop, for example, in milk until it becomes extremely sour and then the organisms responsible for the formation of the acid are inhibited as well as others that cannot tolerate any appreciable amounts of acid. However, some organisms are called acid tolerant because they can survive for long periods of time in an acid environment.

Starch, one of the complex carbohydrates, is also attacked by certain micro-organisms. However, the formation of acid is much slower than in sugars because the starch must be hydrolyzed by organisms that produce diastase. The amounts of sugar and acids formed will depend upon the production of diastase by micro-organisms. One reason why proteolytic bacteria may become predominant is because they are not hampered by the small amounts of acid formed.

Biological Importance of Carbohydrates

Carbohydrates play a major role in foods. They are formed directly in the process of photosynthesis in green plants. Approximately three-fourths of the weight of plant material is made up of carbohydrates, on a dry basis. Over one-half of the American diet is composed of carbohydrates. They are also found in animals in such forms as lactose in milk and glycogen or animal starch in the liver. In order to use the carbohydrates, the body cells must convert them into glucose, the sugar in the blood. In this form it can be assimulated by the body. Surplus glucose is converted into glycogen and stored in the liver.

Most of the organic compounds found in animals and plants are derived from carbohydrates. In fact, proteins are synthesized from amino acids which are the result of a reaction between portions of the carbohydrate molecules and ammonia.

Carbohydrates may be stored in animals and plants and under appropriate conditions can be changed to simpler compounds and oxidized to furnish energy. Glucose-glycogen and glucose or blood sugar are soluble forms that can be readily transformed into energy by the animal. In plants glucose-starch, fructose-inulin and monosaccharide-hemicellulose combinations are stored in the plant.

The biological significance of monosaccharides is interesting to food technologists because they are the basis for the formation of more complex carbohydrates in plants and animals. Starch and glycogen are formed from d-glucose and inulin from levulose. Monosaccharides are built up into the fat and protein found in living cells. Micro-organisms have this remarkable power also. (Galactose, d-glucose, mannose, and fructose can be converted into alcohol by yeast.) Citric and gluconic acids as well as glycerol and butyl alcohol are but a few of the biological products resulting from the action of micro-organisms.

Occurrence of Carbohydrates—

1. In plants:
   a. First product of photosynthesis: glucose.
   b. Reserve food: starch, inulin, and hemicelluloses.
   c. Supporting tissue: cellulose.
   d. Degradation products: gums and mucilages.
   e. Miscellaneous products: glucosides.
2. In animals:
   a. Blood sugar: d-glucose.
   b. Milk sugar: lactose.
   c. Reserve food: glycogen.
   d. In nucleic acids: d-ribose, d-oxyribose.

Moreover, sugars may be classified further as reducing and non-reducing. This will depend on the freedom of the aldehyde or ketone group such as in the case of glucose or maltose which represent reducing sugars because they can reduce Fehling's solution. If the aldehyde and ketone groups are involved in binding the monosaccharide units together such as sucrose then the sugar is said to be non-reducing and will not react with Fehling's solution.

All monosaccharides are reducing sugars because they contain free aldehyde or ketone groups and will react with Fehling's solution.

GENERAL PROPERTIES OF PROTEINS

Protein is composed of several amino acids. At the present time 22 or more of these compounds are known. At least ten amino acids must be secured from the food one eats if the human body is to function in a normal way. Fortunately nature has very generously distributed most of the essential amino acids in various foods.

Amino acids containing large numbers of nitrogen atoms are component parts of proteins. The ten most essential amino acids for animal nutrition are arginine, histidine, leucine, iso-leucine, lysine, methionine, phenylalanine, threonine, tryptophane, and valine. Those that are not absolutely essential to human nutrition can be synthesized in the body from other amino acids.

The word protein is derived from the Greek term meaning "holding first place." All living cells contain proteins. Even enzymes and nucleic acids are proteinlike in structure. In general they are considered as complex nitrogenous compounds. They have a high molecular weight and even in molecular dispersions they are classified as constituted colloidal systems rather than true solutions. When proteins are hydrolyzed they break down into amino acids. All proteins conform quite closely to the following average chemical analysis:

Proteins

```
Carbon.........................50 per cent
Oxygen.........................25   "
Nitrogen.......................16   "
Hydrogen....................... 7   "
```

Sometimes small amounts of sulfur and phosphorus are present.

Classification of Proteins

1. Simple proteins. They are never found in combination with non-protein substances.

   a. Albumins. Soluble in water, coagulable by heat. They are widely distributed in plants and animals, usually in small amounts. Example: egg albumin.

   b. Globulins. Insoluble in water, soluble in dilute salt solutions, coagulable by heat. Occur in many seeds. They can be synthesized in crystalline form. Example: Edestin from hemp seed.

   c. Glutelins. Insoluble in water and dilute salt solutions. Soluble in dilute acids and bases. Example: Glutenin of wheat.

   d. Prolamines. Insoluble in many common solvents, soluble in 80 per cent alcohol. Example: Gliadin of wheat and zein of corn.

   e. Albuminoids. Insoluble and extremely resistant to hydrolysis. Example: Collagen of bones and cartilage, keratin of hoofs, horns, and feathers.

2. Conjugated proteins. Simple proteins usually combined with non-protein material.

   a. Chromoproteins. Presence of a colored non-protein group. Example: Hemoglobin of blood.

   b. Glycoproteins. A carbohydrate forms the non-protein group. Example: Mucin of saliva.

    c. Phosphoproteins. Presence of phosphoric acid which forms the non-protein group. Example: Casein of milk.
    d. Nucleoproteins. Nucleic acids form the non-protein group. Example: Components of the chromosomes of cells.

    3. Derived protein. This includes the protein decomposition products of the naturally occurring proteins.

    a. Primary Derivatives.
       (1) Coagulated proteins. Insoluble products formed when heat or alcohol is used.
       (2) Metaproteins. Principal products formed when acids or bases are used on naturally occurring proteins.
    b. Secondary Derivatives. Products of protein digestion.
       (1) Proteoses. Soluble in water and not coagulated by heat.
       (2) Peptones. Perhaps an advanced stage in protein hydrolysis.
       (3) Peptides. Principally condensation products with very few amino acid residues.

Distribution of Protein in Foods

Cheese, eggs, meats, certain nuts, and dry legumes are foods rich in proteins. In these foods the protein content ranges from 10 to 35 per cent. Different kinds of cereals rank next in protein content at from 5 to 15 per cent protein. Fresh fruits and vegetables are low in protein and range from one to five per cent.

Biochemical Changes in Protein Decomposition

Protein decomposition is much more complex than the breakdown of carbohydrates and the end products are more varied. The protein molecule is quite complex as indicated in the formula of gelatin $C_{49}H_{42}O_{96}N_{105}$. Micro-organisms, through their complex enzyme systems, break down the protein into simpler substances to carry on their normal functions. The breakdown usually follows this pattern: Protein → proteoses → peptones → polypeptides → peptides → amino acids → NH_3 and elemental nitrogen. The intermediate and end products of amino acids are quite varied. In addition, alcohol, gases such as carbon dioxide, methane, hydrogen, and ammonia are liberated. The latter is formed in appreciable amounts in advance stages of protein decomposition.

Odoriferous compounds such as H_2S or mercaptans, indole, skatol, putrescine, and cadaverine are frequently liberated as some of the end products of protein decomposition.

Proteins in Milk

The proteins in milk will serve to illustrate what happens to animal or plant proteins under selected conditions when attacked by certain kinds of micro-organisms.

Casein is the principal protein in milk. It contains the following protein fractions, casein 3 per cent, lactalbumin 0.5 per cent, and lactoglobulin 0.05 per cent. The proteins in milk are very complex in chemical composition as illustrated by the empirical formula $C_{162}H_{254}N_{41}SPO_{52}$.

When the protein molecule is broken down into amino acids it can be utilized by the living cell. Possibly through a dipeptide linkage, amino acids are built up into the complex protein molecule.

The formation of a dipeptide, a tripeptide, or a polypeptide can also take place.

All amino acids have one or more NH_2 groups, and all of them also have carboxyl groups. The simplest amino acid is amino acetic acid, commonly known as glycine. The chemical structure is as follows:

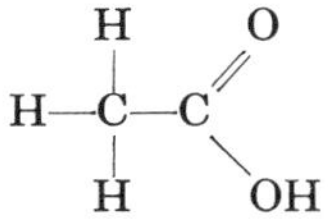

Acetic Acid

By removing one of the "H" atoms and replacing it with an NH_2 group the compound glycine is formed.

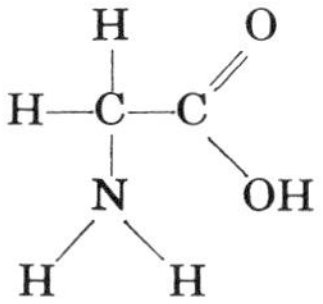

Glycine

Casein is an amphoteric protein having both acid and basic properties, but it usually possesses acidic properties. The protein molecules are broken down into the 18 or more amino acids which are found in milk. Tryptophane is a good example of one of these acids and this occurs in lactalbumin ranging from 2 to 8 per cent.

Tryptophane, one of the essential amino acids for humans, is also required by several different groups of bacteria. *E. coli* and certain other bacteria, have the ability to produce indole, a metabolic end product of tryptophane. Because of a specific enzyme, tryptophanase, tryptophane and water break down to form indol, pyruvic acid and ammonia, according to the following equation:

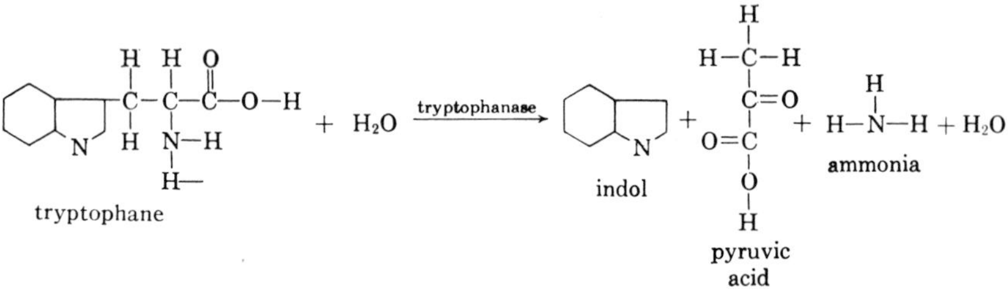

This reaction, called the indole test, is used to help identify certain species of bacteria, especially among the coliforms. The organisms are grown in a tryptophane broth for several days. Then a few drops of sulfuric acid and 1 cc of a 0.1 per cent solution of sodium nitrite are added to the incubated culture. If indole is present in the medium, a red compound, nitroso-indole is formed.

The amino acid, tryptophane, is also responsible for some of the disagreeable odors found in spoiled foods. Organisms containing the enzyme, tryptophanase, break down tryptophane into indole, pyruvic acid, and ammonia. Both indole and methyl indole have disagreeable odors associated with putrefaction.

The kind of organisms and amino acids utilized will determine very largely the end products of the metabolism. Some of these products are poisonous as shown in the following illustration:

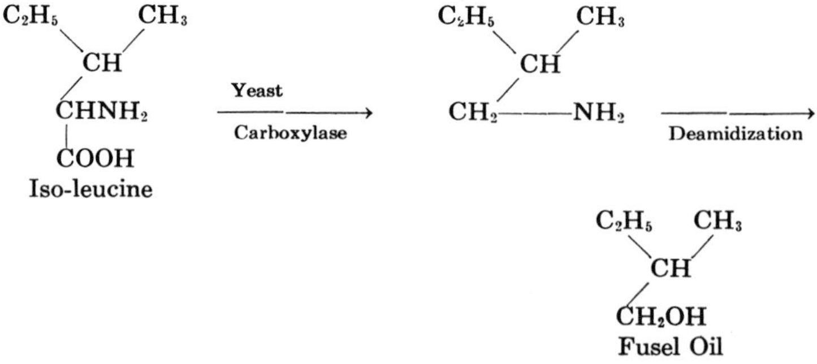

Iso-leucine is one of the many amino acids found in milk. When conditions are favorable and the right kind of yeasts and bacteria are present one of the end products of this protein breakdown is fusel oil which is poisonous.

Ptomaines

Ptomaines constitute another group of compounds resulting from the breakdown of certain proteins by protein-splitting micro-organisms. However, not all ptomaines are poisonous, for instance, those found in Limburger cheese. Ptomaines may be defined as decarboxylated amino acids and may be shown as follows:

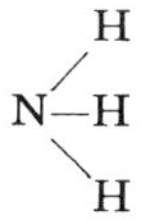

$$
\begin{array}{c}
H \\
N{-}H \\
H
\end{array}
$$

Ammonia

If each H molecule is replaced with a CH_3 on the N, one obtains:

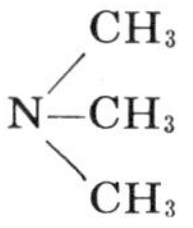

$$
\begin{array}{c}
CH_3 \\
N{-}CH_3 \\
CH_3
\end{array}
$$

Tri-methyl Amine

A ptomaine is the result of the decarboxylation of lysine:

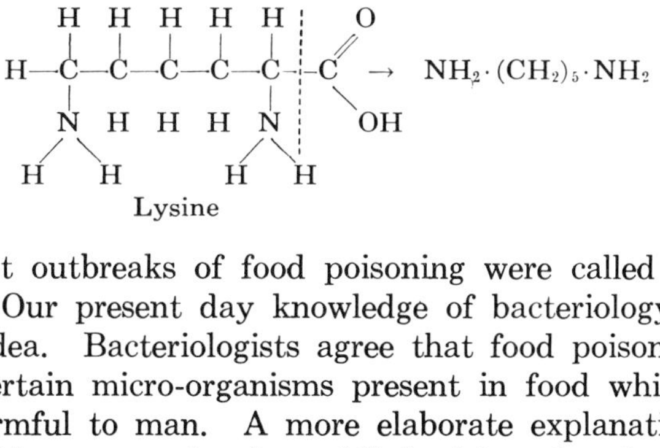

$$
\begin{array}{c}
H \quad H \quad H \quad H \quad H \quad\quad O \\
\mid \quad \mid \quad \mid \quad \mid \quad \mid \quad\quad \mathbin{/\!\!/} \\
H{-}C{-}C{-}C{-}C{-}C{-}C \quad \rightarrow \quad NH_2 \cdot (CH_2)_5 \cdot NH_2 \\
\mid \quad\quad\quad\quad\quad \mid \quad\quad OH \\
N \quad H \quad H \quad H \quad N \\
H \quad H \quad\quad H \quad H
\end{array}
$$

Lysine

In the past outbreaks of food poisoning were called "ptomaine poisoning." Our present day knowledge of bacteriology has eliminated this idea. Bacteriologists agree that food poisoning can be caused by certain micro-organisms present in food which produce exotoxins harmful to man. A more elaborate explanation of food poisoning will be presented under public health and sanitation.

Plants differ from animals in their ability to synthesize proteins. Animals depend on various foods for their protein source while plants mysteriously synthesize and store their protein requirements. The classical "nitrogen cycle" shown in Fig. 1 illustrates how plants build up protein with the aid of certain kinds of micro-organisms from the elemental or uncombined "N" present in the atmosphere.

The end result of nitrogen fixation is the accumulation of nitrogenous compounds in the bacterial cell which are ultimately made

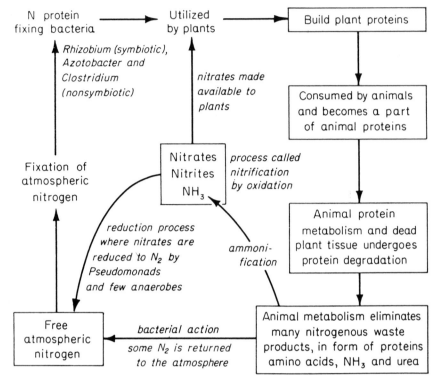

FIG. 1.   THE NITROGEN CYCLE

Protein → peptones → proteoses → polyptides → peptides → amino acids → NH₃ → N₂.

NH₃ is oxidized to nitrites by *Nitrosomas* bacteria.
Nitrites oxidized to nitrates by *Nitrobacter* organisms.
Denitrification is undesirable, since the nitrates are reduced to elemental N₂ and returned to the atmosphere before they are utilized by the plant.

available to the plant. The dry residue of bacterial cells contains about 10 per cent of nitrogen and approximately 65 to 75 per cent of nitrogenous compounds, such as globulins, albumens, and nucleoproteins. These constituents make up the protoplasm and enzyme systems of the cell. Although bacteria may contain the same amino acids as do plants and animals, they differ from them as to the nature of the nitrogenous materials which they can use as a source of nitrogen Obviously bacteria differ from each other in their nitrogen metabolism. It is common knowledge that certain groups of bacteria can use elemental nitrogen from the air, others simple salts, while a few use certain amino acids only.

When bacteria break down proteins very little energy is produced, but they use the nitrogen to build up the protoplasm in the cell, while the energy required to bring about this synthesis is derived largely from carbohydrates.

The dissolution of proteins is often called putrefaction and is largely due to the decomposition of amino acids. Intracellular enzymes act upon these protein compounds within the bacterial cell thus breaking the protein down to simpler substances which gives rise to foul smelling compounds.

One of the great mysteries of biological life is how bacteria can, under ordinary temperatures and pressures, cause nitrogen to combine with other elements. In the laboratory the chemist has difficulty in making nitrogen enter into combination with other elements to form such well known compounds as NH_3 and nitrates.

The decomposition of proteins by micro-organisms is very important in the processing of many kinds of foods. For instance the ripening of cheese by microbiological activity is known to everyone interested in the manufacture of cheese. The tenderization of meat is another form of protein breakdown under carefully controlled conditions.

Green plants or animals cannot utilize atmospheric nitrogen. However certain bacteria can utilize this form of N_2 and convert it into nitrates which plants can use. Plants convert the nitrate nitrogen into plant protein; thus animals, including man, can use this protein. Through the process of metabolism urea is excreted but it cannot be utilized readily by plants as a source of nitrogen. However, bacteria convert this urea into ammonia, nitrites, and nitrates which can be used by plants. Micro-organisms play an important role in breaking down dead organic matter thus liberating complex nutrients for plant growth.

The nitrogen cycle would not exist if it were not for bacteria. Destroy all the micro-organisms in the world and man would soon cease to exist.

Proteins are attacked by some organisms of the genus *Clostridium*, an anaerobic, sporulating organism which causes putrefaction and produces many offensive sulfur compounds, i.e., mercaptans and hydrogen sulfide; also indol, hydrogen, ammonia, phenols, and carbon dioxide.

The decomposition of protein by aerobic organisms is called decay. Proteins containing amino acids with sulfur as a component, such as cystine and methionine, can be broken down with no unpleasant odor, because the end products are completely oxidized and stabilized. In the case of anaerobes the end products are not completely stabilized; hence foul odors are present.

In food processing, the texture of the food may be altered, perhaps by a denaturation of the protein, which may alter the metabolic behavior of the endogenous organisms and enzyme systems. This may be desirable or undesirable and the food technologist should be aware of this phenomenon.

FATS AND THEIR IMPORTANCE IN FOODS

Fats are widespread in nature especially in animal and vegetable matter. Fats are composed of glycerol combined with fatty acids in the ratio of one molecule of glycerol with three molecules of fatty acids. There are many different fatty acids. The characteristics of various fats are determined by the fatty acids that combine with the glycerol. With the exception of a few fatty acids from unusual sources, the fatty acids are straight chain carbon compounds with an even number of carbon atoms and only one acid group (the —COOH group) in each molecule.

This is illustrated below, using stearic acid for this purpose.

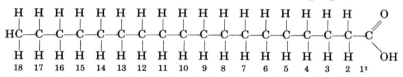

Fatty acids may be grouped according to the even number of H atoms into saturated and unsaturated.

Saturated:
Butyric acid	C_3H_7COOH
Caproic acid	$C_5H_{11}COOH$
Caprylic acid	$C_7H_{15}COOH$
Capric acid	$C_9H_{19}COOH$

Saturated:
Lauric acid	$C_{11}H_{23}COOH$
Myristic acid	$C_{13}H_{27}COOH$
Palmitic acid	$C_{15}H_{31}COOH$
Stearic acid	$C_{17}H_{35}COOH$

Fatty acids which contain the maximum number of H atoms are known as saturated fatty acids. Suet and tallow are examples of fats that contain a large percentage of saturated fatty acids. The unsaturated fatty acids, easily attacked by micro-organisms, do not contain all the hydrogen atoms possible. Various liquid oils are good examples. However, it is possible to add hydrogen to an unsaturated fatty acid and make it a solid saturated fat which can be used in shortenings.

Many of the lower fatty acids have an offensive odor upon hydrolysis. Consequently, milk fat, which has a high percentage of lower

---

[2] The numbers are here given to illustrate the numbering system used for carbon atoms so that their location may be identified in the systematic naming.

fatty acids, especially butyric, has a strong offensive odor on hydrolysis.

$$
\begin{array}{ccccc}
& \text{H} & & \text{H} & \\
& | & & | & \\
\text{C}_3\text{H}_7\text{COO—C—H} & \text{HOH} & \text{HO—C—H} & \text{C}_3\text{H}_7\text{COOH} \\
& | & & | & \\
\text{C}_3\text{H}_7\text{COO—C—H} + \text{HOH} & \rightarrow & \text{HO—C—H} + & \text{C}_3\text{H}_7\text{COOH} \\
& | & & | & \\
\text{C}_3\text{H}_7\text{COO—C—H} & \text{HOH} & \text{HO—C—H} & \text{C}_3\text{H}_7\text{COOH} \\
& | & & | & \\
& \text{H} & & \text{H} &
\end{array}
$$

Glyceryl Butyrate Water Glycerol Butyric Acid

Those fats, such as lard and certain vegetable fats, which contain fatty acids of higher molecular weights such as stearic and palmitic, yield very little offensive odor on hydrolysis.

$$
\begin{array}{ccccc}
& \text{H} & & \text{H} & \\
& | & & | & \\
\text{C}_{17}\text{H}_{35}\text{COO—C—H} & \text{HOH} & \text{HO—C—H} & \text{C}_{17}\text{H}_{35}\text{COOH} \\
& | & & | & \\
\text{C}_{17}\text{H}_{35}\text{COO—C—H} + \text{HOH} & \rightarrow & \text{HO—C—H} + & \text{C}_{17}\text{H}_{35}\text{COOH} \\
& | & & | & \\
\text{C}_{17}\text{H}_{35}\text{COO—C—H} & \text{HOH} & \text{HO—C—H} & \text{C}_{17}\text{H}_{35}\text{COOH} \\
& | & & | & \\
& \text{H} & & \text{H} &
\end{array}
$$

Stearin
Glyceryl Stearate Water Glycerol Stearic Acid

This union takes place by the reaction of the —OH groups of glycerol with the —COOH groups of fatty acids, water splitting out for each such union. Glycerol has three —OH groups. Fatty acids have only one —COOH group. Thus three fatty acid molecules join with one glycerol molecule to produce a pure fat.

A homologous series of fatty acids are given as they occur in different kinds of foods.

Formic acid	HCOOH	Heptylic acid	$C_6H_{13}COOH$
Acetic acid	CH_3COOH	Myristic acid	$C_{13}H_{27}COOH$
Propionic acid	C_2H_5COOH	Lauric acid	$C_{11}H_{23}COOH$
Butyric acid	C_3H_7COOH	Palmitic acid	$C_{16}H_{31}COOH$
Valeric acid	C_4H_9COOH	Stearic acid	$C_{17}H_{35}COOH$

Where a mixture of fatty acids is present in the fat, it is unusual for the fatty acids in any one molecule of fat to resemble each other. If the three radicals, represented by R, are different, then further differences are introduced according to their position. Thus:

$$
\begin{array}{ccc}
& \text{H} & \\
& | & \\
\text{R}_1\text{COO}\!-\!\text{C}\!-\!\text{H} & & \\
| & & \\
\text{R}_2\text{COO}\!-\!\text{C}\!-\!\text{H} & & \\
| & & \\
\text{R}_3\text{COO}\!-\!\text{C}\!-\!\text{H} & & \\
| & & \\
\text{H} & &
\end{array}
\qquad
\begin{array}{c}
\text{H} \\
| \\
\text{R}_2\text{COO}\!-\!\text{C}\!-\!\text{H} \\
| \\
\text{R}_1\text{COO}\!-\!\text{C}\!-\!\text{H} \\
| \\
\text{R}_3\text{COO}\!-\!\text{C}\!-\!\text{H} \\
| \\
\text{H}
\end{array}
\qquad
\begin{array}{c}
\text{H} \\
| \\
\text{R}_1\text{COO}\!-\!\text{C}\!-\!\text{H} \\
| \\
\text{R}_3\text{COO}\!-\!\text{C}\!-\!\text{H} \\
| \\
\text{R}_2\text{COO}\!-\!\text{C}\!-\!\text{H} \\
| \\
\text{H}
\end{array}
$$

The diagrams represent the three possible arrangements, and the three fats although consisting of exactly the same components, will differ in melting point and other properties. This has been proved by the synthesis of fats from mixtures of known fatty acids.

$$
\begin{array}{l}
\text{H} \\
| \\
\text{R}_1\text{COO}\!-\!\text{C}\!-\!\text{H} \\
| \\
\text{R}_2\text{COO}\!-\!\text{C}\!-\!\text{H} \\
| \\
\text{R}_1\text{COO}\!-\!\text{C}\!-\!\text{H} \\
| \\
\text{H}
\end{array}
$$

has a higher melting point, higher refractive index and lower solubility than . . .

$$
\begin{array}{l}
\text{H} \\
| \\
\text{R}_2\text{COO}\!-\!\text{C}\!-\!\text{H} \\
| \\
\text{R}_1\text{COO}\!-\!\text{C}\!-\!\text{H} \\
| \\
\text{R}_1\text{COO}\!-\!\text{C}\!-\!\text{H} \\
| \\
\text{H}
\end{array}
$$

A possible explanation for the relative abundance of the low molecular weight fatty acids in milk fat is that they originate from fermentations in the rumen of cows. This possibility has not been fully explored and deserves further study. In support of this idea there are a limited number of analyses of milk fats from various animal species, which show large amounts of low molecular weight fatty acids only in the case of ruminants. Non-ruminants, including humans, produce milk fats with much less butyric acid and other low molecular weight fatty acids.

Distribution of Fat in Foods

Fats or "ether extracts" separated from foods likewise show considerable variation. Vegetable oils and lard contain nearly 100 per cent fat in contrast to fresh fruits and vegetables which contain less than 1 per cent. Avocados having a fat content of 25 per cent, and ripe olives which have about 19 per cent fat are exceptions. Dry vegetables and soybeans have 18 per cent fat and nuts are rich in fats; varying from 33 per cent in coconuts to 70 per cent or more in pecans. Meats, of course, are variable in fats depending upon the condition of the animal and the way the meat is cut and trimmed.

The wide variety of fatty acids present in milk fat gives this fat one of its outstanding characteristics, i.e., a gradual transition from hard (fully solidified) to liquid (fully melted) over a wider temperature range than is true for other fats. The fatty acids of low molecular weight and unsaturated fatty acids contribute low melting point tendencies, while the high molecular weight saturated fatty acids tend toward high melting points.

In many fats one saturated fatty acid and one unsaturated fatty acid are present in large amounts with other fatty acids dropping off in quantity as you go in either direction, with respect to more or less carbons and lesser or greater unsaturation, from the predominant fatty acids.

Biochemical Changes Induced in Fat by Microbial Activity

The oxidation of fat by microbial activity involves a breakdown of the fatty acid portion of the fat by enzymes forming short chain acids, aldehydes, ketones, and peroxides. Lipase, a fat splitting enzyme, is normally present in many kinds of foods. For example, milk contains an appreciable amount of this enzyme. Many varieties of bacteria and molds are capable of producing lipase.

A food such as butter, which contains over 81 per cent fat, may serve as an excellent example of fat hydrolysis. If one can visualize a fat globule in butter, and there are innumerable fat globules, fused together to form what is commonly called butter as in Fig. 2, then a clearer conception of the hydrolytic changes may be gained.

FIG. 2. BUTTER FAT GLOBULE

Fat globule membrane magnified ×200. The numbers 1, 2, 3, etc. represent fatty acids singly or collectively that make up the variable percentage of fatty acids.

Butter may contain the following percentages of fatty acids: Oleic 33.5, palmitic 28, myristic 11, stearic 9, linoleic 4.5, lauric 4, butyric 3, caproic 2, capric 2, caprylic 1 per cent.

Lard contains numerous fatty acids of the higher series and is not so easily attacked. Certain vegetable fats are comparable to lard in composition.

Fats are more difficult for micro-organisms to attack than carbohydrates and proteins, although a few organisms produce an enzyme lipase that can hydrolyze the fat to free fatty acids and glycerol.

The latter can be attacked by organisms in the same manner as any carbohydrate.

Molds produce an appreciable amount of lipase and usually they attack foods high in fats. Cheese is a good example. Some varieties of cheese are ripened by molds.

Phospholipids and sterols are compounds associated with milk fat. The former are called phosphorized fats since some part of the fatty acid is replaced by phosphoric acid and a nitrogenous base. A typical phospholipid is lecithin found in milk fat, egg yolk, soybeans, and in nearly all vegetables. The nitrogen base in lecithin is choline, a substance which is part of the vitamin B complex. It plays an important role in fat metabolism. Lecithin from egg yolk or soybean is used in the manufacture of mayonnaise, chocolate, and oleomargarine. It aids in emulsifying the fat. Wax-like solid alcohols are called sterols. Cholesterol is the principal sterol in milk. Since cancerous tissue may contain more cholesterol than does healthy tissue it has been claimed that milk in the diet causes cancer. The statement has no scientific basis.

Although true fats are triglycerides of fatty acids as discussed above, it is to be emphasized that the term "fat," as used in the analysis of dairy products (and of foods and feeds in general), includes everything that is ether soluble. In this sense milk fat must be considered as including true fat, phospholipids (principally lecithin), sterols (principally cholesterol) and carotene, xanthophyll, and fat soluble vitamins, A, D, E, and K. There may also be traces of essential oils from weeds or feeds, e.g., allyl sulfide from garlic and allyl thiocyanates from onions. If the fat has undergone any fat hydrolysis under the influence of the lipase in milk (or under the influence of micro-organisms as in cheese ripening), the true fats will have been modified to some degree with the production of free fatty acids, diglycerides, mono-glycerides, and in extreme cases free glycerol.

Oxidase Producing Bacteria

Other undesirable changes in fatty foods such as butter, fish and chilled meats, are due to "oxidase producing bacteria." These organisms are capable of causing an oxidation of fatty foods under certain conditions.

The oxidized flavor in milk is due largely to the formation of aldehydes and ketones as the result of the oxidation of the unsaturated fatty acids such as oleic in milk.

Bacteria are capable of causing more than one type of reaction; in fact, one reaction may mask another. Many oxidase-producing bacteria not only hydrolyze the fat but may initiate the decomposition of the proteins.

Fishy flavor in butter is due to the formation of trimethylamine $N(CH_3)_3$, a compound having a fish odor. It is caused by the hydrolysis of lecithin which is present in fats and fatty materials. Many micro-organisms are capable of forming trimethylamine, although there may be other substances in fats that catalyze the hydrolysis of fats.

Organisms Associated With Oxidase Production

According to Castell and Garrand (1941A,B), *Pseudomonas* and *Achromobacter* genera are oxidase positive. Members of the *Alcaligenes* and *Brucella* are positive while the *Aerobacter*, *Escherichia*, and *Proteus* show a weak oxidase production. These authors observed that strong oxidase producers were Gram-negative, while the Gram-positive organisms were very weak in this respect.

Since *Pseudomonas* and *Achromobacter* genera produce an appreciable amount of oxidase and can grow at storage and refrigerator temperatures, many off-flavors in addition to rancidity may be produced in butter, lard, chilled beef, and other fatty products.

Castell and Garrard (1941A,B) studied the sources of oxidase producing organisms. They concluded that these organisms were widely distributed in many foods. Milk drawn aseptically from the cow's udder failed to show any oxidase formers. They tested 120 samples of milk from different cows. Molasses yielded many of these organisms. In corn silage both positive and negative oxidase producers were found in about equal numbers. Plates exposed to laboratory dust did not reveal many of these organisms, although the dust in dairy barns showed numerous organisms that were positive. Many were found in decayed plant tissue as well as in soil and surface waters. Various types of cheese examined failed to show many of these organisms. Greater numbers of oxidase-positive bacteria were found in butter than in any other food product, especially when the butter was off-flavor, cheesy, putrid, rancid, or fruity.

Lipids

Lipids are esters of fatty acids. These compounds are esters of fatty acids and they can be combined with additional groups.

Bloor has classified lipids very effectively as follows:

1. Simple lipids. Esters of fatty acids combined with various alcohols.
    a. ✓Fats. Esters of fatty acids with glycerol.
    b. ✓Waxes. Esters of fatty acids with alcohols other than glycerol.

2. Compound lipids. Esters of fatty acids containing groups in addition to alcohol and fatty acid.
   a. Phospholipids. Substituted fats containing phosphoric acid and nitrogen.
   b. Glycolipids. Fatty compounds containing carbohydrate and nitrogen residues.
3. Derived lipids. Compounds formed from the groups listed by hydrolysis.
   a. Fatty acids of various series.
   b. Sterols. Alcohols of higher molecular weights.

It is interesting to note that these compounds as a group are too complex for extensive microbial activity. However, the phospholipids as they exist in milk may be significant in contributing an unusual flavor to the product.

Unusual Lipids.—Waxes.—These compounds differ from fat in that they contain no glycerol. They serve as a protective covering on various fruits and leaves and some waxes have marked germicidal properties. Perhaps this is nature's way of protecting certain products from harmful microbial activity.

Sterols.—They are solid alcohols of high molecular weight. Sterols occur in both animals and plants. Cholesterol is present in the animal body especially in tissues, brain, and nervous tissue. It is also found lining the arteries of individuals suffering from arteriosclerosis or "hardening of the arteries" a common metabolic disease in the present generation. Ergosterol, another sterol found in certain plants, can be a very important accessory food substance when subjected to ultraviolet light thus forming vitamin D. The role of sterols in food cannot be truly evaluated, however, many nutrition investigators believe these substances play an important part in our diet.

Importance of Fats in the Diet

Fat is a good energy producing food. It is digested slowly and contributes to the texture and flavor of foods. Examples are milk and cheese. Fats may also carry fat soluble vitamins A, D, E, and K and are essential parts of body tissues. Fats may aid the body in utilizing calcium, reduce the need for vitamin B_1, aid in the metabolism of milk sugar and the utilization of carotene by the body. Fats are also necessary in the diet because of their vitamin content.

Fats can be classified as saturated and unsaturated. Saturated fats are generally solid at room temperature and unsaturated ones are liquid. Chemically, unsaturated fats contain double bonds between some carbons and fewer hydrogen atoms than saturated ones. Unsaturated fats are more reactive than saturated ones. Some unsaturated fatty acids such as linoleic acid cannot be synthesized in the body. For this reason they must be included in the diet and are called *essential fatty acids*. The absence of these essential fatty acids may cause such pathological conditions as kidney lesions. It has been demonstrated many times that the amounts of saturated and unsaturated fats and sterols, especially cholesterol, in the diet play a major role in the development of athero-sclerosis.

Physical Factors That Induce Chemical Changes in Fat

Heat can cause changes in the flavor of milk through the formation of certain compounds (sulfides) formed from the milk constituents, such as sulfur compounds associated with the fat and milk protein. Metallic oxides of copper and iron from the equipment may cause off-flavors. Copper and copper alloys may cause a perceptible oxidized flavor to develop in milk even in minute traces (1 p.p.m.).

The last group of food constituents, the enzymes, are important enough to be discussed in Chapter 3.

BIBLIOGRAPHY

Bloor, W. R. 1926. Biochemistry of fats. Chem. Revs. 2, 243–300.
Burrell, R. C. 1931. Chemistry for Students of Agriculture and Home Economics, 1st ed. McGraw-Hill Book Co., New York.
Castell, C. H., and Garrard, E. H. 1941A. The actions of micro-organisms on fat. III. Oxidation and hydrolysis of triolein by pure cultures of bacteria. Can. J. Res. C19, 106–110.
Castell, C. H., and Garrard, E. H. 1941B. The actions of micro-organisms on fat. IV. Observations on the changes produced in globules of triolein by pure cultures of bacteria. Can. J. Res. C19, 111–120.
Clifton, C. E. 1957. Introduction to Bacterial Physiology, 1st ed. McGraw-Hill Book Co., New York.
Dack, G. M. 1956. Food Poisoning, 3rd ed. The University of Chicago Press, Chicago.
Green, D. E., and Stumpf, P. K. 1944. Biological oxidations and reductions. Annual Review of Biochemistry 13, 1–24.
Gray, W. D. 1959. The Relation of Fungi to Human Affairs. Henry Holt Co., New York. York.
Jacobs, M. B. 1951. The Chemistry and Technology of Food and Food Products. Interscience Publishers, Inc., New York.
Lamanna, C., and Mallette, M. F. 1953. Basic Bacteriology. Williams and Wilkins Co., Baltimore.
Neurath, H., and Bailey, K. 1953. The Proteins. Academic Press, New York.
Oginsky, E. L., and Umbreit, W. W. 1959. An Introduction to Bacterial Physiology, 2nd ed. W. H. Freeman Co., San Francisco.
Pelczar, M. J., and Reid, R. D. 1967. Microbiology, 2nd ed. McGraw-Hill Book Co., New York.
Stephenson, M. 1930. Bacterial Metabolism. Longmans-Green and Co., New York.
Werkman, C. H., and Wilson, P. W. 1951. Bacterial Physiology. Academic Press, New York.
West, E. S., Todd, W. R., Mason, H. S., and Van Bruggen, J. T. 1967. Textbook of Biochemistry, 4th ed. The Macmillan Co., New York.

CHAPTER 3

Enzymes

An enzyme is an organic catalyst. The word comes from a Greek word "en" meaning in and "zyme" meaning yeast.

Enzymes play an important role in the food industry. For the baker, brewer, and confectioner, they liquefy and saccharify starches, convert sugars, and modify proteins. In fruit juice and wine making, they increase yield of juice, improve the juice, and clarify and speed filtration.

The properties of enzymes may be summarized as proteinaceous biocatalysts produced by living cells to perform a specific biochemical reaction necessary for cell metabolism.

A feature common to all enzymes is that they act as catalysts. This means, of course, that they speed up chemical reactions without actually taking part in them. In fact, they are called the "catalysts of life" because there can be no life without enzymes.

All living things, plant and animal, from the smallest to the largest depend on chemical reactions for life, and these reactions in turn depend on the enzymes. Therefore, as one eminent scientist said, "Life is just one enzyme reaction after another."

In addition, even though they do not live, enzymes are somewhat like micro-organisms in that they are affected by acids and bases and have maximum, minimum, and optimum temperatures at which they are active.

However, the most amazing feature about enzymes is their high degree of specificity. Each enzyme has a particular job to do and usually cannot do another. For example, there is one enzyme which influences one form of tartaric acid, but will have nothing to do with its chemical isomer which bears the same relation to it in appearance as a mirror image does to its original.

Classification of Enzymes

Intracellular or endoenzymes never leave the living cell and play an important role in transforming the food absorbed into the cell thus making it available for the metabolism of the cell. In this process large amounts of energy are liberated and made available to the cell.

Extracellular, or exoenzymes, are enzymes produced and excreted by the cell. They diffuse through the cell wall into the surrounding medium and act independently from the cell that secreted them by breaking down the organic substances in the medium, such as the proteins, starches, and fats. In this way the insoluble materials are reduced to a form in which they can be absorbed through the differentially permeable cell wall and utilized by the cell. The energy liberated by the enzyme outside the cell is not important to the cell. In fact, exoenzymes liberate very little energy in the form of heat.

Characteristics of Endo and Exoenzymes

Endoenzymes	Exoenzymes
1. Act within the cell.	1. Act outside the cell which secretes them.
2. Oxidizing-reducing.	
3. Liberate large amounts of energy.	2. Hydrolytic.
4. Energy formed within the cell is directly available.	3. Liberate small amounts of energy.
	4. Energy thus formed not directly useful to the cell.

Action of Enzymes on Food Constituents

a. Carbohydrases—act on carbohydrates.

b. Proteinases—act on proteins.

c. Lipases—act on fats.

Classification of Enzymes

The International Union of Biochemistry (Anon. 1965) recommended the following general key for numbering and classifying of enzymes.

1. Oxidoreductases
   1.1 Acting on the CH-OH group of donors
      1.1.1 With nicotinamide-adenine dinucleotide (NAD) or nicotinamide-adenine dinucleotide phosphate (NADP) as acceptor
      1.1.2 With a cytochrome as an acceptor
      1.1.3 With O_2 as acceptor
      1.1.99 With other acceptors
   1.2 Acting on the aldehyde or keto-group of donors
      1.2.1 With NAD or NADP as acceptor
      1.2.2 With a cytochrome as an acceptor
      1.2.3 With O_2 as acceptor
      1.2.4 With lipoate as acceptor
      1.2.99 With other acceptors
   1.3 Acting on the CH-CH group of donors
      1.3.1 With NAD or NADP as acceptor
      1.3.2 With a cytochrome as an acceptor
      1.3.3 With O_2 as acceptor
      1.3.99 With other acceptors
   1.4 Acting on the CH-NH_2 group of donors
      1.4.1 With NAD or NADP as acceptor
      1.4.3 With O_2 as acceptor

1.5   Acting on the C-NH group of donors
    1.5.1   With NAD or NADP as acceptor
    1.5.3   With O_2 as acceptor
1.6   Acting on reduced NAD or NADP as donor
    1.6.1   With NAD or NADP as acceptor
    1.6.2   With a cytochrome as an acceptor
    1.6.4   With a disulfide compound as acceptor
    1.6.5   With a quinone or related compound as acceptor
    1.6.6   With a nitrogenous group as acceptor
    1.6.99 With other acceptors
1.7   Acting on other nitrogenous compounds as donors
    1.7.3   With O_2 as acceptor
    1.7.99 With other acceptors
1.8   Acting on sulfur groups of donors
    1.8.1   With NAD or NADP as acceptor
    1.8.3   With O_2 as acceptor
    1.8.4   With a disulfide compound as acceptor
    1.8.5   With a quinone or related compound as acceptor
    1.8.6   With a nitrogenous group as acceptor
1.9   Acting on haem groups of donors
    1.9.3   With O_2 as acceptor
    1.9.6   With a nitrogenous group as acceptor
1.10   Acting on diphenols and related substances as donors
    1.10.3 With O_2 as acceptor
1.11   Acting on H_2O_2 as acceptor
1.12   Acting on hydrogen as donor
1.13   Acting on single donors with incorporation of oxygen (oxygenases)
1.14   Acting on paired donors with incorporation of oxygen into one donor (hydroxylases)
    1.14.1 Using reduced NAD or NADP as one donor
    1.14.2 Using ascorbate as one donor
    1.14.3 Using reduced pteridine as one donor
2.   Transferases
2.1   Transferring one-carbon groups
    2.1.1   Methyltransferases
    2.1.2   Hydroxymethyl-, formyl- and related transferases
    2.1.3   Carboxyl- and carbamoyltransferases
    2.1.4   Amidinotransferases
2.2   Transferring aldehydic or ketonic residues
2.3   Acyltransferases
    2.3.1   Acyltransferases
    2.3.2   Aminoacyltransferases
2.4   Glycosyltransferases
    2.4.1   Hexosyltransferases
    2.4.2   Pentosyltransferases
2.5   Transferring alkyl or related groups
2.6   Transferring nitrogenous groups
    2.6.1   Aminotransferases
    2.6.3   Oximinotransferases

2.7   Transferring phosphorus-containing groups
       2.7.1   Phosphotransferases with an alcohol group as acceptor
       2.7.2   Phosphotransferases with a carboxyl group as acceptor
       2.7.3   Phosphotransferases with a nitrogenous group as acceptor
       2.7.4   Phosphotransferases with a phospho-group as acceptor
       2.7.5   Phosphotransferases, apparently intramolecular
       2.7.6   Pyrophosphotransferases
       2.7.7   Nucleotidyltransferases
       2.7.8   Transferases for other substituted phospho-groups

2.8   Transferring sulfur-containing groups
       2.8.1   Sulfurtransferases
       2.8.2 Sulfotransferases
       2.8.3   CoA-transferases

3.   Hydrolases
3.1   Acting on ester bonds
       3.1.1   Carboxylic ester hydrolases
       3.1.2   Thiolester hydrolases
       3.1.3   Phosphoric monoester hydrolases
       3.1.4   Phosphoric diester hydrolases
       3.1.5   Triphosphoric monoester hydrolases
       3.1.6   Sulfuric ester hydrolases

3.2   Acting on glycosyl compounds
       3.2.1   Glycoside hydrolases
       3.2.2   Hydrolyzing N-glycosyl compounds
       3.2.3   Hydrolyzing S-glycosyl compounds

3.3   Acting on ether bonds
       3.3.1   Thioether hydrolases

3.4   Acting on peptide bonds (peptide hydrolases)
       3.4.1 α-Amino-acyl-peptide hydrolases
       3.4.2   Peptidyl-amino-acid hydrolases
       3.4.3   Dipeptide hydrolases
       3.4.4   Peptidyl-peptide hydrolases

3.5   Acting on C-N bonds other than peptide bonds
       3.5.1   In linear amides
       3.5.2   In cyclic amides
       3.5.3   In linear amidines
       3.5.4   In cyclic amidines
       3.5.5   In cyanides
       3.5.99 In other compounds

3.6   Acting on acid-anhydride bonds
       3.6.1   In phosphoryl-containing anhydrides

3.7   Acting on C-C bonds
       3.7.1   In ketonic substances

3.8   Acting on halide bonds
       3.8.1   In C-halide compounds
       3.8.2   In P-halide compounds

3.9   Acting on P-N bonds

4.   Lyases
4.1   Carbon-carbon lyases
       4.1.1   Carboxy-lyases

           4.1.2   Aldehyde-lyases
           4.1.3   Ketoacid-lyases
    4.2   Carbon-oxygen lyases
           4.2.1   Hydro-lyases
           4.2.99 Other carbon-oxygen lyases
    4.3   Carbon-nitrogen lyases
           4.3.1   Ammonia-lyases
           4.3.2   Amidine-lyases
    4.4   Carbon-sulfur lyases
    4.5   Carbon-halide lyases
    4.99   Other lyases
5.   Isomerases
    5.1   Racemases and epimerases
           5.1.1   Acting on amino acids and derivatives
           5.1.2   Acting on hydroxyacids and derivatives
           5.1.3   Acting on carbohydrates and derivatives
           5.1.99 Acting on other compounds
    5.2   Cis-trans isomerases
    5.3   Intramolecular oxidoreducatases
           5.3.1   Interconverting aldoses and ketoses
           5.3.2   Interconverting keto- and enol-groups
           5.3.3   Transposing $C=C$ bonds
    5.4   Intramolecular transferases
           5.4.1   Transferring acyl groups
           5.4.2   Transferring phosphoryl groups
           5.4.99 Transferring other groups
    5.5   Intramolecular lyases
    5.99   Other isomerases
6.   Ligases
    6.1   Forming C-O bonds
           6.1.1   Amino-acid-RNA ligases
    6.2   Forming C-S bonds
           6.2.1   Acid-thiol ligases
    6.3   Forming C-N bonds
           6.3.1   Acid-ammonia ligases (amide synthetases)
           6.3.2   Acid-amino-acid ligases (peptide synthetases)
           6.3.3   Cyclo-ligases
           6.3.4   Other C-N ligases
           6.3.5   C-N ligases with glutamine as N-donor
    6.4   Forming C-C bonds

Sources of Enzymes

Some general characteristics of enzymes are the following: (a) They are produced by living cells including micro-organisms. (b) Because they are part of the cells or intercellular tissue they continue to react with these tissues after harvest or slaughter. (c) Enzymes can be extracted and purified from certain biological materials such as plant sap and glandular tissues to provide industrial enzymes.

Enzymes are normally present in all living tissues, both animal and vegetable. Metabolism is usually carried on in a well-defined order by independent enzyme reactions linked in a complex enzyme system. The conversion of glucose in respiration aerobically to carbon dioxide and water takes place through a series of enzymatic reactions. In the first phase pyruvate is formed from glucose. Enzymes bring about this change in 12 separate steps. According to Krebs (1943), in each step an intermediate product is formed as a product of the preceding reaction in which one or more enzymes take part.

Ordinarily, these intermediate products do not accumulate within the cell. Although the reactions are confined to the cell, they are carefully regulated. No one knows the secret of how this regulation is accomplished. Enzymes such as catalase, peroxidase, and phenolase are present in the living cell and play an unknown role in normal cell metabolism. However, if the cell becomes damaged by some physical or mechanical means, then these or other enzymes may accelerate biochemical changes which may result in decomposition of the cell wall and its protoplasm. Enzymes apparently have a normal role to play in the cell and anything that interrupts this role speeds up their activity.

Enzymes are similar in some respects to certain normal intestinal bacteria. If death occurs, these bacteria leave the intestinal tract and invade other parts of the body. Similarly, enzymes can react on the tissues which produced them if these cells are killed or damaged.

Enzymes are inherent compounds intimately associated with food; in fact, they are part of it. They are necessary for carrying on the complicated life processes. After the living tissue or food material dies, many of the enzymes continue to function. It is in this stage that the food substances may undergo disintegration commonly associated with food spoilage, a process known as autolysis.

Fruit that is removed from the vine or tree before it is mature continues to carry on internal biochemical changes. Inherent enzymes take an active part in this process. Green bananas and tomatoes will continue to ripen after being plucked from the plant. This is a good illustration of enzymatic activity. Fruit is still alive when stored and will continue to respire by taking in oxygen and giving off carbon dioxide. This process will go on until the fruit is fully ripe. This is why precooling of the fruit is important in order to slow down respiration before shipping or storage of the product. Removing the skin of an apple or potato accelerates enzyme activity.

A pea in a pod removed from the vine may continue to follow all the changes associated with normal ripening. However, if the pea is removed from the pod these biochemical changes are greatly accelerated. An alteration in flavor and tenderness of meat is obvious long after an animal is dead. These practical everyday processes are due primarily to a group of enzymes which catalyze or hasten these chemical reactions. The tenderization of meat is largely a controlled enzyme process and resembles protein digestion. However, if allowed to continue, a true spoilage is the result. Carbon dioxide and other gases are sometimes used to slow down this respiration process while the food product is in transit.

Micro-organisms like all living cells owe their activity to enzymes. Certain molds liberate lipase, an enzyme, which plays an important role in the ripening of Roquefort cheese. While many bacteria possess enzyme systems that produce profound changes, some are desirable and others undesirable in foods.

Enzyme Activity

Peroxidase activity plays a more important role than catalase in the production of off-flavors, but the correlation values of the two enzymes vary over a wide range. According to Joslyn and Marsh (1933), peroxidase activity varies in different vegetable tissue and with the indicator used. Obviously it is essential to select the proper indicator for each vegetable tested. The work of Joslyn et al. confirmed this principle when they used benzidine as the indicator in studying peroxidase activity in spinach, peas, and lima beans. They concluded that this enzyme may not be entirely responsible for deterioration in unblanched vegetables.

Four peroxidases have been isolated in pure crystalline form but not their chemical structures. According to Green and Stumpf (1944), they are horseradish peroxidase, verdo-peroxidase, milk peroxidase, and cyto-chrome-C-peroxidase. Cytochrome catalyzes the oxidation of ferro-cytochrome-C only. The other peroxidases are responsible for a variety of compounds such as aromatic amines, phenols, diamines, ascorbic acid, iodides, and ferro-cytochrome-C.

Environmental Factors Affecting Enzyme Activity.—Enzymes have many characteristics of living cells and they respond to environmental conditions. An attempt to preserve food is nothing more than creating an unfavorable environment for enzyme activity. Low temperature delays or retards enzymatic activity. Meat kept in a frozen condition may keep for years without any appreciable deterioration. According to reports, dogs have eaten the flesh of prehistoric animals that were frozen in the great artic regions without any ill effect. Eggs deteriorate very rapidly after being laid, if temperature conditions are favorable. Proper cooling of freshly-laid eggs is essential to maintain a high quality product.

Industrial Enzyme Applications. Not only do enzymes make the fermentation process possible, but they are used for other things too.

Clear beer is an enzyme product. Ordinary beer will become cloudy when the beer cools. When treated with a protein-splitting enzyme the beer remains clear, even though cool.

Enzymes are also used to clarify wine and fruit juices. In the closely related jelly industry other enzymes are used to improve gel strength by reducing the sugar content.

One of the most interesting uses of enzymes in foods is in the manufacture of chocolate-covered, liquid center candies. If cherries are used, they are first covered with a semi-solid sugar solution to which the enzyme sucrase has been added. After the chocolate covering is added the enzyme hydrolyzes the sugar to the more soluble glucose and fructose and produces the liquid center.

Enzymes are also used widely in the textile industry. Wool processors use certain enzymes to produce a non-felting product which has less shrinkage. In the cotton industry other enzymes aid in making the material for the housewife's calico dress. Many patents are held for processes using enzymes to degum silk. The use of enzymes in the textile industry is not restricted to the processing of natural fibers because they can also be used to dissolve the size on filament viscose and acetate rayon as well as other synthetic fabrics.

In the leather industry enzymes are used commerically in the softening of hides. They produce a soft, silky grain with a luxurious feeling which cannot be obtained by any other means.

In the paper industry the use of enzymes to convert starch for sizing and coating paper appears to be the most economical way. The Industrial Products Division of Pillsbury Mills has developed tailor-made enzymes in capsule form for the paper industry.

Still other enzymes have been used in the commercial preparation of organic chemicals such as citric acid, acetone, glycerin, and lactic acid.

Pectolytic enzymes are used to digest pectins contained in the mucilaginous layer of the seed of the coffee fruit in the commercial curing of coffee. This may reduce the "natural" fermentation time in the preparation of washed coffee, which normally requires 18–36 hours, to 6 hours or less.

Although the commercial enzyme industry is expanding into a large scale operation, enzymes were used industrially long before anything was known about their chemical composition. For example the manufacture of cheese and the fermentation of beer and other alcoholic beverages have always depended on enzyme action for their production.

The advantages of using purified, standardized industrial enzymes instead of those in the tissues are that industrial enzymes have known standards of purity and concentrations. Because of this the enzyme processes can be better controlled, a more uniform product is produced, and the entire process can be reproduced with reasonable accuracy in batch after batch.

How an Enzyme Works

The action of a single enzyme reaction may be illustrated by observing the enzyme carboxylase that catalyzes the reaction in which acetaldehyde is formed from pyruvic acid.

$$CH_3COCOOH \rightarrow CH_3CHO + CO_2$$

Many yeasts and a few bacteria when grown on glucose produce ethyl alcohol (C_2H_5OH). Conversely, after the bacteria have shown growth and pyruvic acid is added to the medium, large amounts of acetaldehyde will be formed. Again, when the bacteria are dried at low temperature under conditions which kill the cells, if cells are ground into a fine powder, the powder will produce acetaldehyde from pyruvic acid. Although the cells are dead, the enzyme involved in converting pyruvate to acetaldehyde has been retained. Yeast cells behave very much in the same way as the bacteria in converting pyruvate to acetaldehyde. The enzyme carboxylase may be obtained by grinding, filtration, and precipitation as acetone powder. Yeasts are ground to destroy the cell wall and membrane, filtered and then precipitated as acetone powder. The powdered yeasts are suspended in 1 per cent KCl, and centrifuged. The liquid contains the enzyme and will catalyze the above reaction.

If carboxylase or similar enzymes are dialyzed, they apparently lose all biological activity, but with the addition of concentrated dialysate, activity becomes normal. In the dialysate, thiamine pyrophosphate has been identified. Although the dialyzed protein or the thiamine pyrophosphate of magnesium acting separately seems to have no action on pyruvate, when all three are added to the substrate, the reaction proceeds. A coenzyme is a non-protein organic compound, such as thiamine pyrophosphate, which is necessary for this enzyme to function.

Oginsky and Umbreit (1959) state that there are two factors usually associated with carboxylase coenzyme activity. They are the role of the magnesium ion and the role of thiamine pyrophosphate. These investigators state that there are four requirements for this enzymic reaction.

(1) Coenzyme requirement. Presumably the surface of the protein has the necessary configuration for a reaction.

(2) It is assumed that the protein surface will not support a reaction. However, a metal ion is adsorbed at various places on the protein thus giving the surface the proper configuration for adsorption of the substrate or other transformations necessary for surface reaction.

(3) The organic coenzyme and not the ion is adsorbed on the protein surface, thus effecting the proper configuration.

(4)   Both the ion and an organic coenzyme are interrelated in such a way that the ion favors the attachment of the coenzyme to the surface, thereby making the adsorption of the coenzyme complete. On the other hand, the ion and coenzyme may be adsorbed in different spots on the enzyme surface.

Food Spoilage.—All foods are the result of living cells and these cells produce inherent enzymes. Micro-organisms also are present, and they too liberate enzymes. Deterioration of food does not take place in normal healthy tissue, but when injury occurs or the tissue reaches maturity the enzymes assume a new role. They may start a series of biochemical changes many of which are undesirable and bring about spoilage.

Let us consider enzymes in connection with the storage of food. Meat is stored in a non-living state. Respiratory enzymes cease to function but others carry on and induce undesirable changes in the meat. Micro-organisms play an important role in spoilage so low temperature and the use of carbon dioxide are employed to create an unfavorable environment for the organisms and the enzymes. Under practical storage temperatures autolysis goes on at a very slow rate. Studies made by the chemists in the U.S. Dept. of Agriculture established that protein is broken down into simpler substances such as peptones, peptides, amino acids and ammonia. Phosphate, normally present in the tissue, is separated from organic compounds.

Fats undergo hydrolysis with the liberation of fatty acids. If these acids are members of the lower fatty acid series, offensive odors are usually evident.

The blanching of vegetables before storage is necessary in order to inactivate the enzymes. The chemical changes that take place in frozen vegetables are not very well understood.

The Action of Enzymes on Complex Foods

The manner in which enzymes act on food materials has been studied extensively by many biologists. Obviously many theories have been suggested of which two seem to be most widely accepted. One theory suggests that the enzyme is divided into two components; a colloidal carrier and a specific reactive part held on this carrier. Another idea is that all enzymes are pure proteins and the arrangement of the atoms of the molecule determines the specificity of the enzyme. The latter viewpoint has accumulated considerable support in that the biochemists have been able to isolate many enzymes in a pure crystalline form. However, not all enzymes have been obtained in a highly purified state.

Enzymes in Relation to Spoilage in Canned Foods.—Enzymes play a minor role in spoilage of canned foods because they are usually destroyed by the heating process. However, if enzymes in foods are not completely inactivated they may contribute to undesirable flavors, alter the color and texture and thus lower the quality, transform starch to sugar which may tend to increase the toughness and consistency of the food, and lastly destroy ascorbic acid (vitamin C).

Table 2 gives a view of the variety of enzymes which have been studied.

TABLE 2

A FEW MICROBIAL EXTRACELLULAR HYDROLYTIC ENZYMES

Enzyme	Substrate	Catabolic Products
1. Esterases		
A. Lipases	Glycerides (fats)	Glycerol + fatty acids
B. Phosphatases		
a. Lecithinase	Lecithin	Choline + H_3PO_4 + fat
2. Carbohydrases		
A. Fructosidases	Sucrose	Fructose + glucose
B. Alpha glucosidases (maltase)	Maltose	Glucose
C. Beta glucosidases (cellobiase)	Cellobiose	Glucose
D. Beta galactosidases (lactase)	Lactose	Galactose + glucose
E. Amylase	Starch	Maltose
F. Cellulase	Cellulose	Cellobiose
G. Cytase	. . . . .	Simple sugars
3. Nitrogen carrying compounds		
A. Proteinases	Proteins	Polypeptides
B. Polypeptidases	Proteins	Amino acids
C. Desamidases		
a. Urease	Urea	CO_2 + NH_3
b. Asparaginase	Asparagine	Aspartic acid + NH_3
D. Desaminases	Amino acids	NH_3 + organic acids

Energy Relationships

The energy evolved in an active fermentation is the result of energy liberated in the individual enzymatic reaction. In large masses of fermenting liquid, billions of cells are active and large amounts of heat may be generated. If this heat is not removed the active cells are affected. For instance, in vinegar making the heat generated during the

TABLE 3

ENERGY LIBERATED FROM ONE GRAM OF SUBSTRATE BY ENZYMES

Exoenzymes	Calories	Endoenzymes	Calories
Pepsin	0	Lactic	82.
Trypsin	0	Dehydrogenase	149.5
Rennet	0	Urease	239.
Lipase	4	Oxidase (Vinegar)	2530.
Invertase	9.3		
Maltase	10		
Lactase	23		

fermentation, if uncontrolled, may be sufficient to inhibit biological activity. Table 3 shows some typical energy values.

All fermentative processes are exothermic. Stephenson (1950) has calculated that one gram (net weight) of *Micrococcus urea* decomposes 180 to 1200 gm. of urea per hour. Also 1 gm. (net weight) of a lactose fermenting organism can break down 178 to 14,890 gm. of lactose per hour. These observations indicate the ease and rapidity in which microorganisms may attack food for energy and their ability to maintain themselves under a variety of environmental conditions.

Some Specific Characteristics of Enzymes—Chemical Units

Most are soluble in water, with the possible exception of plant tyrase. Certain of these diffuse out of the cell. There are others which are held in the cell and in order to get these enzymes free it is necessary to destroy the cells. Extraction by water, dilute glycerin, or dilute acid or alkali is facilitated if cells have previously been dried, frozen, and allowed to thaw, plasmolyzed or allowed to autolyze, so as to disintegrate cell structures and render membranes more permeable.

The first enzymatic fractions extracted from the living cells always consists of a mixture of several enzymes and a host of accompanying inactive substances.

Since the amount of enzyme present in a given product cannot yet be measured by ordinary quantitative methods of analysis, activity is taken as the measure of concentration. By this means the amount of substrate undergoing a change in unit time is measured under defined conditions, such as temperature, pH, initial concentration of substrate when acted on by a unit mass of the product possessing enzymatic activity. When crude enzyme preparations are purified their enzyme activity increases, but their mass decreases.

Individual Enzymes

Hydrolytic Enzymes.—In this group are included those enzymes which catalyze hydrolysis (esterases, carbohydrases, proteolytic enzymes, and amidases).

Other hydrolytic enzymes are cellulase, hemicellulase, and pentosanase. They may be useful in recovering cellulosic wastes and tenderizing cellulosic food products. Pentosanase increases the yield of high quality starch from wheat by hydrolyzing insoluble pentosans.

Non-Hydrolytic Enzymes.—Glucose oxidase and catalase are two enzymes that have industrial food applications. Glucose oxidase acts in the presence of oxygen to convert glucose to gluconic acid and hydrogen peroxide, and catalase converts hydrogen peroxide to water and oxygen.

The shelf life of dried eggs is greatly extended by removing glucose.

$$C_6H_{12}O_6 + O_2 + HOH \xrightarrow{\text{Glucose Oxidase}} C_6H_{12}O_7 + H_2O_2$$
glucose   gluconic acid

$$2H_2O_2 \xrightarrow{\text{Catalase}} 2H_2O + O_2$$

It prevents "browning" and preserves the color and flavor of the product. Glucose oxidase and the catalase complex is used as an antioxidant. Oxidase enzyme may be coated on the inside of cheese wrappers for this purpose.

Invertase is present in yeast and in the shoot and root system of higher plants. It hydrolyzes cane sugar to reducing sugars. Cane sugar is dextro-rotatory. The hydrolysis product contains equal amounts of glucose and fructose and is levo-rotatory since fructose is more levo-rotatory than glucose is dextro-rotatory. Because of the change of rotation, this mixture was termed invert-sugar. The hydrolysis was described as an inversion and the enzyme received the name invertase. Invertase can also act on trisaccharides containing the same linkage between glucose and fructose as occurs in cane sugar. For example, raffinose is hydrolyzed to fructose and melibiose.

Esterase.—The hydrolysis of substances containing an ester linkage with the formation of free acids and alcohols is catalyzed by these enzymes.

Lipase is found in resting and germinating seeds containing oils as reserve food. It is found in milk, bacteria, etc. It hydrolyzes fats to free fatty acids and glycerol. In resting seeds the properties of lipase are different from those in germinating seeds. Some maintain that the enzyme is in the pro-enzyme stage, or zymogen, and is activated by H ions. Some are active in the neutral or even weakly alkaline stage, while others are active only in acid stages.

Phosphatase is probably present in all living cells. Yeast serves as a useful source of the enzyme. It attacks the hexosephosphate yielding hexose and phosphoric acid. It may also act on other organic phosphates, nucleotides, and phytin.

Chlorophyllase is present in green leaves. In the presence of ethyl alcohol, ethyl cholorphyloid, which is crystallizable, is produced.

Some Specific Characteristics of Enzymes

Carbohydrases.—In this group it is convenient to separate the polysaccharases which hydrolyze polysaccharides, from glycosidases, which cause hydrolytic cleavage of glycosidic linkages in di- and trisaccharides. Conversion of starches to sugars by use of carbohydrases is an important commercial application of enzymes. Probably amylases have the greatest commercial use.

$$\text{Starch} \xrightarrow[\text{Liquefying Amylase}]{\alpha\text{-amylase}} \text{Dextrins} + \text{Maltose}$$

$$\text{Starch} \xrightarrow[\text{Saccharifying Amylase}]{\beta\text{-amylase}} \text{Maltose} + \text{limit dextrins}$$

$$\text{Dextrins} \xrightarrow{\text{Dextrinase}} \text{Maltose}$$

$$\text{Starch or Dextrins} \xrightarrow{\text{Amyloglucosidase}} \text{Glucose}$$

Polysaccharases.—Amylases or diastases are most likely present in all living cells that contain starch. It is known that the activity of this enzyme may be depressed by tannins. Amylases are probably compounded of several enzymes. In the presence of a thermostable substance of unknown composition, which is known as a complement, amylases show extended activity. They readily hydrolyze dextrin. Possibly the fact that dextrins are never found in the free state in the cell may be accounted for by the association of amylases with a complement in living cells. Autolyzing yeast serves as a source of complement.

Amylases are used extensively in the baking industry, because α-amylase stimulates sugar production through greater starch conversion, which in turn increases gas formation and improves crust color. Softening of bread dough is largely due to protease action.

The low inactivation temperature of fungal α-amylase, 159°F (71°C), allows the baker to use high levels of this enzyme rather than cereal amylase, without causing excessive dextrinization of starch during baking. The higher inactivation temperature 177°–194°F (81°–90°C) requires that it be used at low levels of activity.

Bacterial amylase is not permitted by Federal Standards, whereas fungal amylase obtained from *Aspergillus oryzae* is allowed.

In the brewing industry amylases help to liquefy the starch to produce a free flowing slurry.

In syrup production amylases produce a made-to-order hydrolysis because they have a specificity for certain linkages. By using different types of amylases it is possible to obtain numerous hydrolyzed starch products and therefore syrups with any desired properties.

Bacterial, cereal, and fungal amylases are used in preparation of food dextrin and sugar mixtures, as well as in the processing of cereals for dry breakfast foods.

Chocolate syrups and licorice are kept free flowing by the use of starch liquefying amylases. In certain fruit extracts and juices, amylases are used to remove the starch.

Cellulase occurs in many fungi and bacteria, and may be present in the germinating seeds of certain flowering plants. It hydrolyzes cellulose to form glucose, cellobiose being an intermediate product. Hemicellulases or cytases are found in some seeds. It is probable that this group is resolved into several enzymes. Cytases can cleave galactans to form galactose and mannans to form mannose. Inulase has been detected in the sprouting buds of stored artichokes containing inulin as a reserve food. It affects the hydrolysis of inulin to fructose.

Pectinases are used in fruit and wine processing as pectolytic enzymes. Pectinesterase hydrolyzes methyl groups of the soluble pectin molecule. Polygalacturonase hydrolyzes polygalacturonate chains to monogalacturonic acid. The reactions are:

Pectin $\xrightarrow{\text{Pectinesterase}}$ Methanol + polygalacturonic acid

Polygalacturonic acid → Mono and oligogalacturonic acid

Pectins are colloidal in nature thus making viscous solutions which hold the materials in suspension. Pectinesterase removes the methyl groups from the pectin and thereby exposes the reactive carboxyl groups. In the presence of multivalent cations such as calcium, insoluble salts are formed which can be removed.

Proteolytic Enzymes.—A second way of classifying enzymes is on the basis of the substrate attacked. All enzymes which take part in the hydrolysis of proteins to peptones, polypeptides, and amino acids belong to this group and possess in common the power of effecting the hydrolytic cleavage of the polypeptide linkage with the formation of free amino and carboxylic groups. The classification given by West *et al.* (1967) is as follows.

Animal proteinases or endopeptidases. These include such enzymes as pepsin, rennin, trypsin and chymotrypsin, and cathepsin.

Plant proteinases or endopeptidases. Examples of enzymes in this grouping are papain, chymopapain, ficin, and bromelin.

A third grouping consists of the exopeptidases which are subdivided into polypeptidases of which aminopeptidase or aminopolypeptidase, carboxypeptidase, dipeptidase, and tripeptidase are examples. Other more specific peptidases have also been characterized of which leucylpeptidase and iminodipeptidase are examples.

Enzymes Concerned with Oxidation and Reduction.—Many substances which are stable in the presence of molecular oxygen rapidly undergo aerobic oxidation in living cells. Therefore, it appears that every living cell contains enzymes which cause oxidation by activating other oxidizing substances. In the course of the oxidation reaction, the oxidizing agent itself becomes reduced except when oxidation occurs by the addition of molecular oxygen which apparently is a rare event in living cells. Thus the same enzyme system may be concerned with oxidation and reduction. For example, there is present in the cells of the potato tissue an enzyme which oxidizes certain aldehydes in the presence of nitrates, with the reduction of the latter to nitrites.

Cells which cannot directly stimulate the aerobic oxidation of gum guaiacum contain an enzyme peroxidase. For example, neither horseradish root alone nor hydrogen peroxide alone can oxidize guaiacum, but a blue color develops if both guaiacum and hydrogen peroxide are applied to the cut surface of horseradish root. Catechol-oxidase is considered as the main enzyme in the system which causes the color changes we have described and is a compound of two enzymes—catechol oxygenase and peroxidase. The essential properties of a direct oxidase may be attributed to the catechol oxygenase component. This enzyme is a dehydrase or dehydrogenase, and activates a cellular substance containing a catechol grouping, which then becomes converted by dehydrogenation into an orthoquinone. It is supposed that molecular oxygen is also activated and then functions as a hydrogen acceptor and is reduced.

Orthoquinone is a very strong oxidizing agent and can itself effect all the color changes by which direct-oxidases are characterized. It may be that peroxidase will immediately act on the hydrogen peroxide and so contribute to the oxidation powers of direct-oxidases. Accordingly the color changes would be due to mixtures of a catechol compound, oxygenase, molecular oxygen, and peroxidase.

The experimental investigations of certain oxidation systems in the test tube have in recent years been greatly helped by the use of methylene blue (MB) as an oxidizing agent. Upon reduction this dye is converted into a colorless leuco compound (MBH_2). Now it has been found that methylene blue is rapidly reduced by certain living cells under aerobic conditions. It is supposed that such cells contain oxidizable substances (AH_2) with labile hydrogen atoms which are activated by dehydrase enzymes, and in donating hydrogen to a hydrogen-acceptor (methylene blue) are as a result themselves oxidized.

$$AH_2 + MB \xrightarrow{\text{Dehydrase}} A + MBH_2$$

Certain oxidizable substances may be removed from cells and tissue by washing with water. Then by adding selected substances, potential hydrogen-donators, to the washed cells or tissues, the types of dehydrase enzyme present may be determined. Thus Thunberg has found that the seeds of species of mallow, orange, and plum decolorize methylene blue in the presence of oxalates, and inferred that the cells contained an oxalic-dehydrase. He also reported the presence of malic-, formic-, and succinic-dehydrases in the seeds of the runner bean.

In living cells oxidized substances act as hydrogen-acceptors. Molecular oxygen may participate in cellular oxidations by receiving hydrogen directly from an oxidizable metabolite. Hydrogen peroxide may in consequence be produced, and it is probable that the enzyme catalase, which is invariably present in the cells of aerobic organisms, by decomposing the peroxide as soon as it is produced, has the functional value of preventing this compound from exerting a toxic effect.

$$2H_2O_2 \xrightarrow{\text{Catalase}} 2H_2O + O_2$$

It has been demonstrated that an oxido-reductase system exists in yeasts and higher plants which can convert methyl glyoxal into lactic acid. This enzyme has been called methyl-glyoxatase.

$$CH_3CO \cdot CHO + H_2O \xrightarrow{\text{Methyl-Glyoxatase}} CH_2 \cdot CHOH \cdot COOH$$

Enzymes as Thermo-Labile, Colloidal, Biochemical Catalysts Showing Specificity

Enzymes which have been separated from living cells appear to fulfill the principal requirements of a catalyst, in that without themselves serving as the sources of the end products, they either accelerate reactions which are produced spontaneously but slowly or promote reactions which could not occur in their absence. An enzyme may enter into chemical combination during the course of the reaction, but the end products are entirely derived from the substrate.

Indeed, for reactions of short duration, at moderate temperatures and constant and favorable pH, with a limited amount of substrate rather than the enzyme, the concentration of enzyme will be the same at the end as at the beginning of the reaction. The initial catalytic powers of the enzyme system remain unimpaired. It must be remembered, however, that enzymes are readily inactivated under unfavorable conditions such as sometimes arise during the course of a reaction. For example, trypsin is only active in alkaline solution and is gradually inactivated by the hydrogen ions set free when this enzyme cleaves proteins into amino acids in unbuffered solutions. This particular inactivation is reversible since lytic activity is restored by once more making the solution alkaline.

The velocity of an enzyme action, like that of any other catalysts, is proportional to the concentration of the substrate and to that of the enzyme. The quantitative relations which depend on these concentrations, temperature, pH, and often other factors, are various and complex.

With few exceptions enzyme preparations do not pass through the membrane of a dialyzer, and estimations of their molecular weights by physical methods have given figures ranging from 20,000 to 300,000. They have always been regarded as colloidal catalysts, which develop extensive active surfaces when dispersed in a reaction medium. It is supposed that enzymic reactions take place on these surfaces. However, certain enzymes (lipase) can actually bring about chemical changes when dispersed in liquids in which they are quite insoluble. Such enzymic reactions resemble surface catalysis induced by certain metals (colloidal platinum). The degree of dispersion of enzymes appears to exercise an important influence on surface activity.

Chemical forces also play an important part. The whole surface of enzyme particles is probably chemically active. The chemically active regions possess affinities for and powers of effecting change in the appropriate substrate or substrates. What may happen during the reaction is that the enzyme combines chemically with and activates the substrate, which is then decomposed. The products of the reactions may have little affinity for the enzyme. Accordingly, by diffusing from the enzyme surface, they would make room for further activation of substrate.

Certain substances may be absorbed by enzymes and thus inactivate them. Others may combine chemically at the active centers, as happens when oxidation enzymes containing iron are inactivated by hydrogen cyanide or hydrogen sulfide.

Enzymatic Action and Other Biochemical Changes in the Development of Oxidized Flavor in Milk

The fat-water interface is the site of chemical reactions concerned in the production of off-flavors in milk. By forces active at interfaces concentration effects are produced which greatly accelerate such changes. Certain other "pro-oxygenic" factors aid such changes, e.g., (a) increases in temperature; (b) sunlight or ultraviolet light; (c) time or aging.

Autolytic Enzymes

Autolytic means self destruction—these enzymes may be an inherent part of the food or present in the microbial cell. Regardless of their origin, these enzymes play an important role in foods. Although all living cells contain autolytic enzymes, their activity is not well understood. When a cell dies these enzymes act very promptly and literally digest the cell.

Some microbiologists believe that most enzyme actions are reversible, perhaps some of the synthetic enzyme processes of cells during life reverse their action after death. The optimal growth temperatures for the organisms favor the enzyme action. An excellent example is the tenderization of meat. Leafy vegetables undergo the same enzyme action until spoilage is apparent. Bananas as well as other fruits become very soft during autolysis followed by loss of weight, color, and flavor.

When excessive autolysis has taken place, bacteria molds and yeasts find a most favorable environment for growth.

All of the food that we eat may be classified on the basis of stability such as: (a) staple foods: cereals, flour, and sugar, (b) semi-perishable foods: potatoes and corn and (c) perishable foods which include dairy products, meats, fish, fruits and vegetables.

Obviously the perishability of any food is determined very largely by the manipulation of the moisture content. The activity of micro-organisms in any food may be classified on a functional bases—(1) those causing spoilage or rendering the food inedible, (2) those producing desirable changes, and (3) those causing disease.

A fundamental knowledge of the biochemical activities of micro-organisms is important in order to control their action when they are present in various foods.

Biochemical Behavior of Enzymes in Frozen Foods

Enzymes in frozen foods: Enzymes in foods continue to function, very slowly to be sure, in foods held at low temperature. If the quality of the frozen food is to be maintained, the enzymes must be inactivated. Otherwise, they will cause off-flavors and discolor the food. Even at 0°F (−17.78°C) the enzymes are not inactivated, but only slowed down and within a week or month the frozen food may show evidence of abnormal odors and tastes.

Inactivating enzymes: Many kinds of fruits become dark after the skin is removed due primarily to oxidizing enzymes. By excluding atmospheric oxygen, these enzymes are successfully inactivated. Chemical inhibitors such as sulfurous acid and the addition of sugar or syrup may suppress the activity of these enzymes.

Blanching of Foods Prior to Freezing.—Heat treatment of foods is desirable in order to improve the keeping quality of the product during the time it is held in cold storage. The following advantages are accomplished during the "blanching process": (1) destruction of large numbers of micro-organisms on the surface of the food, thereby decreasing the microflora of the product during the processing stages, (2) inactivation of many inherent enzymes in the food which would otherwise contribute to the deterioration of the product during the storage period, (3) removal of much of the mucilage-like substances from the raw material which contributes to off-flavors, (4) the heat treatment sometimes referred to as "color set," which prolongs the natural color of the food, (5) an appreciable amount of extraneous substances are removed, which would otherwise contribute to many undesirable flavors in frozen foods.

The Enzyme Phosphatase

The phosphatase test is considered to be a reliable method for measuring the efficiency of pasteurization of milk and cream. Unfortunately there are conditions which may alter the accuracy of the test. For example, reactivation of phosphatase has been observed. Milk and cream heated to high temperatures for short periods give negative phosphatase results, then upon holding the samples for 3 or 4 days at 40°–50°F (4° to 10°C) a positive reaction again occurs.

There are two sources of the enzyme phosphatase. It is normally present in milk as well as other animal and plant cells. Phosphatase is also produced by certain bacteria including *Lactobacillus enzymo thermophilus*, *Streptococcus*, *Micrococcus*, *Aerobacter*, *Escherichia*, *Salmonella*, and *Pseudomonas*.

It has been noted that bacterial phosphatase seems to be more heat stable than milk phosphatase. A temperature of 170°F (76.7°C) for 30 minutes is required to inactivate the bacterial phosphatase enzyme, whereas milk phosphatase is inactivated at 145°F (62.8°C) for 30 minutes.

In one instance pasteurized cream gave a negative phosphatase test, then upon standing at 40°–50°F (4° to 10°C) gave a positive reaction. The positive test was caused primarily by *Bacillus cereus* and *B. mesentericus*. Since both organisms are spore formers they were able to survive the pasteurization temperature. Obviously bacterial phosphatase production by microorganisms may partially explain the reactivation of phosphatase in the pasteurization of selected food products.

The role of phosphatase is not well defined in food products. However it is normally present in raw milk and cream. Due to its heat sensitivity the phosphatase test is used by regulatory and quality control laboratories to detect the efficiency of pasteurization.

The heat stability of the enzyme is slightly higher than the heat required to destroy *Mycobacterium tuberculosis*. Either pasteurization process long time low temperature (LTLT) or flash pasteurization (HTST) will inactivate phosphatase.

This test is based upon the presence in milk of an enzyme (phosphomonoesterase) which can cause the hydrolysis of monoesters of phosphoric acid. The enzyme is totally destroyed by efficient pasteurization 61.7°C (143°F) for 30 minutes, or 71.5°C (160°F) for 15 seconds. In order to determine whether the enzyme has been destroyed (i.e. whether the milk has been subjected to proper pasteurization), a phenyl phosphoric ester is added to the milk. If present, the enzyme will hydrolyze the ester, releasing free phenol. To the milk is then added a compound (2,6-dibromo-quinone-chloroimide) which reacts with phenol to give a colored product, an indophenol. The intensity of the resulting color is an index of the amount of phenol released, and hence, in turn, the activity of the enzyme and the degree of pasteurizing efficiency.

The chemical equations involved in the test are as follows (it must be noted that the phenylphosphoric ester is undoubtedly a salt of the acid. For simplicity, the reaction is written with the ester in its acid form):

phenylphosphoric ester   phenol   phosphoric acid

phenol   2,6-dibromoquinone-chloroimide   an indophenol (blue)

Thus the appearance of a blue color in the finished test is an indication of improper pasteurization. Commercially, however, a certain amount of leeway is permitted, and standards may be obtained indicating the limits of this tolerance. For more accurate work, butyl alcohol (high-grade, neutralized) may be used to dissolve the colored compound and separate it into a distinct layer, which eliminates any error caused by opaqueness of the milk.

BIBLIOGRAPHY

Anon. 1939. Enzymes in Foods and Food Preservation; Food and Life. Yearbook Agr., U.S. Dept. Agr.

Anon. 1965. Enzyme Nomenclature. Elsevier Publishing Co., New York.

Barron, E. S. 1943. Mechanisms of carbohydrate metabolism. An essay on comparative biochemistry. Advan. Enzymol. 3, 149–189. Interscience Publishers, New York.

Clifton, C. E. 1957. Introduction to Bacterial Physiology. McGraw-Hill Book Co., New York.

Green, L. A., and Stumpf, S. 1944. Ann. Rev. Biochemistry 13, 1–24.

Heid, J. L., and Joslyn, M. A. 1967. Fundamentals of Food Processing Operations. The Avi Publishing Co., Westport, Conn.

Joslyn, M. A., and Marsh, G. L. 1933. The role of peroxidase in the deterioration of frozen fruits and vegetables. Science 78, 174–175.

Kerr, R. W. 1950. Chemistry and Industry of Starch, 2nd ed. Academic Press, New York.

Lamanna, C., and Mallette, M. F. 1953. Basic Bacteriology. The Williams and Wilkins Co., Baltimore.

Miller, B. S., and Johnson, J. A. 1955. Fungal enzymes in baking. Baker's Dig. 29, 95–100.

Oginsky, E. L., and Umbreit, W. W.   1959.   An Introduction to Bacterial Physiology, 2nd ed.   W. H. Freeman & Co., San Francisco.

Reed, G.   1952.   Fungal enzymes in bread baking.   Food Technol. 6, 339–341.

Reed, G.   1966.   Enzymes in Food Processing.   Academic Press, New York.

Schultz, H. W.   1960.   Food Enzymes.   Avi Publishing Co., Westport, Conn.

Stephenson, M.   1950.   Bacterial Metabolism.   Longmans-Green & Co., London.

West, E. S., Todd, W. R., Mason, H. S., and Van Bruggen, J. T.   1967.   Textbook of Biochemistry, 4th ed.   The Macmillan Co., New York.

CHAPTER 4

Morphology of Micro-organisms

BACTERIA

Micro-organisms may be classified, as other forms of life, into two main groups, animals and plants: In the animal kingdom, we may think of (a) single-celled animals (protozoa) and (b) many celled animals (includes all other forms except protozoa). The plant kingdom or *Thallophytes*, are characterized by no true roots, stems, or leaves. Members of this group are: algae (contains chlorophyll), fungi (no chlorophyll). This group contains mushrooms, molds, yeasts and bacteria. Various morphological types of bacteria are shown in Figs. 3 and 4.

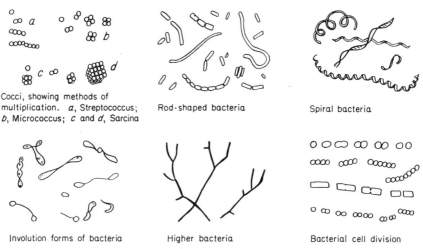

Cocci, showing methods of multiplication. *a*, Streptococcus; *b*, Micrococcus; *c* and *d*, Sarcina

Rod-shaped bacteria

Spiral bacteria

Involution forms of bacteria

Higher bacteria

Bacterial cell division

FIG. 3. MORPHOLOGY OF BACTERIA (MAGNIFIED)

The bacteriologist must use special units of measurement in determining the size of micro-organisms. The following information is useful to a food microbiologist in comparing the size of different organisms.

Micron (μ) $\frac{1}{1000}$ of a millimeter or $\frac{1}{25,400}$ of an inch.
Millimicron (mμ) $\frac{1}{1,000,000}$ of a millimeter.
Angstrom $\frac{1}{10,000,000}$ of a millimeter.

The smallest common bacteria are 0.15 micron in diameter and 0.3 micron in length. A large bacillus may vary from 0.8 to 2.5 microns in diameter and 8 to 10 microns in length. Most of the bacteria of importance in foods will range from 2 to 10 microns in length and 0.5 to 2.5 microns in diameter.

Yeast cells as a rule are much larger than bacterial cells. Some yeasts may range from 2.0 to 7 microns in diameter.

Molds are multicellular. Their components will vary with different kinds of molds.

Viruses and bacteriophages are the smallest units of living matter known. Their features will be discussed elsewhere.

The class *Schizomycetes* includes most of the bacteria that are associated with foods. *Eubacteriales* and *Pseudomonales* make up the

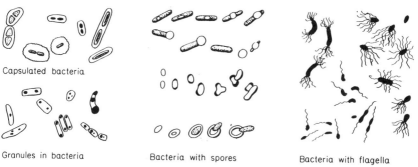

Capsulated bacteria

Granules in bacteria   Bacteria with spores   Bacteria with flagella

FIG. 4. BACTERIAL STRUCTURES (MAGNIFIED)

two principal orders. The order is divided into several families in which the following are of importance in foods:

(a) Pseudomonadaceae

The principal genus in this group is *Pseudomonas*. The organisms are gram-negative and usually motile. Organisms in this group are responsible for many kinds of food spoilage. Their action on carbohydrates is minor; however, in foods containing proteins and fats they demonstrate considerable proteolytic and lipolytic activity. The *Pseudomonas* organisms grow rapidly at refrigerator temperatures and in many cases produce slime on the surface of meats. *Pseudomonas fluorescens* produces a greenish pigment; some species, such as *P. nigrificans*, form a black pigment on protein foods.

The biological activity of the *Pseudomonas* group may be in many cases identified by their proteolytic and lipolytic activity and pigment production.

(b) Achromobacteriaceae

These bacteria are Gram-negative rods, aerobic to facultative and most of them are motile. Carbohydrates are not usually utilized. There are three genera that are important in foods because of their ability to grow at low temperatures. For instance, *Alcaligenes viscolactis* may cause ropiness in milk. *Achromobacter* causes spoilage of meat products by producing slime and off-odors. *Flavobacterium* produces an orange pigment on meats and dairy products. All of these organisms may be found widely distributed in nature.

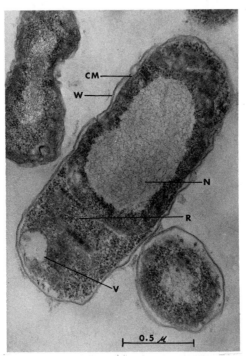

FIG. 4A. BACILLUS CEREUS CELLS MAGNIFIED 71,000 TIMES WITH AN ELECTRON MICROSCOPE

W-Cell Wall, CM-Cell Membrane, V-vacuole, R-ribosome, N-nucleus.

(c) Brevibacteraceae

Brevibacterium lineus and *B. erythrogenes* produce orange and red pigments in certain cheeses, and these may have a role in their ripening processes. These organisms are gram-positive rods. Their carbohydrate and oxygen requirements are variable. Morphological features range from gram-positive short rods to coccoid as shown in Fig. 5. Variation also exists in motility characteristics. All members in this classification are asporogenous.

FIG. 5.   BREVIBACTERACEAE (MAGNIFIED)

Showing diagrammatically typical arrangements of rod and coccoid forms.

(d) Bacillaceae

Bacillus subtilis, B. polymyxa, and *B. stearothermophilus* are heat resistant spore formers. *Bacillus coagulans* is used to produce commercial lactic acid. *Bacillus stearothermophilus* may cause flat sours in canned vegetables. *Clostridium* are typical anaerobic bacteria. *Clostridium thermosaccharolyticum* produces a gaseous spoilage in canned vegetables. *Clostridium sporogenes* produces a stormy fermentation of milk. *Clostridium butyricum* can be a troublesome organism in foods, especially in large blocks of cheese where the center area of the cheese offers ideal anaerobic conditions. A variety of gases with objectionable odors are produced;   many are odoriferous which is objectionable and also create a favorable environment for other spoilage organisms. *Clostridium botulinum* produces toxins in food which cause botulism food poisoning. The *Bacillaceae* are widely distributed in nature. Those shown in Fig. 6 are typical.

FIG. 6.   BACILLACEAE SPORES FORM IN
THE CENTER OF THE ROD (MAGNIFIED)

Bacillus subtilis cells at left, *Clostridium sporogenes* at right.

(e) Corynebacteriaceae

These organisms are of special interest from the public health standpoint. *Corynebacterium diphtheriae* is the causative agent of diphtheria in man. *Corynebacterium pyogenes* may cause mastitis in dairy cattle. The characteristic feature of this group is the granules in the rod. (See Fig. 7.)   They can be easily observed by appropriate staining techniques.   These organisms have no special significance in spoilage of foods.

FIG. 7.   CORYNEBACTERIACEAE (MAGNIFIED)

Characteristic features of these organisms, represented here
by *Corynebacterium diphtheriae*, are the granules in the rods.

(f) Enterobacteriaceae

These organisms are gram-negative non-spore forming rods.   The
genera are *Aerobacter, Erwinia, Escherichia*, and *Serratia*.   All may
bring about biological changes in food spoilage, while *Proteus, Salmonella*, and *Shigella* are significant in public health.   *Salmonella*
especially is involved in food poisoning and will be discussed more
completely under food poisoning.   *Aerobacter aerogenes* and *Escherichia coli* are often called the coliform group.   Their presence in foods
is usually undesirable.   The two species should be distinguished because of their source.   *Aerobacter aerogenes* is usually of plant origin,
while *Escherichia coli* is of intestinal origin in animals.   They can
utilize carbohydrates, with production of gases and other metabolic
by-products which are undesirable.   Coliforms are indicators of sewage pollution, especially when present in oysters and hence may indicate other intestinal pathogens that may be of major importance in
foods.

Erwinia may cause wilts, soft rots, or necrosis in vegetables and
fruits.   *Erwinia carotovora* often causes soft rot in carrots.

Serratia is noted for its red pigment production on the surface of
many foods, especially if carbohydrates are present.   Bread is a good
example of the condition and is referred to as blood bread when it
occurs.

Proteus are gram-negative, motile rods.   Morphologically they are
difficult to distinguish from other members of the intestinal group.
Proteus vulgaris is the type species.   It produces acid and gas from
glucose but not lactose.   They have been identified in spoilage of eggs
and meats and also have been suspected in food poisoning.   Ammonia is readily formed from urea.   Putrefactive odors have been
associated with the breakdown of proteins.

Salmonella.—At present there are over 1,000 species generally called
serotypes.   Organisms in this genus include *S. enteritidis, S. paratyphi,
S. schottmuelleri, S. typhimurium,* and *S. typhi,* the cause of typhoid
fever.   All have been involved in food borne infections.   *Salmonella
pullorum,* the cause of pullorum in chickens, has also been isolated in
several food borne outbreaks involving humans.

Like *Proteus*, the *Salmonella* group are similar in morphological features (see Fig. 8). All are gram-negative, non-sporulating organisms. Serological techniques are more useful than cultural features in identifying the different species. However, they can produce acid from glucose but not lactose. Their proteolytic properties are negligible.

FIG. 8.   TYPICAL CELL GROUPING OF SALMONELLA GENERA (MAGNIFIED)

Shigella. Microscopic features are similar to *Proteus* and *Salmonella*, except they are non-motile and produce no gas from glucose. One species, *S. dysenteriae* is the type species. They may be associated with food borne infections.

(g) Propionibacteriaceae

Propionibacterium shermanii is the best example in this group and is typical of other species. They are gram-positive, asporogenous, anaerobic to microaerophilic rods, sometimes resembling cocci in short chains. Their metabolic activity is interesting because they can produce acetic and propionic acids and carbon dioxide from lactic acid. These organisms play an important role in Swiss cheese ripening in that they ferment the lactates to produce gas which contributes to the characteristic eyes in this variety of cheese. They also contribute to the fine delicate flavor of Swiss cheese. No doubt they play an important role in other desirable food fermentations, in the production of desirable flavors and odors in foods.

(h) Lactobacillaceae

Members of this family are important in foods because of their ability to produce lactic acid as a desirable fermentation in many foods. Some are homofermentative, producing principally lactic acid, but some acetic acid and carbon dioxide may be produced. The heterofermentative members of this family not only produce lactic acid, but several volatile compounds and small amounts of alcohol. *Lactobacillus acidophilus, L. bulgaricus, L. casei, L. pentoaceticus, L. brevis,* and *L. thermophilus,* are all gram-positive rods, non-motile and microaerophilic. They require for the most part complex foods for their energy requirements.

Lactobacillus leichmannii is used for microbiological assays for vitamins and antibiotics in foods.

Since most of the members of this group are microaerophilic, they grow poorly on the surface of culture media but produce colonies submerged beneath the surface. *Lactobacilli* predominate in nearly all types of acid fermentation in foods.

Morphologically, these organisms are quite pleomorphic, even within the species. Some species produce metachromatic granules comparable to those formed in *Corynebacterium diphtheriae.*

(i) Streptococcae

Some of the *Streptococci* are pathogenic for man and animals. *Streptococcus pyogenes* may cause infections in man while *S. agalactiae* is largely responsible for mastitis in dairy cattle. Fortunately it has a low virulence in man. More appropriate discussion will occur under food poisoning.

Streptococcus lactis and *S. cremoris* are important starter organisms in fermented dairy products. They are largely responsible for the ordinary souring of milk. They are gram-positive, ferment lactose, and produce "d" type of lactic acid. They are easily cultivated on whey agar. The temperature for growth may range from 50°F (10°C) to 113°F (45°C).

Streptococcus faecalis has been identified in the spoilage of canned hams and sometimes in bacon. The temperature range for growth may vary from 50°F (10°C) to 122°F (50°C). Their thermoduric tendency makes them unique in that they can survive pasteurization of milk, tolerate 7 per cent salt and can grow at a pH of 10.0.

Streptococcus liquefaciens produces a rennin-like enzyme which slowly coagulates milk; it is often called "sweet curdling." Later an actual proteolysis takes place. The acid production generally equals that produced by *S. lactis.* The organism produces "d" type of lactic acid and produces acetyl-methyl-carbinol. Except for proteolysis of milk, the cultural features are comparable to *S. lactis.*

Streptococcus faecalis and *S. liquefaciens* may be referred to as belonging to the enterococcus group because of their presence in the intestinal tract of man and animals. Therefore, their presence in foods and on utensils may be significant from a sanitary viewpoint. However, *S. liquefaciens* due to its rennin-like enzyme may play an important role in the ripening of certain cheeses. The ability of this group of organisms to grow over a wide temperature range makes them all the more significant in foods.

Leuconostoc mesenteroides is associated especially with sauerkraut and pickle fermentations. This organism initiates the desirable lactic acid fermentation in these products. It differs from the other species in its ability to tolerate fairly high concentrations of salt and sugar. The organism can tolerate up to 50 per cent sugar. These bacteria produce an undesirable slimy or gummy fermentation in syrups and ice-cream mixes. A desirable feature is the ability of *L. mesenteroides* to produce dextran, a product that has a potential use in blood plasma.

Leuconostoc citrovorum (*Streptococcus citrovorus*) and *L. dextranicum* (*S. paracitrovorus*) are important organisms in dairy starter cultures. They are able to ferment citric acid with the production of diacetyl, the compound that contributes to the fine delicate flavor of butter. Diacetyl is also found in bread, coffee, and other fermented food products in varying amounts. The morphological features are comparable to *Streptococcus lactis*. They are gram-positive and asporogenous. These organisms are considered non-pathogenic for humans. This group of organisms will be discussed more fully under lactic acid fermentation.

MOLDS

Molds like bacteria and yeasts play an important role in foods. Some molds are desirable because they produce products that en-

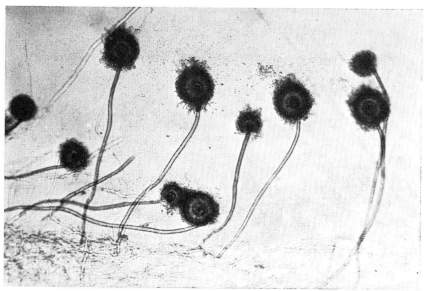

Courtesy of Continental Can Co.

Fig. 9. *Aspergillus ochraceous*

Showing mycelia and conidial heads (×100).

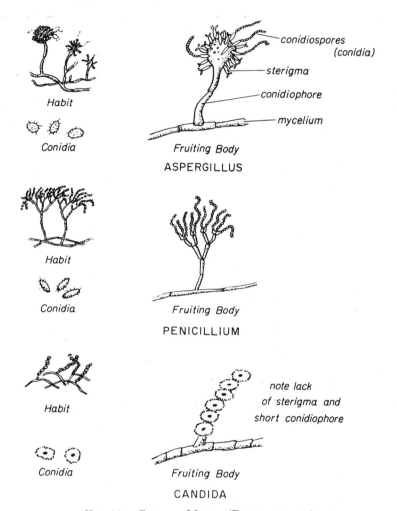

FIG. 10.   COMMON MOLDS (DIAGRAMMATIC)

hance the flavor of foods, such as blue, Roquefort, and Camembert cheeses.   The latter owe their characteristic flavor to the growth of the molds in the cheese.   Molds are useful in producing certain enzymes, such as amylase for bread making or the production of commercial citric acid.   Some molds are undesirable in that they contribute to certain kinds of spoilage in foods.   Other molds may be significant from the public health standpoint.

The classification of molds, like bacteria and yeasts, is complicated. However, they are members of the plant kingdom and classified in

Courtesy of Continental Can Co.

FIG. 11.   PENICILLIUM

With mycelia and brush-like conidial heads (×200)

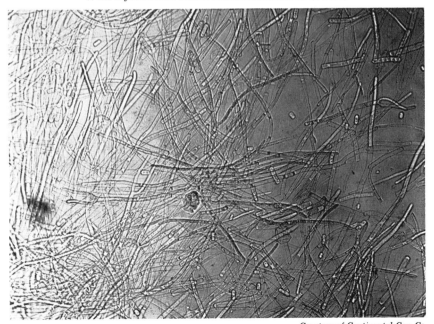

Courtesy of Continental Can Co.

FIG. 12.   OOSPORA ON TOMATO (×150)

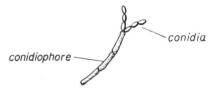

FIG. 13.   *Geotrichum candidum* (*Diagrammatic*)

the phylum, Thallophyta, which may be defined as plants devoid of roots, stems, and leaves and producing no photosynthetic pigments.

Some of the common molds in foods may be classified as follows:

The order *Mucorales* has spores borne in sporangia. Some forms of these are illustrated in the frontispiece, a photomicrograph of Mucor mycelia and sporangia. Perhaps the genus and species of a few molds commonly found in foods will be sufficient to emphasize their importance in foods and food products.

Aspergillus glaucus and *A. repens* are often responsible for undesirable changes in foods. These varieties grow well in high concentrations of salt and sugar.

Aspergillus niger is frequently found in foods. *Aspergillus ochraceous* is found on growing tomatoes, Fig. 9. The fruiting bodies are black with a variation in colors. Some strains are used to produce citric, gluconic, and oxalic acids. Fig. 10 illustrates a few of the many mold forms.

The genus *Penicillium* is characterized by branching of the conidophore as shown in Fig. 10. *Penicillium camemberti* and *P. roqueforti* with blue-green conidia are used in ripening Blue and Camembert cheeses (see Fig. 11).

Geotrichum candidum (*Oospora lactis*) or "dairy mold" gives a white cottony growth on dairy products as shown in Fig. 12. It also appears on tomatoes, Fig. 13.

Monilia or the genus *Neurospora* produces asexual spores. It may be characterized by a long mycelium. The aerial hyphae forms branched chains and pigmented budding conidia. *Neurospora sitophila* produces a pink conidia and is sometimes called "red bread mold," or blood bread as shown in Fig. 14.

FIG. 14.   *Neurospora sitophila Diagrammatic*

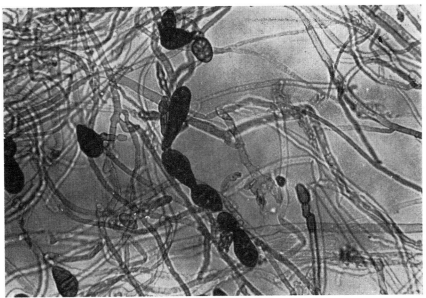

Courtesy of Continental Can Co.

FIG. 15. *Alternaria*, A CAUSE OF ROT IN TOMATOES

Spores show the typical Indian-club shape; filaments are septate and of medium thickness (×200).

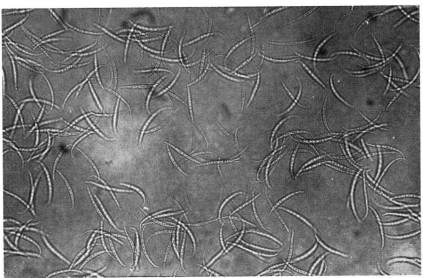

Courtesy of Continental Can Co.

FIG. 16. SICKLE-SHAPED SPORES OF *Fusarium* (×200)

Courtesy of Continental Can Co.

FIG. 17.   MYCELIA AND SPORES OF *Botrytis* (×100)

White spots on refrigerated meat may be due to the genus *Sporotrichum* or *S. carnis*. The conidia are oval shape and may be branched out from all parts of the mycelium.

The genus *Alternaria* or *A. tenuis* (see Fig. 15) forms a mass of mycelium with dark brown conidia. It may be associated with spoilage of citrus fruits and tomatoes.

The great variety of mold forms is illustrated in Figs. 16 and 17.

The morphological features of molds can be examined satisfactorily by the slide culture technique (see Fig. 18). This method permits examination with all of the parts intact and thus makes identification of the mold comparatively easy.

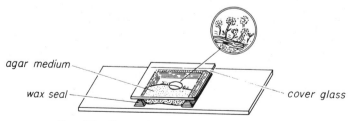

agar medium —   cover glass

wax seal —

FIG. 18.   SLIDE CULTURE CELL TECHNIQUE

Further reference should be made to the many reference books on fungi for complete identification and environmental factors for growth.

YEASTS

Yeasts and yeast-like fungi may be desirable or undesirable in foods. These organisms are widely distributed in nature. They are found in orchards and vineyards, also in the soil, air, intestinal tract of animals, and certain insects.

Physiologically yeasts have no chlorophyll and are dependent on plants and animals for their energy. Yeasts may be grouped as saprophytic or parasitic.

Although they may appear pleomorphic in size and shape, yeasts are unicellular organisms. Some appear as cylindrical or elongated changing at one end into a filamentous form. Others appear ellipsoidal. Yeasts range in size from 2 to 6 μ in width and from 10 to 30 μ in length. As a rule most yeasts are larger than most varieties of bacteria.

Yeasts may reproduce asexually by budding. All true yeasts produce ascospores which is part of the sexual process. Ascospores are encased in a sac called ascus. Therefore all true yeasts are called "sac fungi" and should be included in the class *Ascomycetes*. In sexual reproduction a fusion takes place prior to spore formation. The fused nuclei divide and ascospores are formed. When two yeast cells meet, a tube is formed to allow passage of nuclei, then they fuse into a single nucleus. *Schizosaccharomyces odosporus* is an example of this type. Asexual or binary fission is comparable to bacterial reproduction. This type of reproduction is characteristic of *Schizosaccharomyces* (see Fig. 19). False yeasts produce no ascospores and they belong to the *Fungi imperfecti* group.

Fig. 19.   Vegetable and Ascospore Yeast Cells (Diagrammatic)

Saccharomyces cerevisiae, showing vegetative cells at left, ascus and ascospore formation at right.

Most yeasts play an important role in the food industry, because they produce enzymes that favor desirable chemical reactions, such as leavening of bread, the production of alcohol, glycerol, or invertase.

They are also capable of synthesizing certain essential vitamins of the B group.

The type of end products desired can be controlled within certain limits by the oxygen supply. Most yeasts require an abundance of oxygen for growth, but in certain industrial fermentations, an exclusion of oxygen determines the yield and kind of end product. The temperature range for yeast growth varies from 32°F (0°C) to 122°F (50°C), although the optimum range is 68°F (20°C) to 86°F (30°C).

Some yeasts are chromogenic and produce a variety of pigments including green, yellow, pink, and black.

False yeasts or class *Fungi imperfecti* include several genera that are important in foods. *Cryptococcus utilis* is a food yeast and *C. kefyr* is a lactose-fermenting yeast. *Candida mycoderma* is a film-forming yeast, growing in an acid environment such as beer, pickles, and sauerkraut. They utilize the acid, thereby making conditions more favorable for other spoilage organisms to survive. *Candida krusei* is used in a starter culture along with *Lactobacillus bulgaricus* in Swiss cheese making, to stimulate a uniform acid production. Since *L. bulgaricus* is microaerophilic, the yeast may create a metabiotic state that is beneficial to *L. bulgaricus*.

Rhodotorula glutinus produces a pink pigment that is undesirable in sauerkraut which is sometimes called pink kraut. It produces a water-soluble pigment that accumulates in the kraut juice giving it a pink color.

ALGAE

The role of algae in food should not be underestimated. In fact, some algae, like bacteria can use atmospheric nitrogen and combine it with oxygen, thus making it available to plants and animals in much the same way as nitrogen-fixing bacteria. Some algae form a sheath that serves a useful purpose in protecting nitrogen-fixing bacteria from dehydration and at the same time the algae provide carbohydrates as a source of energy. A form of metabiosis exists in this relationship.

Some algae produce pigments that may be of interest in foods. One variety of algae produces carotene, a precursor of vitamin A, while other algae synthesize vitamin D. When fish eat the phytoplankton, the vitamins are stored in the liver of the fish, thus making a rich source of vitamins for man.

Red algae or (Irish moss) and brown varieties known as kelp are harvested by the Japanese as a source of food. Agar, a common bacteriological culture medium, is used in fruit juices and beverages as a clarifying agent. Irish moss is used in chocolate milk to hold the chocolate in suspension.

Algae are rich in iodine, bromine, and potassium; therefore certain varieties of algae can be used as commercial fertilizers. France and Germany have already used algae in this way.

Unfortunately there are some forms of algae that when eaten by shellfish make the shellfish toxic to humans, animals, and birds that eat the fish.

Algae may play an important role in food waste stabilizing ponds by supplying the oxygen to oxidize the food wastes in lagoons. However, more information is needed before any definite conclusions can be drawn as to the feasibility of such a process.

VIRUSES AND BACTERIOPHAGES

Viruses are on the threshold between living matter and chemicals. They rely on other living tissues to survive. Viruses are capable of causing diseases in plants and animals.

Viruses are included in the order *Virales*. They vary in size from 0.2 to 0.012 μ in diameter as compared to bacteria which may be around 1.0 μ in diameter. Bacteriophages are called bacterial

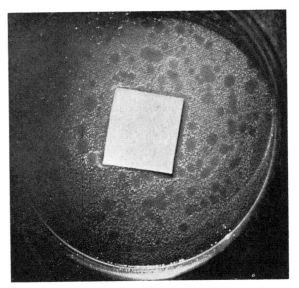

FIG. 20. ACTION OF BACTERIOPHAGE ON A PURE CULTURE
OF *Streptococcus lactis*
Note the clear zones of lysis surrounding the colonies.

viruses. Viruses and bacteriophages are not visible under the ordinary compound microscope. Both have the ability to multiply very rapidly, while attacking the host cells. In comparing a cell with bacteriophage and a virus, the cell contains DNA (desoxyribonucleic acid) and RNA (ribonucleic acid). The phage contains *only* DNA. Bacteriophage is derived from nucleic acid, and, while the cell is able to grow and divide, a virus cannot undergo fission. It must be formed from the material in the host cell.

The phage is so small that it passes through a bacterial filter while bacteria remain on the filter. This is one way of separating these agents.

Bacteriophages are of interest in foods, especially dairy starter cultures. They parasitize the bacterial cells and thereby impair their ability to produce acid as shown in Fig. 20. This is a serious problem with butter and cheese cultures, e.g. *Streptococcus lactis, S. thermophilus*, and *S. cremoris*.

BIBLIOGRAPHY

Anon. 1961. The ultimate parasite (virus). Time Magazine *78*, No. 20, Nov. 17, 60–66.
Carpenter, P. L. 1967. Microbiology, 2nd ed. W. B. Saunders Co., Philadelphia.
Frazier, W. C. 1967. Food Microbiology, 2nd ed. McGraw-Hill Book Co., New York.
Pelczar, M. J., and Reid, R. D. 1967. Microbiology, 2nd ed. McGraw-Hill Book Co., New York.
Raper, K. B., and Thom, C. 1949. A Manual of the Penicillia. The Williams and Wilkins Co., Baltimore.
Tanner, F. W. 1944. The Microbiology of Foods, 2nd ed. Garrard Press, Champaign, Ill.
Thom, C., and Raper, K. B. 1945. A Manual of the *Aspergilli*. The Williams and Wilkins Co., Baltimore.
Troy, V. S. 1960. Mold Counting of Tomato Products. Continental Can Co., New York.

CHAPTER 5

Factors that Influence Microbial Activity

Six major environmental factors determine the growth or destruction of micro-organisms in foods. They are: moisture, oxygen, temperature, nutrients, pH, and growth inhibitors.

Food supply for micro-organisms varies with the composition of the food on or in which they are found. Organisms may be divided into groups according to their ability to utilize carbohydrates, proteins, and fats as sources of energy.

Temperature is very important for micro-organisms. At high temperatures all organisms are destroyed, while at freezing temperatures microbial activity is slowed down but not necessarily stopped. Since micro-organisms vary in their temperature requirements for growth it is possible to classify them into three groups, namely, psychrophilic, mesophilic, and thermophilic. All are important in bringing about biological changes in food.

All micro-organisms are divided into aerobes and anaerobes with an intermediate group known as facultatives which cannot tolerate strict aerobic or anaerobic conditions. The major difference depends on the mechanism by which the organism obtains its oxygen requirements. Each group of organisms plays an important role in foods; some are desirable and others are undesirable. They will be considered more fully under different types of fermentations.

Moisture

Water is essential for the growth of all viable cells. Most foods contain sufficient water to support growth; however, in the processing of foods such as drying or freezing the water is removed or remains in a solid state which makes it unavailable for the organisms to carry on a normal metabolic activity.

Water in most cases carries food nutrients into the cells and also serves as a means of eliminating the waste products that have accumulated as the result of metabolic activity. Moreover water helps to maintain the natural shape and turgidity of the cell.

Water is present in all foods in varying amounts. A brief comparison of the moisture contents in several foods is shown below. For instance, fresh fruits may vary in moisture from 75 to 90 per cent. Leafy vegetables, such as green beans, spinach, and lettuce have a water content varying from 90 to 95 per cent. In some foods like tomatoes, cucumbers, and watermelons, the moisture will average about 95 per cent. Milk contains about 87 per cent moisture. Fresh eggs range from 70 to 75 per cent while dry beans, cereals, peas, and nuts range from 5 to 15 per cent water. Sugar and lard are practically free of moisture.

In order to understand the relationship of moisture to the microorganism and the food itself, one should consider osmotic pressure and its effects. When two solutions of different substances or two solutions of the same substance in different concentrations are brought together, diffusion takes place. However, if a membrane is used to separate the solutions a pressure results due to the different rates of passage of the two solutions. This process is called osmosis. The rate of diffusion through the membrane depends upon the properties of the two solutions. Water molecules diffuse faster than the solute molecules. The resulting pressure is called osmotic pressure and the process which produces it is known as osmosis. Obviously compounds with large molecules will have lower osmotic pressure than materials with smaller molecules. This is the reason salt exerts a greater osmotic pressure than cane sugar.

TABLE 3A

LOWEST VALUES OF EQUILIBRIUM RELATIVE HUMIDITY (H) PERMITTING DEVELOPMENT OF SPOILAGE ORGANISMS

Group of Micro-organisms	Minimum h-value
Normal Bacteria	0.91
Normal yeasts	0.88
Normal molds	0.80
Halophilic bacteria	0.75
Xerophilic fungi	0.65
Osmophilic yeasts	0.60

Alarm Water Content of Some Common Foods
(Assuming $h + 0.70$ and $T - 20°C$)

Food	Alarm Water Content (%)
Whole milk powder	8[1]
Dehydrated whole egg	10-11
Wheat flour	13-15
Rice	13-15
Separated milk powder	15
Dehydrated fat-free meat	15
Pulses (peas, beans, lentile, etc.)	15
Dehydrated vegetables	14-20
Starch	18
Dehydrated fruits	18-25

Source: Mossell, D. A. A., and Ingram, M. (1955).
[1]Calculated.

There are three recognized solutions: (a) Isotonic solutions of salts have the same density as the cell liquid. Isotonic solutions are the most favorable for all biological life. Physiological saline or 0.85 per cent sodium chloride in water is isotonic normal salt solution.

(b) A hypertonic solution is more dense than the bacterial cell liquid. When two solutions of different densities are separated by a membrane, water passes from the less dense to the more dense. Therefore, when a bacterial cell is placed in a more dense solution, water leaves the cell and passes into the solution and the cell shrivels. The organism has lost its turgidity. This phenomenon is called plasmolysis.

Salt and sugar or mixtures of the two are frequently used to preserve food. Meats are often cured and preserved in brine solutions. If the salting of meats is properly done, there is no better way to stop microbiological activity which may result in spoilage of the product than by using hypertonic solutions.

(c) Hypotonic solutions have a lower density than the cell, and water passes from the less dense to the more concentrated medium. Water passes into the cell, resulting in a swelling or bursting of the cell. Hypotonic solutions have no practical value in food preservation. For instance, if one crushed fruit, a hypotonic condition would be attained which could be harmful to micro-organisms, but the fruit itself would also be damaged.

Significance of Free and Bound Water in Biological Life.— The form in which water exists in the food is important from the microbiological standpoint. Bound water is present in the tissue itself and is a component part of the composition just as much as the proteins and carbohydrates. It is a part of the living tissue and is vital to all the physiological processes associated with the cell. Free water exists in and around the tissue or cell. It can be removed from the cell without seriously interfering with the vital processes. Free water is important for the survival and metabolism of micro-organisms that may be present in the food. Hence dehydration is an important method of preserving food. Free water governs the microbial activity whereas bound water has very little effect upon the organisms.

Water Activity

Micro-organisms are dependent on water for growth. The amount of water available for micro-organisms is referred to as "water activity" (a_w). Pure water has a "water activity" of 1.00 and is in equilibrium with a relative humidity of 100 per cent. In freezing the pure water freezes out and the solution becomes more concentrated. Because some water exists as bound water the "water activity" of a system is not exactly the same as its water content. Bacteria require more water than yeasts which require more than molds.

Oxidation—Reduction Potential

All forms of life require oxygen to carry on their metabolic activities. Free atmospheric oxygen (O_2) exists in the air and is readily available to certain groups of micro-organisms. Oxygen also exists in the combined form such as C-H-O, the elemental form in a simple carbohydrate. Certain organisms have a mechanism which enables them to utilize the oxygen in the compound.

Micro-organisms may be classified according to their oxygen requirements.

1. Aerobic organisms grow in the presence of atmospheric oxygen.

2. Anaerobic organisms grow in the absence of atmospheric oxygen.

3. Facultatively anaerobic organisms grow in either the absence or the presence of atmospheric oxygen.

4. Microaerophilic organisms grow in the presence of a reduced oxygen supply.

The presence of aerobes and anaerobes in a food supply may change the oxidation-reduction potential in the food to a point where certain organisms are inhibited in growth.

Many fresh foods have a low O-R potential because they have reducing substances such as vitamin C, reducing sugars, and other compounds. They tend to keep the oxidation potential at a low level, hence there is a slow diffusion of oxygen from the atmosphere.

In the case of Swiss cheese the heating of the milk may alter the texture of the food or change the reducing and oxidizing compounds so that anaerobic organisms may find a favorable environment in the center of the cheese.

The biochemical behavior of micro-organisms in food is largely determined by the amount of oxygen present. If atmospheric oxygen is present most food materials are completely though slowly oxidized. Carbon dioxide and water are the end products when sugar is oxidized. If amino acids are oxidized, ammonia, carbon dioxide, and water are formed. Free fatty acids, carbon dioxide, and water are the result of the oxidation of fats.

However, if the oxygen tension is lowered, more intermediate products and less end products are formed by microbial action. In this case the organisms may produce alcohol, lactic, acetic, and formic acids. The protein breakdown usually results in amino acids with varying amounts of ammonia, hydrogen sulfide, sulfites, carbon dioxide, and water. Fats are broken down to glycerol and fatty acids, with very little carbon dioxide and water formation. Under strictly anaerobic conditions foul smelling compounds are formed from proteins such as butyl alcohol, mercaptans, and hydrogen sulfide. The formation of these is frequently referred to as putrefaction.

In an alcoholic fermentation of sugar by yeasts, in which alcohol is the desired product, a small amount of oxygen is necessary for the yeasts to convert the sugar into alcohol. If yeast and vitamins are desired, then large amounts of oxygen must be supplied. Here the sugar is completely oxidized, thus producing more energy per gram than under anaerobic conditions and a greater yield of yeast cells.

Consequently oxygen plays an important role in the type and amount of biological product obtained, the amount of food consumed, and the energy released in the breakdown.

Sugar fermentation by yeasts is familiar to all biologists. With an abundance of oxygen available for yeast production, the principal reaction is

$$C_6H_{12}O_6 + 6O_2 \rightarrow 6CO_2 + 6HOH + 674 \text{ calories}$$

Under anaerobic conditions for alcohol production, there is little increase in the yeast present and the main reaction is

$$C_6H_{12}O_6 \rightarrow 2C_2H_5OH + 2CO_2 + 22 \text{ calories}$$

Thus, some 30 times as much heat is produced in the first process as in the second.

TABLE 3B

GENERATION TIMES OF SEVERAL SPECIES OF BACTERIA

Organism	Medium	Temp. (°C)	Generation Time (Min.)
Aerobacter aerogenes	Broth or milk	37	16-18
	Synthetic	37	29-44
Bacillus mycoides	Broth	37	28
Bacillus thermophilus	Broth	55	18.3
Escherichia coli	Broth	37	17
	Milk	37	12.5
Lactobacillus acidophilus	Milk	37	66-87
Mycobacterium tuberculosis	Synthetic	37	792-932
Rhizobium japonicum	Mineral salts + Yeast + mannitol	25	344-461
Salmonella typhi	Broth	37	23.5
Staphylococcus aureus	Broth	37	27-30
Streptococcus lactis	Lactose broth	37	48
	Milk	37	26
Treponema pallidum	Rabbit testes	37	1,980

Molds grow very poorly under anaerobic conditions, consequently they are not a serious factor in food spoilage under these conditions. Ensilage is an excellent example of the influence of oxygen on the by-products of fermentation.   If the ensilage is well packed in the silo, lactic acid and gassy fermentations are the result.   If it is loosely packed then lactic acid is produced in small amounts but mold growth will be pronounced.

Temperature

Temperature is an important physical factor affecting growth and metabolic activity of all living cells.   Micro-organisms are no excep-

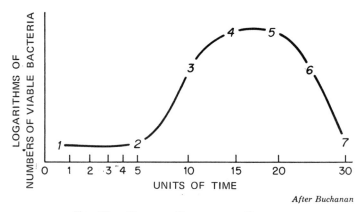

After Buchanan

Fig. 21.   Growth Phases in a Culture

1.   Initial phase.   The number of bacteria remains constant or they may actually decrease in numbers.   Perhaps this is due to an adjustment to their environment.   (1–2)

2.   Log phase.   The bacteria increase in numbers due to a plentiful supply of food.   (2–3)

3.   Negative growth phase.   Multiplication is beginning to slow down.   Due to decrease in food supply and accumulation of waste products which may be toxic to the organism.   (3–4)

4.   Stationary phase.   The death rate is in balance with the birth rate, due to less food and accumulation of waste products.   (4–5)

5.   Accelerated death phase (5–7).   Birth rate conditions as shown in 4–5.

tion.   Obviously, a slight range of optimum temperatures can be designated for each organism or for groups of closely related ones. The minimum temperature for growth may be several degrees below the optimum.   Naturally the rate of growth decreases as the temperature is lowered.   This is the basic principle of preserving foods by refrigeration and freezing.   Maximum temperature refers to the temperature slightly above the optimum at which growth will occur. An increase in temperature above the maximum will destroy the organisms.

TABLE 3C

EFFECT OF TEMPERATURE, NUTRITION, AND AERATION ON THE Q_{10} OF GROWTH OF
Pseudomonas Fluorescens

Media	Culture	Q_{10} Values at Various Temperature Intervals				
		4° to 10° C	10° to 15° C	15° to 20° C	20° to 25° C	25° to 32° C
Glucose	Stationary	4.04	3.10	1.90	2.31	0.018
	Shake	3.52	1.69	1.88	2.50	.028
Citrate (Na)	Stationary	4.25	2.96	1.96	2.02	.019
	Shake	3.89	2.10	2.59	1.66	.024
Casamino acids	Stationary	4.49	3.77	1.69	1.49	1.27
	Shake	2.26	2.72	1.93	1.64	.019

Source: Jezeski, J. J., and Olson, R. H. (1962). Proc. Low Temperature Microbiology Symp. 1961, Campbell Soup Co., Camden, N.J.

Prof. Barber (1929) at the University of Chicago perfected a single cell isolation technique in which he studied the generation time of Escherichia, coli with respect to different temperatures and time intervals.

68°F (20°C)	60	
77°F (25°C)	40	
86°F (30°C) required	29	minutes for the cell to divide
98°F (37°C)	17	
104°F (40°C)	19	
113°F (45°C)	32	
122°F (50°C)	no growth	

TABLE 4

CLASSIFICATION OF MICRO-ORGANISMS WITH RESPECT TO THEIR TEMPERATURE REQUIREMENTS

Grouping of Bacteria	Temperature Range of Growth Expressed in Degrees Centigrade			General Sources of These Bacteria
	Minimum	Optimum	Maximum	
Cryophilic or Psychrophilic	0 to 5	15 to 20	30	Water and frozen foods
Mesophilic	10 to 25	30 to 40	35 to 50	Pathogenic and many non-pathogenic bacteria
Thermophilic	25 to 45	50 to 55	70 to 90	Many spore forming bacteria usually from soil and water

Table 4 shows favorable temperatures for different types of organisms. Buchanan (1951) suggested several distinct growth phases that are applicable to all micro-organisms growing in food material suitable but limited in quantity. This is summarized in Fig. 21.

Since micro-organisms are a series of enzyme systems some of the factors which influence enzyme reactions also influence growth of cultures of micro-organisms. One of these is temperature which is sometimes measured by an index referred to as a temperature coeffficient (Q_{10}). Temperature coefficient is defined by Elliott and Michener (1965) as the ratio of growth rate or activity rate at one temperature to that at a temperature 10°C lower. In general the rate of reaction increases two- to fourfold with each 10°C increase in temperature. Biological organisms do not follow this pattern as close as pure enzyme systems.

Nutritional Requirements

With almost no exception micro-organisms must depend on nutrients for both energy and growth. Because of the surface/volume ratio of micro-organisms energy requirements are high. Generally those organisms found in a particular foodstuff are there because the required nutrients are also in the food. Where they do not exist that particular species of micro-organisms does not survive. Energy requirements vary from simple carbon sources all the way up to complex cellulose compounds which can be broken down by only a very few organisms. Proteins and amino acids can also be used as energy sources. Growth requirements also vary. Some cannot break down proteins; others can grow with very crude nitrogen sources. Accessory food substances influence growth. Some organisms are so sensitive to a particular vitamin that they are used as an assay organism. Occasionally trace mineral deficiencies can prevent growth.

Hydrogen Ion Concentration or pH

Although different micro-organisms grow best at different pH levels, most bacteria grow best at a pH near neutral; yeasts grow in a pH range of 4 to 4.5; and molds can grow over a wide pH range from pH 2–8.5 but favor an acid pH. Some microbiological reactions in food are controlled by pH when one group of organisms ferment sugars so the pH becomes so low other micro-organisms cannot survive.

Inhibitors

Many chemical compounds can inhibit the growth of micro-organisms by inactivating a vital metabolite needed for growth of the organism, by denaturing the protein portion of the cell or by causing physical damage to the parts of the cell.

BIBLIOGRAPHY

Anon. 1947. The Canned Food Reference Manual, 3rd ed. American Can Co., New York.

Buchanan. R. E. and Buchanan, E. D. 1951. Bacteriology, 5th ed. The Macmillan Co., New York.

Elliott, R. P., and Michener, H. D. 1965. Factors Affecting the Growth of Psychrophilic Micro-organisms In Foods. U.S.D.A. Tech. Bull. *1320.*

Frazier, W. C. 1967. Food Microbiology, 2nd ed. McGraw-Hill Book Co., New York.

Goldblith, S. A., Joslyn, M. A., and Nickerson, J. T. R. 1961. Introduction to Thermal Processing of Foods. Avi Publ. Co., Westport, Conn.

Jezeski, J. J., and Olson, R. H. 1962. The activity of enzymes at low temperatures. Proc. Low Temperature Microbiology Symp. 1961, Campbell Soup Co., Camden, N.J.

Morrey, C. B. 1929. Fundamentals of Bacteriology, 4th ed. Lea and Febiger Co., Philadelphia.

Mossell, D. A. A., and Ingram, M. 1955. The physiology of the microbial spoilage of foods. J. Appl. Bacteriol. *18,* 233–268.

Paley, C., and Isaacs, M. L. 1941. The Effect of pasteurization on *escherichia coli* in milk and ice cream mix. J. Dairy Sci *24,* 421–427.

CHAPTER 6

Role of Temperature in Microbial Activity in Foods

The Effect of Temperature upon Micro-organisms

The bacterial cell has no unique mechanism for surviving at temperatures lower or higher than its usual natural environment. A wide temperature range from 32°F to 185°F (0° to 85°C) will permit bacterial cultures to grow, but the speed of growth will vary with each species of bacteria. The biologists think of the optimum temperature as that temperature at which the organisms grow most rapidly in a relatively short time, 2 to 24 hours. A lower temperature than the optimum for a particular organism may produce a large number of cells over a longer incubation period, while increasing the temperature may cause a rapid multiplication but it also speeds up chemical reactions. These reactions may result in synthesis of protoplasm or the generation of energy or both. Finally, they may lead to the destruction of all proteins.

High temperatures tend to accelerate metabolic activities accompanied by very little destruction of enzyme proteins.

Oginsky and Umbreit (1959) have cited references where attempts have been made to show that the maximum growth temperature is slightly below the minimum temperature necessary for the inactivation of cell enzymes. For instance, at least one *Bacillus subtilis* enzyme is inactivated at 131°F (55°C) so that the organism will grow at 130°F (54°C) but not at 131°F (55°C).

These authors also observed that the malic dephosphorylating adenosine triphosphate of thermophilic organisms showed marked resistance to heat. This observation is a new concept in that the enzymes of thermophilic bacteria are no longer protected by a temperature-insensitive protein colloid. It is likely that variations in the sensitivity of most mesophilic organisms to heat may be due to variations in the nature of their enzyme proteins.

Enzyme heat sensitivity may explain why an enzyme capable of synthesizing an essential metabolite is inactive at high incubation temperature. However, the cells may grow if the essential metabolite is added to the culture medium. The enzyme is present and capable of synthesis, but only functions at lower temperatures.

Lactobacillus arabinosus is a good example of an organism which grows at 79°F (26°C) in air, without tyrosine, aspartic acid, or phenylalanine. When this organism is incubated at 98.5°F (37°C) phenylalanine and tyrosine are essential nutrients, and at 103°F (39.4°C) aspartic acid is required. If this culture is incubated at 79°F (26°C) in the absence of CO_2 then all three amino acids must be supplied. Conversely, if CO_2 is added to the medium at a high incubation temperature the organism will grow without aspartic acid or phenylalanine. Oginsky *et al.* (1959) explain this temperature dependence of nutritional requirements on the inactivation of the requisite enzyme(s) at higher incubation temperatures.

One hypothesis explains the enzyme synthesizing pantothenic acid in a genetic mutant of *Escherichia coli* requiring this vitamin if the temperature is above 86°F (30°C). The parent strain of *E. coli* not dependent on pantothenic acid at any temperature showed no comparable inactivation.

Causes of Death by Heating

Lamanna and Mallette (1954) have presented several theories in an attempt to explain (1) the exact physical and chemical mechanisms which bring about the death of a bacterial cell in the presence of water when heated and (2) why there is such a great variation among cultures of the same species in the amount of time and the temperature required to destroy these organisms. ⌊The three theories most generally accepted are that heat inactivates vital enzymes, the cells become intoxicated with their metabolic waste products, or that certain destructive changes take place in the physical state of essential lipids.⌋ Although the exact changes which occur are not completely understood, there are several facts which lend support to each theory.

Denaturation of Proteins by Heat.—Heat causes an irreversible change in proteins called denaturation or coagulation. Since enzymes have a protein structure, they are denatured and inactivated upon heating. The isolation of heat resistant enzymes such as apyrase, cytochrome oxidase, dehydrogenase, and succinoxidase from heat resistant bacteria give support to this theory.

Intoxication.—It is possible that when cells are heated, the metabolism of the cell accelerates to the point where the cell is poisoned by its own metabolic products. However, it is doubtful that sufficient time elapses between heating and the death of the cell for enough toxic substances to accumulate to kill the cell.

Changes in Essential Lipids.—A general relationship exists between the melting points of the fats found in an organism and the temperature range which will bring about its death. Fat from mammals is solid at room temperature, whereas fats from fish have low melting points and are liquid at room temperature. Killing temperatures are lower for fish than for warm blooded animals. Further support of this theory is found in the fact that the heat resistance of spores of *Clostridium botulinum* is much greater when there is an accumulation of higher molecular weight fatty acids in the medium in which the cells are grown.

Effect of Heat on Bacterial Spores

It has been observed that a slight heat shock will stimulate the metabolic activity of an organism. In the case of the endospores and vegetative cells of *Bacillus subtilis* in the presence of methylene blue, the vegetative cells will dehydrogenate glucose at 104°F (40°C) much more rapidly than do the endospores. Also when the vegetative cells and endospores are heat shocked at 176°F (80°C) for 30 minutes and then the temperature reduced to 104°F (40°C), the vegetative cells will no longer reduce methylene blue in the presence of glucose, while the endospore activity has been markedly increased. A second phase of this heat treatment is heating the spores to 176°F (80°C). If the spores that have been activated are heated to this temperature the enzyme systems are destroyed leaving them comparable to the vegetative cells.

The Application of Heat in the Canning Industry

Historical.—In 1782, Scheele suggested the application of heat to preserve vinegar in bottles. In 1810, Appert, a scientist and French confectioner, was awarded 10,000 francs by Napoleon for suggesting the best method for preserving food for his armies. He boiled the food and placed it in bottles under an air-tight seal. It was in the same year that Peter Durand secured a patent from the English government for preserving fruits, fish, and vegetables in sealed cans. About 1819, Ezra Daggett and Thomas Kensett introduced the process in America for packing salmon, lobsters, oysters, and other sea foods. The next year, 1820, Underwood and Mitchel built a canning factory in Boston. They successfully canned cranberries, currants, plums, and quinces.

It is interesting to note that glass jars were used exclusively in the early days of canning. However, they were gradually abandoned because the inferior quality of the glass made them unable to withstand high temperatures. Then too, the jars were expensive, bulky, and costly to transport.

Kensett in 1825 obtained a patent to use tin cans. He built a canning factory for the use of tin cans.

The original Appert method of preserving food by heat was to cook the food in open kettles and then put it into sealed containers.

TABLE 5

STEAM TEMPERATURES RELATED TO PRESSURE

Pressure, Lb. per Sq. In.	Temperature °F	Temperature °C
0	212	100
5	228	109
10	240	115.5
15	251	121.5
20	260	126.5
40	287	141.5

The boiling point, around 212°F (100°C), was the highest temperature obtainable. However, in 1874 a closed kettle was developed which allowed for superheating water with steam. Later steam pressure was used, a forerunner of the present autoclave and more recently the pressure cooker. Relations between steam pressures and temperatures are shown in Table 5.

Factors that may influence the sterilization of canned goods:

1. Number of organisms present in the food prior to sterilization.
2. Kind of organisms present in the food.
3. Size of container in which food is preserved.
4. Reaction, or pH of the food. Fruits are more easily sterilized than foods having a neutral reaction such as corn or peas.
5. Amount of moisture initially present in the food.
6. Ease of heat conduction and convection.
7. Agitation of food during sterilization.
8. Volume of food.
9. Composition of food

Work done at the Idaho Experiment Station several years ago showed the effects of pH associated with different foods and the influence of sporulation on heat resistance. The results are shown in Table 6.

TABLE 6

TIME REQUIRED TO DESTROY THE VIABLE SPORES OF *Clostridium botulinum* IN DIFFERENT FOODS AND AT VARIOUS PH LEVELS

Kind of Food	pH of Food	Temperature 90°C	95°C	100°C	110°C	115°C
		Minutes				
Hominy	6.95	600	495	345	34	10
Corn	6.45	555	465	255	30	15
Spinach	5.10	510	345	225	20	10
String Beans	5.10	510	345	225	20	10
Pumpkin	4.21	195	120	45	15	10
Pears	3.75	135	75	30	10	5
Prunes	3.60	60	20	..	..	..

Time and Temperature Required to Destroy *C. botulinum*, *B. anthracis* (Spore Formers), and *E. coli* (Non-spore Former)

Bacillus anthracis:
8 minutes at 221°F (105°C)
10 minutes at 212°F (100°C)
25 minutes at 203°F (95°C)
45 minutes at 194°F (90°C)

Escherichia coli:
2 minutes at 212°F (100°C)
4 minutes at 170°F (77°C)
10 minutes at 125°F (52°C)
30 minutes at 115°F (46°C)

Clostridium botulinum:
0.78 minutes at 260°F (126.7°C)
1.45 minutes at 255°F (123.9°C)
2.78 minutes at 250°F (121.1°C)
5.27 minutes at 245°F (118.3°C)
10   minutes at 240°F (115.6°C)
36   minutes at 230°F (110.0°C)
150   minutes at 220°F (104.4°C)
330   minutes at 212°F (100.0°C)

Tables 7 and 8 show the importance of temperature to bacterial life.

TABLE 7

TEMPERATURE RELATIONS TO BACTERIAL LIFE

Degrees Fahrenheit	Degrees Centigrade	Temperature Effects on Organisms
250	121	Wet steam temperature at 15 lb. pressure kills all forms including spores in 15 to 20 minutes.
240	115.5	Wet steam temperature at 10 lb. pressure kills all forms including spores in 30 to 40 minutes.
230	110	Wet steam temperature at 6 lb. pressure kills all forms including spores in 60 to 80 minutes.
220	104.5	Wet steam temperature at 2 lb. pressure
212	100	Boiling temperature of pure water at sea level. Kills in vegetative stage quickly but not spores after long exposure.
200	93.3	Growing cells of bacteria, yeasts, and molds are usually killed (180° to 200°F).
190	87.8	
180	82.2	
180	82.2	Thermophilic organisms grow in this range (150° to 180°F).
170	76.7	
160	71.1	
150	65.6	
170	76.6	Pasteurization of milk in 30 minutes kills all the important pathogenic bacteria as far as humans are concerned except the spore forming pathogens (140° to 170°F).
160	71.1	
150	65.6	
140	60.0	
100	37.8	Active growing range for most bacteria, yeast and molds (60° to 100°F).
98.6	37.0	
90.0	32.2	
80.0	26.7	
70.0	21.1	
60.0	15.6	
60	15.6	Growth retarded for most organisms (60°–50°F).
50	10.0	
50	10.0	Optimum growth of psychrophilic organisms (50° to 40°F).
40	4.4	
32	0.0	Freezing. Usually the growth of all organisms is stopped.
0	−17.8	Bacteria preserved in a latent state.
−420	−250	Many species of bacteria are not killed by the temperature of liquid hydrogen.

Adapted from Research Dept. Bulletin, Glass Container Association.

TABLE 8

TEMPERATURE RANGE FOR SAFE STORAGE OF FOODS

Zone I. Sub-freezing Temperatures 0° to 15°F (0° to −18° to −9.4°C)
  a. Frozen meat, fish, and vegetables
  b. Frozen fruits
  c. Ice cream
  d. Homemade frozen desserts

Zone II. High Humidity (85 per cent) and Moderate Air Circulation. 34° to 37°F (1.1° to 2.7°C)
  a. Fresh meat, chicken, and fish
  b. Sliced smoked ham and bacon
  c. Sliced cold cuts of meat
  d. Leftover canned and cooked meat

Zone III. 38° to 40°F (3.3° to 4.4°C)
  a. Fresh milk, cream, and buttermilk
  b. Cottage cheese and butter (both covered)
  c. Fresh orange and tomato juice (covered)
  d. Bottled beverage (for chilling)

Zone IV. 40° to 43°F (4.4° to 6.1°C) Moderate Humidity
  a. Berries, pears, and peaches
  b. Ripe grapefuit and oranges
  c. Ripe tomatoes (short time only)
  d. Fresh eggs
  e. Oleomargarine
  f. Custards and puddings (day or two only)
  g. Prepared salads (for chilling)

Zone V. 40° to 45°F (4.4° to 7.2°C) High Humidity
  a. Cherries and cranberries
  b. Lettuce and celery
  c. Spinach, kale, and other greens
  d. Beets, carrots, parsnips, and turnips
  e. Peas and lima beans
  f. Cucumbers and eggplant (short time only)

Zone VI. 55° to 60°F (12.7° to 15.5°C) Fairly High Humidity and Moderate Circulation. (Good Fruit Cellar or Storage Cellar Well Ventilated.)
  a. Apples, cabbage, potatoes, pumpkin, squash, unripened tomatoes, and maple syrup (in tight container)

Zone VII. Normal Room Temperature. Dry Storage
  a. Ready prepared cereals
  b. Crackers
  c. Bottled beverages

Zone VIII. Normal Room Temperature Storage
  a. Peanut butter and honey
  b. Salad oils and vegetable shortenings
  c. Catsup and pickles
  d. Jelly and preserves
  e. Dried fruits and bananas (short time)
  f. Flour
  g. Dried peas and beans
  h. Sugar and salt

Methods of Preserving Food by Heat

Cooking of Foods.—Boiling is one of the common methods in the preparation of many foods for consumption. In most instances it makes the food more palatable and perhaps more easily digested.

However, boiling the food at atmospheric pressure, which rarely produces a temperature as high as 212°F (100°C) does not insure a complete destruction of all the organisms. [The addition of sugar to the food will raise the temperature above the boiling point.] This procedure was one of the first methods used to preserve food. The food is usually cooked in an open kettle and the contents poured into jars and then securely sealed. This method does not insure sterile food because many of the organisms are not destroyed during the cooking process, especially the spore forming microorganisms and many kinds of thermophilic bacteria.

Cooking does destroy many pathogenic organisms that may be present in foods. Organisms that cause diseases such as tuberculosis, typhoid, paratyphoid, brucellosis, dysentery, tularemia, sore throat, scarlet fever, and diphtheria are easily destroyed by boiling, providing sufficient temperature and time of exposure have been maintained.

[The toxin produced by *Staphylococcus aureus* is heat labile, but not at the temperatures and times ordinarily used for cooking. Food recently contaminated by these bacteria and then eaten may not cause any ill effects. It is the toxin produced by the organisms as a result of their ability to grow in the food when conditions are favorable which causes the ill effects.] Moreover, the mechanism of food poisoning by various species of the *Salmonella* group is not well understood. Illness may result by ingesting the organisms in the food. It appears in this case that food intoxication takes place by the liberation of a toxin after the bacteria have entered the intestinal tract. A more adequate consideration of food poisoning is presented under "Food Poisoning" (Chapter 20). [In general most of the sporulating bacteria which may be present in food at the time it is eaten will cause no ill effects in man.]

[*Clostridium botulinum* spores are not usually pathogenic to man when taken into the body through food. However, when conditions are favorable for their growth in food products, this organism will produce an extremely potent toxin which is often fatal. Fortunately, heating the food to a boiling temperature usually inactivates or destroys *botulinum* toxin. However, the spores of *Cl. botulinum* are very resistant to heat and can withstand boiling temperature for several hours.]

Baking.—An oven temperature of 350° to 400°F (175° to 205°C) in the baking industry is usually misleading. During the baking process just as long as the food remains moist the maximum temperature reached is rarely over 212°F (100°C).]

[Baked goods are likely to have low heat conductivity. Lack of convection currents prevents heat penetration and moisture loss also has a cooling effect. All of these factors make baking less effective than boiling as a means of destroying micro-organisms in food.]

Frying.—Although frying kills most micro-organisms it may not destory all micro-organisms in food. Obviously, spore forming organisms, thermophilic and heat resistant strains of bacteria are not killed by frying. This is especially true for those organisms present in the interior of the food.

Trichinella—It is important to relate the effect of cooking on other organisms beside bacteria. A disease known as trichinosis, caused by a parasite infecting pork, can cause serious illness in man especially when the meat is not properly cooked. Investigations have shown that *Trichinella spiralis* larvae are usually killed by heating the meat to 137°F (59.2°C) or storing the product at a cold temperature of 5°F (−15°C) for 30 days. Adequate cooking of the pork is absolutely necessary to destroy the larvae since meat inspection fails to detect their presence.

Cooking garbage fed to swine is one way to control this disease. It has been estimated that 5 per cent of the swine were infected as the result of eating raw garbage and 10 per cent from receiving raw offal from slaughterhouses.

Cold Pack.—The cold pack method has been widely used in the past. However, it is not generally used at the present time for preserving many kinds of vegetables and fruits. The raw food is packed in jars cold and then a brine or syrup is usually added. The jars are closed loosely and heated in a water bath at a temperature well under the boiling point of water. Sometimes the food is blanched before packing in the jar. Certainly this is advantageous in reducing the microflora on the raw product. In the past "cold pack" has been responsible for much of the spoilage of foods. There have been many outbreaks of "botulism" since the method was introduced in 1917. It is a very poor method for preserving vegetables and meats since the entire load of micro-organisms on the raw material go into the jar unless the microbial load is reduced by blanching.

Hot Pack.—The "hot pack" is a modification of the "cold pack," except that the food is given a short precooking before packing in the jars. The temperatures obtained in the "hot pack" method are comparable to boiling or cooking the food in an open kettle. The fundamental factors are temperature and time.

Oven Process—Another method widely used is the "oven process" and it is often recommended by stove manufacturers. Needless to say this method is expensive and certainly unsafe to use. Food is placed in presumably sterile jars and remains unsealed during the heating period in the oven. The temperature of the food rarely reaches 212°F (100°C), and the heat penetration into the center of the food in the jar is very slow.

Studies at Purdue University have dealt with the slow heat penetration in the oven process. A quart of water at 68°F (20°C) was placed in a preheated oven at 275°F (135°C) and it required from 95 to 110 minutes for the water to reach the boiling point.

Pasteurization.—Another method used is to heat food, e.g., milk, to 142° to 145°F (61° to 63°C), holding it at that temperature for 30 minutes. In ice cream, the pasteurization temperature is several degrees higher because cream serves to protect the organisms from destruction as compared to raw whole milk. Recently, flash, or short time pasteurization, is gradually replacing the holding method in the pasteurization of raw milk. Briefly, the milk is exposed in a thin film at a temperature of 160° to 171°F (71° to 77°C) from 15 to 19 seconds. This later method is more economical and has several advantages over the holding method of pasteurization.

Many foods can be preserved, at least for short periods of time, by the pasteurization process. However, its application to food preservation should not be confused with complete sterilization of the food product as in many kinds of canned foods. Perhaps the pasteurization of dried fruits may serve to show the effect upon the survival of micro-organisms associated with these products.

Dried fruits as a rule contain micro-organisms. Pasteurization of figs, prunes, and raisins at temperatures ranging from 159.8° to 185°F (71° to 85°C) and held from 30 to 90 minutes showed a reduction around 90 per cent in the microbial content. Likewise, when dates, figs, prunes, or raisins were suspended in a viable broth culture of *Escherichia coli* and the fruits subjected to 160°F (71°C) for 30 minutes, with a humidity of 75 per cent or above, the test organisms were destroyed.

Pasteurization of dates and figs has been recommended from the public health standpoint. Some French packaged dates were examined several years ago and the investigators found large numbers of *Escherichia coli* present. The survival of several varieties of intestinal organisms is a reflection of the general sanitary practices employed in handling and processing dried fruits. The author has immersed dried dates in a viable culture of *Salmonella typhi* and recovered the live test organisms 72 days after inoculation. Obviously dried fruits can be an important factor in the spread of certain enteric organisms that are important to public health.

Pasteurization of different types of food: At the present time there is a tendency to pasteurize all foods that may be consumed in the raw state. Some states have recommended, or have enacted laws requiring the pasteurization of all milk before it is processed into cheese or ice cream. Many kinds of food cannot be preserved by pasteurization because the heat treatment will damage the physical properties, the texture, and flavor of the food. The temperature and time of pasteurization will vary with the method used and the food product. This process should not be confused with sterilization. The latter means complete destruction of all life.

Fellers (1930) studied the survival of Coliforms and Salmonella typhi on dried fruits. He found these organisms were killed in 30 minutes at 160°F (71.1°C) when the humidity was 75 per cent or more.

Few organisms are found on sulfured fruits or on very acid fruits, due to the sulfurous or natural acid present in these products. Hence, these foods are much easier to sterilize than those of less acidity.

The work of Auzulovic and Reedy (1942) on the pasteurization of crab meat showed that it kept as long as 5 weeks when stored at 41° to 43°F (5° to 6°C) after heating to 145°F (63°C) for 30 minutes, or 150°F (66°C) 20 minutes, or 170°F (77°C) for one minute. Moreover, the meat was free of Escherichia coli and there was no appreciable change in the color, odor, or flavor.

The effect of pasteurization on the microflora in milk and other dairy products is well known. The process is so firmly established in the dairy industry that it is considered a routine practice and the results of pasteurization are unchallenged by public health officials. Public health reports show a steady decline in Brucellosis, Streptococcus infections, and tuberculosis when pasteurization of milk is carried on routinely in the dairy plant. Probably no other food product can show as good a public health record as milk and other dairy products. Obviously the infected animal must be eliminated from the herd in order to insure the safety of the product. Good herd management together with proper pasteurization has made milk, although one of the most perishable foods, one of the safest food products consumed by man.

Since ice cream is widely consumed, this product can be an important vehicle in the spread of pathogenic bacteria. The low temperature at which this product is kept is not sufficient to insure its safety for the public.

Hammer and Sanders (1919) examined several samples of ice cream mix before and after pasteurization at 141.8° to 150.8°F (61 to 66°C) for 20 minutes. The counts ranged from 56,000 to 15,300,-

000 per ml. before pasteurization and were reduced to from 170 to 66,000 per ml. after pasteurization.

Fay and Olson (1924) showed that pasteurization of the ice cream mix at 150.8°F (66°C) for 30 minutes reduced the average bacterial count by 98.69 per cent.

Paley and Isaacs (1941) stated that *Escherichia coli* survived twice as long in ice cream mix as in milk at 143.6°F (62°C). They attributed the protective action to the presence of stabilizers. Their results are shown in Table 9.

TABLE 9

SURVIVAL OF *E. coli* IN MILK AND ICE CREAM AT 143°F[1]

Experiment No.	No. Organisms/Ml. Before Heating		No. Organisms/Ml. Surviving After				
			10 Min.	20 Min.	25 Min.	30 Min.	35 Min.
			Milk				
1	1,000,000[2]		0.0	0.0	0.0		
2	"		3.7	0.0	0.0		
3	"		450.0	0.0	0.0		
4	"	(0.7)	0.0	0.0	0.0		
5	"	(2.0)	0.0	0.0	0.0		
6	"	(0.7)	29.0	0.0	0.0		
7	"	(1.1)	0.0	0.0	0.0		
8	"	(0.9)	0.0	0.0	0.0		
Average	1,000,000	(1.4)	0.0	0.0	0.0		
			Ice Cream Mix				
1	1,000,000[2]	(2.6)	6,400	1,500.0	170.0	18.0	35.0
2	"	(2.2)	7,700	0.4	0.0	0.4	0.4
3	"	(0.5)	120,000	1,600.0	36.0	0.0	0.0
4	"	(1.8)	890	0.6	1.2	2.4	1.2
5	"	(16)	5,100	180.0	5.0	0.3	0.0
6	"	(1.0)	2,100	14.0	2.0	1.0	1.0
7	"	(0.6)	1,100	33.0	0.0	0.0	0.0
8	"	(0.5)	44	2.0	0.0	0.0	0.0
Average	1,000,000		18,000	416.0	27.0	2.8	0.2

[1] Paley and Isaacs, (1941).
[2] The data have been calculated on the basis of an initial 1,000,000 organisms. The actual counts in millions are given in parentheses.

Thermophiles and Thermodurics.—Heat resistant bacteria constitute an important group of organisms in heat treated foods. Their ability to grow at temperatures ranging from 15° to 25°F (8.3° to 13.9°C) above the pasteurization temperature of milk is well known. Yet such a heat treatment will coagulate blood serum and egg albumin and produce painful burns on the skin of human beings.

Another group of organisms closely related to the thermophiles are called thermodurics. The term is not well defined and may be confusing to the layman. Thermoduric organisms, as the name indicates, are "heat tolerant" as contrasted to thermophilic microorganisms which implies "heat lovers or heat resistant." The former group can survive pasteurization of milk for short periods of time. However, the fundamental difference between thermophiles and thermoduric organisms is that thermophiles can grow and survive at high temperatures while thermodurics cannot grow but may survive for short periods of time at high temperature. Lowering the temperature to the minimum range for thermophilic bacteria will greatly favor the growth of thermoduric organisms. How much heat an organism can withstand before it can be classified as a thermoduric or thermophilic is not yet accurately defined.

A tentative classification has been suggested, viz., referring to all organisms as thermoduric if they are not killed by pasteurization at 143°F (61.6°C) for 30 minutes. Bacteria that are metabolically active above 113°F (45°C) may be called thermophilic.

When an organism grows at ordinary temperatures as well as high temperatures it is called a facultative thermophile. Obviously most thermophilic bacteria are also thermoduric.

Heat loving bacteria are widely distributed in nature. They are abundant in decaying organic matter, surface soil, water, sewage, hay, cereals, milk, dust, dirt, and filth. They are commonly associated with dirty dairy utensils. In fact, their frequency on milk equipment can be used by the sanitarian as an index of the sanitary practices that are followed on the dairy farm and in the dairy plant.

Root crops and grains that are grown on heavily manured soils contain large numbers of thermophilic organisms.

It is common knowledge that thermophilic bacteria do not have any public health significance. No toxins, such as those produced by food poisoning organisms, are produced by thermophiles.

Storage at high temperatures: All food products preserved in sealed containers should never be stored near steam pipes, boilers, hot air registers, or direct sunshine. The increase in temperature may be sufficient to permit thermophilic organisms to grow.

In canned food thermophilic bacteria may survive the heating process. If the container is "airtight" then anaerobic spore formers should be suspected. Usually their metabolic activities are marked by putrefactive odors with gas formation. The majority of thermophilic organisms found in foods are aerobic or are facultative with respect to oxygen. Unfortunately, these micro-organisms can survive and grow under a wide variety of conditions. Many of these organisms are spore formers and very resistant to heat. A summary of the properties of these organisms is shown in Table 10.   Fig. 22 shows the relation between temperature and sanitation.

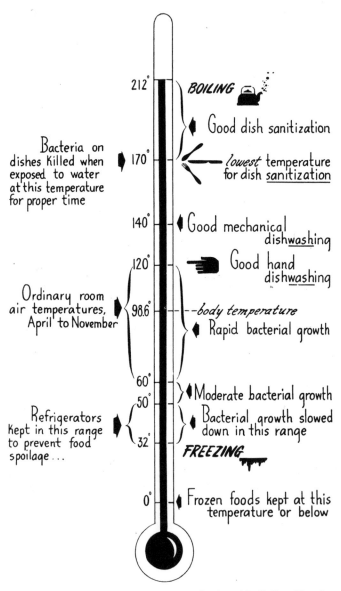

Courtesy of Institutions Magazine

FIG. 22.   TEMPERATURE AND FOOD SANITATION

TABLE 10

THERMOPHILES OF IMPORTANCE TO THE FOOD INDUSTRIES

Name	Economic Importance	Heat Resist-ant Spores	Growth Temperatures		Oxygen Require-ments
			Opti-mum Degrees F	Range, Degrees F	
Streptococcus thermophilus	Grow during pasteurization of milk. Ripening agent in Swiss Cheese.	None	120	77–140	Facultative
Lactobacillus bulgaricus	Bulgaricus milk. In making lactic acid	None	120	77–140	Facultative
Lactobacillus thermophilus	Grow during pasteurization of milk.	None	131	86–150	Facultative
Lactobacillus delbruckii	Acidification of brewery mash. Lactic acid manufacture.	None	113	?	Facultative
Bacillus calidolactis	Coagulates milk at high temperatures	Yes	131–149	113–167	Facultative
Bacillus thermo-acidurans	Flat sour spoilage of tomato juice	Yes	131	?	Facultative
Bacillus stearo-thermophilus	Flat sour spoilage of canned foods	Yes	122	113–169	Facultative
Clostridium thermosac-charolyticum	Hard swells of canned foods	Yes	131–143	110–160	Anaerobic
Clostridium nigrificans	Sulfide-stinkers of canned foods	Yes	131	?–158	Anaerobic

BIBLIOGRAPHY

Anon. 1947. The Canned Food Reference Manual, 3rd ed. American Can Co., New York.

Buchanan, R. E., and Buchanan, E. D. 1951. Bacteriology, 5th ed. The Macmillan Co., New York.

Fay, A. C., and Olsen, N. E. 1924. Bacterial content of ice cream. J. Dairy Sci. 7, 330–356.

Fellers, C. R. 1930. Pasteurization of dried fruits. Am. J. Public Health 20, 175.

Goldblith, S. A., Joslyn, M. A., and Nickerson, J. T. R. 1961. Introduction to Thermal Processing of Foods. Avi Publishing Co., Westport, Conn.

Hammer, B. W., and Sanders, L. R. 1919. A Bacteriological Study of the Method of Pasteurizing and Homogenizing the Ice Cream Mix. Iowa Agr. Expt. Station Bull., 186.

Lamanna, C., and Mallette, M. F. 1953. Basic Bacteriology. The Williams and Wilkins Co., Baltimore.

Oginsky, E. L., and Umbreit, W. W. 1959. An Introduction to Bacterial Physiology, 2nd ed. W. H. Freeman Co., San Francisco.

Paley, C., and Isaacs, M. L. 1941. The effect of pasteurization on *Escherichia coli* in milk and ice cream mix. J. Dairy Sci. 24, 421–427.

CHAPTER 7

Microbiology of Foods at Low Temperatures

Cold has been used since prehistoric times to preserve food. The development of rapid freezing and dehydration of nearly all types of foods makes it possible to preserve them for a long time and to maintain the foods in a good physical state as well as retain nutritional value. The consumption of frozen foods has increased many fold and no doubt will continue to increase each year in the home and commercial cold storage lockers.

It is a well known fact that freezing temperature is not an effective means of destroying micro-organisms in foods. [Although the total number of organisms usually is reduced in foods held at low temperatures, there may be as many generic types present at the end of the storage period as in the original unfrozen food.]

Since cold is not an effective means of destroying micro-organisms, the potential dangers of certain infections may be significant in public health. The danger is increased further by lack of antemortem and postmortem inspection of meat placed in home sized lockers. The handling of such meat under unsanitary conditions and use of infected animals makes the problem all the more important from the public health standpoint. No food product is rendered safe by refrigeration.

Psychrophilic micro-organisms are frequently referred to as "cold lovers." The importance of this group in certain kinds of food has not been fully appreciated. [As a rule this group of organisms does not have any public health significance] However, they can bring about profound undesirable biochemical changes in many kinds of foods held under refrigeration for a long time. Kennedy and Weiser (1950) studied the effects of these organisms in market milk supplies in which these organisms not only increased in numbers but caused a pronounced off-flavor in the milk. It is reasonable to conclude that their presence in other foods besides milk would have similar effects.

[Fortunately most of the psychrophilic bacteria are easily destroyed by heat since the majority of the group are non-spore forming organisms.] A few members of this group may acquire a heat resistant tendency and are able to withstand the conventional method of pasteurization of milk. This may be one explanation for the presence of these bacteria in market milk.

There are many varieties of bacteria that are able to carry on their metabolic activities slightly above the freezing temperature, 32°F (0°C). Low temperature should not be relied upon to destroy microorganisms; it merely slows up their multiplication and thus reduces their metabolic activities. The author has observed that *Staphylococcus aureus*, a food poisoning strain, has survived at 41°F (5°C) for two years in ice cream. Ordinarily such a temperature is not the optimum for this organism to multiply and produce an enterotoxin. This is the basic principle involved in the preservation of many kinds of perishable foods. [Low temperature retards the metabolic activity of the organisms so that growth or multiplication practically ceases./ If the frozen food is allowed to thaw out, the higher temperature favors the growth of the organisms. This is one good reason why frozen food should never be refrozen. It is a practice dangerous to public health.

Low Temperature

At low temperatures cells continue to carry on their metabolic activities very slowly because their enzymatic processes are functioning at a low rate. This does not usually cause a destruction of cell proteins. [At or below the freezing point, ice crystals will form, the size of the crystals depending upon the temperature and rate of cooling. If small crystals are formed, the turgidity of the cell is maintained.] This is the principle of lyophilization where frozen and dried cultures may remain viable for years. The author has kept non-spore forming bacterial cultures for 5 years and they are still viable.

The mechanism of death of bacteria at low temperatures is not well understood and leaves much speculation in the minds of bacteriologists. It is true that low temperature does affect the colloidal state of protoplasm/and in turn would tend to destroy the cell.

\The crystallization of water by freezing would no doubt disturb the colloidal state, or it might result in the mechanical crushing of the bacterial cell. Again, death to the cell may be due to "salt death" or excessive concentration of crystalloids as the pure solvent separates from a solution.] Freezing and thawing can become more destructive by altering the colloidal state of the protoplasm in the cell. Bacteria that survive freezing and thawing several times usually can be kept at low temperatures for a long time. Lyophilization or dehydration below freezing is a well known process for preserving cultures.

The work of Kiser and Beckwith (1942) is especially interesting because it shows how the combination of the acidity of strawberries and the presence of dissolved sugar destroys *S. typhi* in a few hours at room temperature. However, when berries were held at temperatures just above freezing for a few days there seemed to be very little effect upon the survival of the test bacteria at 0°F (−18°C).

A public health hazard is evident when the berries are washed in polluted water at the patch. Assuming that these berries are quick frozen, they would be thawed out only a short time before they are consumed. Obviously, the berries would not be washed in the home because of the loss of juice.

Cold-Sensitive Bacteria

There are a few kinds of bacteria that depend upon the bodies of animals for their existence. When these organisms are removed from their host, they are able to survive only a very short time even at slightly reduced temperatures. Meningococci and gonococci are very quickly destroyed at freezing temperature. Kopeloff and Etchells (1934) state that *Lactobacillus acidophilus* can survive much better at room temperature than when it is placed in a refrigerator. The rough strain[1] of *L. acidophilus*, or the one having the only dependable therapeutic value in man, appeared to have lost its viability at 41° to 49°F (5° to 9.4°C) as compared with storage at 69° to 86°F (20° to 30°C). When the initial titratable acidity ranged from 0.6 to 1 per cent the original count of *L. acidophilus* decreased by approximately 90 per cent, when held in the refrigerator. However when the culture was stored at room temperature only 20 to 75 per cent of the test organisms died.

Because of the wide use of commercial and home freezing units to preserve food, the growth and metabolic activity of organisms at low temperatures becomes more important as to flavor, texture, and public health aspects.

Molds, such as *Cladosporium, Sporotrichum, Penicillium,* and *Monilia* will grow at temperatures ranging from 24.8°F (−4°C) to 20°F (−6.7°C). Yeasts may be grouped in the same temperature range as molds. Bacteria have a comparable temperature range with molds and yeasts. However, some species of bacteria such as *Achromobacter, Alcaligenes, Flavobacterium,* and *Pseudomonas* grow at temperatures above freezing.

A marked reduction of organisms may take place in frozen foods, but the lethal effect may be due primarily to some form of denatura-

---

[1] The term "rough" refers to the typical appearance of a colony of this strain as distinguished from the smooth appearance of the colonies of another strain of the same organism when both are grown on plates.

tion, flocculation of cell proteins or holding the organisms in a bacteriostatic state, comparable to the hibernation of certain animals during the cold months.
The factors influencing the destruction of micro-organisms in frozen foods are (1) kind of organism, and whether or not it sporulates, for instance, mold spores are very resistant to freezing, (2) fast versus slow freezing, fast freezing seems to be less lethal than slow freezing, but there are differences of opinion, and (3) the kind of food substrate. Sugar, salt, proteins, colloids and fat may serve as protective agents, while high moisture and high acidity may accelerate the destruction of organisms. The viability of organisms in frozen foods tends to decrease as time goes on. If death does occur, it may be due to plain starvation of the cell, in other words, the inability of the cell to utilize the nutrients as a source of energy.

Blanching Prior to Freezing

Heat treatment of foods is desirable in order to improve the keeping quality of the frozen product. This process called blanching is done before freezing. The following is accomplished by the blanching process: (1) destruction of large numbers of micro-organisms on the surface of the food, thereby decreasing the microflora of the product during the processing stages, (2) inactivation of most inherent enzymes in the food which would otherwise contribute to the deterioration of the product during the storage period, (3) a removal of much of the mucilage-like substance from the raw material which contributes to off-flavors, (4) the preservation of the natural color of the food, sometimes referred to as "color set," (5) a removal of an appreciable amount of extraneous substances which would otherwise contribute to many undesirable flavors in the canned product, (6) a preheating of the product causing the shrinking, wilting or softening of the tissues thereby making it much easier to fill the container.

Preservation of Fruit Color

The retention of the original color in fruits during storage is very important from the consumer's viewpoint. There are two concepts in regard to the cause of "browning" or discoloration of fruits: (1) chemical reaction between the fruit tissue and the oxygen of the air, and (2) activation of inherent enzymes in the fruit.

Blanching and the use of certain antioxidant chemicals are valuable in minimizing discoloration. Scalding or blanching tends to inactivate the inherent enzymes thus preventing the biochemical changes in the product that may contribute to discoloration. This method is effective and recommended for all vegetables; however, for fruits it has a tendency to destroy some of the fine delicate volatile fruit flavors. The use of antioxidants is gaining in popularity because these compounds tend to overcome some of the disadvantages of blanching. Antioxidants may be classified or grouped as follows: (1) Organic acids such as citric acid which is an inherent and flavorful acid of citrus fruits. This acid has been used with success in preventing the darkening of peaches, apples, apricots, and pears. (2) Sulfuring of fruits, especially those fruits for dehydration, has been used for a long time. Sulfite and sulfur dioxide are the common forms of sulfur used. However, certain precautions as to concentration and time of exposure must be followed in order to make a good product. (3) The use of vitamins such as ascorbic acid which is a good reducing agent prevents browning of cut fruits for freezing. This method has the added advantage of improving the vitamin content of the fruit. More recent use of antioxidants has involved the combination of antioxidants with organic acids for preservation of fruit color.

Blanching Methods for Fruits

Esselen, Fellers, and McConnell (1949) have outlined a splendid review of the literature on "frozen apples and apple products." The darkening or browning of sliced apples is undersirable from the standpoint of the physical appearance and the alteration of the quality of the product. Methods for preventing darkening are outlined as follows.

Blanching is one of the common methods used at the present time. It consists of blanching the sliced apples or any other food product in steam, hot water, or hot syrup long enough to inactivate the oxidative enzymes present in the apple tissue. Steam is preferable over hot water or syrup because there is less loss of soluble solids and flavor constituents.

Deaeration.—This method involves a replacement of the gases in the apple tissue by water, brine, or syrup. The process consists of exhausting the oxygen in the plant tissue through respiration while submerged in a dilute salt brine or under vacuum. However, sliced apples so treated tend to be water logged and show a high degree of shrinkage when baked in pies.

Sulfur Dioxide.—Sulfurous acid has been widely used in the preparation of frozen apples. Liquid sulfur dioxide, sodium bisulfite, sodium, or potassium metabisulfite may be used as a source of sulfur dioxide in the dipping solution. Usually a solution concentration range from 2,000 to 3,000 p.p.m. from 2 to 5 minutes is satisfactory for most fruits. The fruit slices should then be held from 6 to 8 hours before they are frozen to permit complete penetration of the sulfur dioxide.

Ascorbic and Other Acids.—Recently ascorbic acid has been widely used to prevent browning, although in apples the penetration of the acid is very slow. In spite of this objection, there are many advantages attributed to the use of ascorbic acid. No foreign flavors or odors are introduced, no heat is required, and the natural soluble solids and flavors of the fruit are retained.

Food Preservation by Low Temperature

There are many factors involved in the preservation of food by low temperatures. Perhaps specific examples may be emphasized in our discussion of frozen foods.

A technique involving a drying process has been used to preserve bacterial cultures for long periods of time. The "chryochem" or "lyophile" process is based on the principle of rapid freezing of an aqueous solution containing the organisms. This is accomplished by partially sealing the material in small containers and freezing instantaneously in dry ice ($-78°C$). The frozen ampoules are attached to a high vacuum. A modification of this technique has been used to preserve certain kinds of food products such as fruit juices. However, there are many limitations, among them high costs, in the use of this method in the food industry.

Freezing and drying in many cases prolong the life of certain micro-organisms. Swift (1937) stated that when streptococci are completely dried while in a frozen state, they will survive for many years. Some effects of low temperatures on the survival of micro-organisms in refrigerated foods are discussed in the following sections.

Cold Shock.—A 90 per cent cell reduction has been observed in *Escherichia coli* when grown at 113°F (450°C), and then transferred to a culture medium and held at 50°F (10°C). Sudden change in environmental conditions slows up the metabolism of the organisms, but does not necessarily kill all of them.

The freezing of a liquid food product also subjects the micro-organisms to certain physical and chemical changes related to the viscosity of the product, and rate of crystallization. These factors tend to influence dissolved materials in the food during freezing. Obviously if the frozen mass is not uniform throughout the food product, there may be areas favorable for microbial growth or unfavorable areas may result in the destruction of the organisms.

Staphylococcus aureus remained viable after the culture was exposed to −252°C (21°C above absolute zero) for 2 hours. Presumably absolute zero is the temperature at which molecular activity ceases. Many investigators maintain that staphylococci show a greater resistance to freezing as compared to other bacteria occurring in frozen vegetables. Staphylococci isolated from frozen pack vegetables were capable of producing enterotoxin, the toxin usually associated with staphylococcus food poisoning.

It has been shown that many food poisoning strains of staphylococci can grow very rapidly in certain kinds of vegetables held at room temperature.

In the case of *Trichinella spiralis*, refrigeration killed the larvae imbedded in the meat as illustrated in the following summary.

Temperature, Degrees F	Days of Freezing Necessary for Death	
	Large Pieces of Meat	Small Pieces of Meat
−5	30	20
−10	20	10
−20	12	6

Clostridium botulinum spores and toxin are very resistant to freezing. However, if the toxin is produced in the food before it is frozen, it is dangerous for human consumption although the spores of this organism may be eaten along with the food with no particular ill effects. Botulinum toxin is readily destroyed by boiling. The work of Tanner and Oglesley (1936) showed that growth occurred and toxin was produced at 68°F (20°C) when detoxified spores were inoculated. At 59°F (15°C) germination and toxin production from heated spores did not occur very often. Growth at 50°F (10°C) occurred only after 27 days and germination of spores had not taken place in 47 days at this temperature. Hence, frozen foods held at room temperature for a few days may be dangerous, but when they are kept below 50°F (10°C) the food may remain safe for a long time.

The work of McCallum and Kirkpatrick (1934) studied the survival and virulence of *Mycobacterium tuberculosis* (bovis) in milk from an infected cow. The milk was frozen and at stated intervals samples were injected into guinea pigs. The authors showed that the infected milk produced active tuberculosis in the experimental animals after the milk was kept at 32°F (0°C) for 32 months. Moreover, these investigators have shown that high amounts of *M. tuberculosis* (bovis) inoculated into fresh normal raw milk and held at 32°F (0°C) will survive up to 12 months although no virulence test was run on the milk. Again this observation emphasizes the survival of pathogenic organisms in milk during the normal souring process. Apparently the organisms are able to adjust their enzyme systems to such an environment. Similarly if the pH of the milk is adjusted to the point comparable to the sour milk and properly buffered, the organisms will survive only a very short time. McCullough (1945) has indicated that the natural acidity of various fruit juices destroys many kinds of micro-organisms very quickly.

Many kinds of viruses and pathogenic protozoa are likewise very resistant to low temperatures, and thus they may be a threat to public health. Viruses under conditions difficult for bacteria remain viable over long periods of time.

Germicidal Properties of Low Temperatures

The status of cold as a germicide: Alternate freezing and thawing have not proved successful in attenuating organisms. For instance, *Bacillus anthracis* was frozen with carbon dioxide at $-90°F$ and thawed in water 21 times in succession without losing any of its virulence. *Staphylococcus aureus* and *Salmonella typhi* were frozen in liquid air at $-182°$ to $-190°C$ for 20 hours without destroying the viability of these organisms. Likewise, staphylococci have been dried and exposed to liquid air for several months. This treatment also failed to destroy *Brucella abortus* (suis) in the tissues of a swine carcass exposed for 30 days at $-10°F$ $(-23.3°C)$.

TABLE 11

EFFECT OF FREEZING ICE CREAM MIX ON TYPHOID BACILLI

Samples Taken	Typhoid Bacilli per Ml. of Ice Cream Mix
5 days old	51,000,000
20 days old	10,000,000
70 days old	2,200,000
342 days old	660,000
430 days old	51,000
648 days old	30,000
2 years old	6,300
2 years, 4 months old	Viable typhoid bacilli

NOTE: This work clearly indicates how difficult it is to destroy micro-organisms by cold.

Freezing temperatures failed to destroy the organisms in samples of milk from a tuberculous cow even after 32 months. Tanner and Oglesby (1936) inoculated a standard ice cream mix with *Salmonella typhi* and then froze it. They placed the mix in a hardening room where the temperature was maintained about $-40°F$ $(-40°C)$. Table 11 shows the results of this experiment.

THE PHYSICAL PRINCIPLES OF THE FREEZING PROCESS

The freezing of any foodstuff implies the removal of heat from the product until a temperature of 0°F has been reached. Hence a physical change takes place from an unfrozen to a frozen state. The initial freezing process involves cooling the material to the freezing point by the removal of heat in the case of water amounting to one British thermal unit per pound per degree drop in temperature. Foods of low moisture content require fewer B.t.u.'s for freezing than those of high moisture content. This step in the cooling process takes place very rapidly because of the wide differences in temperature between the warm food and the cold refrigerating medium. As the food reaches the freezing temperature, the rate of heat transfer slows down. At this point the actual freezing of the food begins.

TABLE 12

SPECIFIC AND LATENT HEATS OF FOODS

Food Product	Specific Heat (B.t.u./Lb.) Freezing Before	After	Latent Heat of Fusion (B.t.u./Lb.)
Asparagus	0.94	0.48	134
Bacon	0.50	0.30	29
Raspberries	0.85	0.45	122
Strawberries	0.92	0.47	129
Beef (lean)	0.77	0.40	100
Beef (fat)	0.60	0.35	79
Beef (dried)	0.22-0.34	0.19-0.26	7-22
Cabbage	0.94	0.47	132
Carrotts	0.90	0.46	126
Eggs (crated)	0.76	0.40	90
Fish (frozen)	0.76	0.41	101
Fish (dried)	0.56	0.34	65
Green peas	0.79	0.42	106
Milk	0.93	0.49	124
Lamb	0.67	0.30	83.5
Oysters (shell)	0.83	0.44	116
Poultry (frozen)	0.79	0.37	106
Pork (fresh)	0.68	0.38	86.5
Beans (string)	0.91	0.47	128
Veal	0.71	0.39	91

Source: Anon. (1967).

During the freezing process the temperature of the food changes very little while the latent heat of fusion is removed. Latent heat will vary from 22 B.t.u. per pound for dried beef to 144 B.t.u. per pound, the latent heat of water, for fruits and vegetables with a high water content.

Table 12 shows specific heat ranges of various foods before and after freezing and the corresponding latent heat of fusion.

Calculation of the Amount of Heat Removed in the Freezing of Foods

If the initial temperature, the freezing point, and the storage temperatures are known, it is possible to calculate how much heat must be removed per pound of food in order to freeze it. The heat removal can be expressed in the formula $Q = W[C_1(t_1 - t_f) + h_f + C_2(t_f - t_3)]$. Q is the total heat removed from W pounds of food. C_1 and C_2 are specific heats of the food before and after freezing: t_1, t_f, and t_3 represent temperatures before cooling, at the freezing point, and at the end, respectively, and h_f is the latent heat of fusion. If 2 lbs. of shelled oysters having a temperature of 55°F (12.78°C) are frozen and chilled to 0°F (−17.78°C) approximately 0.90 B.t.u. per degree per pound must be removed, in order to lower the temperature from 55°F to 30°F (12.78° to −1.11°C). The heat loss is 2 × 0.90 × (55 − 30) = 45 B.t.u. Also, 124 B.t.u. per pound of latent heat or a total of 248 B.t.u. must be removed. Finally, the oysters are brought to zero °F from 30°F (−1.11°C) by removing 0.46 B.t.u. per degree per pound. Hence, 2 × 0.46 × (30 − 0) = 27.6 B.t.u. is required. The total heat removal is the sum of the three quantities or 45 + 248 + 27.6 = 230.6 B.t.u. for 2 lbs. or 160.3 B.t.u. per pound. This is approximately equivalent to freezing one pound of water at 32°F (0°C), and then lowering it to 0°F (−17.78°C). This would require 161.0 B.t.u.

Mechanism of Freezing

No doubt the formation of ice crystals takes place when food products are frozen, due to the presence of free water in, or on the surface of, the food. In food packages, air will be trapped between the wrapping material and the food or between the portions of food. During the freezing process, moisture from warm food will form as vapor on the surface of the wrapper and will condense and freeze faster than frost forms in the food itself. If quick freezing is employed the moisture will freeze in place, hence the formation of ice crystals. The presence of salt or sugar in the food will lower the freezing point below that of pure water. In weak salt or sugar solutions, the freezing process will result in the formation of ice crystals. Obviously, the remaining solution tends to become more concentrated and thus lowers its freezing point to the eutectic point where all the liquid that remains unfrozen freezes solid. Sometimes the eutectic point may be below 0°F (−17.78°C) so that some of the liquid may remain unfrozen as in a heavy syrup.

In freezing some foods, ice crystals may be formed either within or between the cell tissue. The size of crystals will depend upon the rate of freezing.

In slow freezing, the ice crystals tend to become larger and they actually rupture the cell walls which results in a partial breakdown of the physical structure of the food cell tissue. Such a condition is detrimental and usually contributes to a poor quality product. Fruits and vegetables that are fresh, crisp, and firm before freezing become soft and mushy after being subjected to slow freezing.

Frozen foods tend to dehydrate very rapidly while held in storage unless some precautions are taken to minimize this condition. Dehydration is due to a difference in vapor pressure. The water vapor tends to migrate to the colder area of the cooling coils where the vapor pressure is lower. Here the vapor condenses with the formation of frost.

Unwrapped foods are very susceptible to drying out on the surface. This is sometimes called "freezer burn" as in the case of poultry. Careful wrapping will reduce the air space and thus avoid serious drying.

Effect of Freezing on Enzymes

Enzymes differ in their power to survive at low temperatures. A partial inactivation of some of the more labile enzymes, such as dehydrogenases, may alter the type and rate of biochemical changes produced.

Hepburn (1950) summarized the early literature on the effect of low temperature upon enzyme activity. He reported that many enzymes survived temperatures varying from $-17.78°$ to $-312°F$ ($0°$ to $-191°C$) (liquid air) either in tissues or in solution. Morris and Barker (1932) reviewed the effects of low temperatures on enzyme kinetics and stated that enzymes are not inactivated by storage as low as $-303°F$ ($-186°C$). The author believed that the ice formation in the cell tissue had a retarding effect upon the enzymes, in foods in the frozen state. No doubt the physical and colloidal properties of a system, when it passes from a liquid to solid state, has an effect upon the enzymes.

Inherent enzymes in the food will continue to act in cold storage although the action is very slow. It becomes apparent that any procedure that will inactivate or retard enzyme activity in the food is highly desirable. Heat treatment, commonly called blanching, or the use of harmless chemicals such as vitamin C or citric acid on fruits or vegetables is recommended. Moreover, the addition of syrup to fruit will partially prevent oxidation enzyme reactions or the browning of the product.

Influence of Blanching on Enzymes

In general the effect of the heat treatment is insufficient to inactivate catalase and peroxidase. Hence frozen vegetables will develop off-flavors. Balls stressed the importance of inactivating enzymes by heat. However, there is a possibility of catalytic action as the result of overheating with the formation of decomposition products. Also the revival of enzyme activity after a partial inactivation may be a problem. This is known to occur with proteolytic enzymes and peroxidase. The temperature, time, and heat penetration of blanching must be controlled accurately.

Factors that may influence effective blanching: The physical shape of the vegetables and temperature of the tissue and its heat conductivity are important in an efficient blanch. Other factors are temperature of heating medium, motion of medium and vegetables, and nature of medium. Biological factors are also important. Variety, maturity and growing conditions all influence heat conductivity.

The Effect of Low Temperature on the Survival of Micro-organisms on Raw Fruits, Vegetables, and Meats

The fact that many fruits and vegetables are consumed in the raw state makes these products a potential source of danger from the public health standpoint, especially the enteric organisms which cause dysentery, typhoid, and paratyphoid infections.

During the last ten years many investigators have shown that certain intestinal bacteria could not survive more than 4 weeks in cherry juice sealed in cans without heat treatment, but were viable from 2 to 3 months in frozen whole cherries. It has been generally accepted that food stored at low temperatures tends to reduce the microbial content of the food appreciably. However, one should always bear in mind that low temperature is not a sterilization process but rather a method for creating a set of conditions which are unfavorable for extensive microbial growth to take place.

Smart (1937) concluded that the reduction in microbial content of strawberries held in sealed tins and other containers for a period of a year at 15°F (−9.44°C) amounted to an average of 99.3 per cent.

The author has studied the microbiology of fresh strawberries and found the number of organisms ranged from 600 to 2,000 bacteria per gram of fresh fruit and 80 to 800 molds and yeasts. The microbial content of shelled beans and peas was appreciably higher than the strawberries even though the latter foods were blanched.

Likewise, a study of frozen-pack vegetables was made in order to determine the presence of *Staphylococcus aureus*. Approximately 50 isolations were studied and 12 cultures were capable of producing a potent enterotoxin. However, when the vegetables were maintained at a temperature of 41°F (5°C) an increase in the microflora was observed. Bacterial filtrates of the enterotoxin were potent after being held in a refrigerator for 2 months at 40°F (4.4°C).

TABLE 13

MONTHS TO REACH A PERCEPTIBLE FLAVOR OR COLOR DIFFERENCE

Product	Temperature		
	0°F (−18°C	10°F −12°C	20°F −7°C)
Flavor			
Green beans	10	3	1
Peas	10	3	1
Spinach	6	2	0.7
Cauliflower	10	2	0.5
Color			
Green beans	3	1	0.2
Peas	7	1.5	0.3
Spinach[1]	—	—	—
Cauliflower	2	0.5	0.2

Tressler *et al.* (1968).
[1] Color deterioration of spinach varied. Two lots that were judged by a highly trained panel differed; one of the lots was as unstable as cauliflower, the other was more than twice as unstable as green beans.

The storage periods at various temperatures during which some vegetables change perceptibly in flavor or color are shown in Table 13.

The author studied egg meats subjected to fast freezing by local packers and found the bacterial count ranging from 800 to 200,000 bacteria per gram of egg white, with equally high counts in egg yolks. After 9 months' cold storage of the egg products, a decrease in the microbial content ranged from 95 to 99 per cent.

Studies on the coliform counts of fresh eggs have shown that coliform organisms constitute about 10 per cent of the total microflora of the fresh eggs. However, after 9 months of cold storage the egg products are free of coliform bacteria.

The work of Wrinkle, Weiser, and Winter (1950) indicates that coliforms and gram-positive cocci were the principal bacteria found in high standard plate count samples of liquid egg. Freezing at 2° to 10°F (−17° to −12°C) and storage at the same temperature for

2 to 3 weeks reduced the number of bacteria but did not eliminate any of the groups of bacteria studied.

Pasteurization of liquid whole egg at 143° to 144°F (61° to 62°C) for 3.7 to 4.0 minutes reduced the standard plate count of bacteria more than 99 per cent. This included nearly all the coliforms and gram-positive cocci and many pathogenic gram-negative enteric bacteria.

Alcaligenes, Flavobacterium, Proteus, and Pseudomonas were the principal genera of bacteria found in liquid and frozen egg products. All of these organisms produced spoilage when inoculated into sterile liquid whole egg.

Smart and Brunstetter (1937) reported that only three genera of bacteria failed to survive freezing for 3 to 15 months when the foods were held at 15°F (−9.4°C). As expected the molds and yeasts survived.

According to Smart (1939), fresh washed mushrooms contained 10,000 to 300,000 micro-organisms per gram. However, blanching this product for 5 minutes in steam reduced the microbial content from 275,000 to 720 per gram. Approximately two-thirds of the surviving bacteria died during a six months' storage of the mushrooms in the frozen state. The coliform organisms survived blanching but disappeared after six months' freezing at 15°F (−9.4°C). As expected, all the spore forming bacteria, molds, and yeasts survived.

Studies on shelled raw peas by Diehl, Campbell, and Berry (1936) showed 1,000,000 organisms per gram and the microbial content increased rapidly after six hours at 70°F (21.2°C). Blanching the peas at 210°F (99°C) for 60 seconds destroyed 99 per cent of the microflora; the surviving organisms grew rapidly and the peas spoiled almost as readily as the raw peas. The growth of organisms was largely prevented in both raw and blanched peas at 32°F (0°C) for 48 hours. The usual storage temperature of frozen pack peas is 0°F (−17.8°C). The bacterial population is appreciably reduced in 2 to 3 months.

Lockhead and Jones (1939) have made a comprehensive study on numbers and types of micro-organisms in frozen vegetables. Their studies on asparagus, peas, beans, and corn showed a marked decrease in numbers of organisms during the first two weeks of storage, then the microbial population declined slowly or remained stationary. The method of packaging such as water, brine, or dry-pack did not alter the survival of the organisms.

Frozen vegetables and fruits contain appreciable numbers of organisms even after 9 months' freezing at 0°F (−17.8°C). Obviously when the product is defrosted these organisms may be responsible for spoilage.

A temperature of 41° to 50°F (5° to 10°C) is favorable for the growth of many psychrophilic bacteria especially those found in vegetables.

Staphylococci and several species of *Flavobacterium* can withstand freezing much better than other types of bacteria occurring in fresh pack vegetables. After 9 months' freezing the former varieties of organisms predominate.

Effect of Freezing on Certain Animal Products

Fish.—They may be prepared for freezing by different methods but the fillet is perhaps the most familiar type of frozen fish product. Due to the relatively high fat content in fish, precautions must be observed in order to maintain a good quality product. The fat undergoes oxidation and is readily recognized as rancid. Any method that will reduce the exposed surface of the fish will tend to reduce the oxidation of the fat. Hence, the principle of the brine-immersion process is the formation of a "protein skin" on the surface of the fish. Salt tends to accelerate the oxidation of the fat, so the brine treatment of fish should be followed with caution. The darkening of the surface of herring, mackerel, and salmon is due to oxidation of the fat in the tissues.

During the cold storage of fish, the proteins are denatured thus lowering their ability to absorb and hold the tissue juices. When these juices are free from the tissue, autolytic enzymes and the activity of certain bacteria in the presence of pieces of fish in the juices bring about undesirable changes in the product.

Poultry.—Most processed poultry has part or all of the outer layer of skin removed during the dressing process. Scalding carcasses at temperatures above 128°F (53°C) will result in removal of the skin on at least some parts of the carcass. If the carcasses are scalded at 140°F (60°C) for about 45 seconds (subscalding) complete removal of the skin takes place upon picking. A common practice is to scald broilers for about a minute at 125°F (52°C) (semiscald) and then scald the necks and thighs at a much higher temperature which causes the skin to peel in these areas.

To prevent the surface of the carcass from becoming darkened by dehydration, the carcasses are held in slush ice water or crushed ice until they are consumed or packaged for freezing. It is important to package poultry carcasses while still wet in a moisture-vapor-proof material before freezing. Since poultry fat, relative to other animal fats, is unstable, the air should also be removed from the package.

Eggs.—Frozen whole eggs, whites, and yolks are the forms available to the consuming public at the present time. However, each frozen constituent of the egg has its advantages and disadvantages.

Whole frozen eggs are not an acceptable product for the consumer but freezing during the surplus season is a means of storing eggs to be used later for dried whole eggs. Hence, it is possible to keep an egg drying plant in continuous operation by using the frozen eggs during the offseason. The baking industry uses the whole egg product in ever increasing amounts.

Egg whites that have been frozen are more desirable than fresh egg whites because the former has more desirable whipping properties. Consequently, this product is used as an ingredient in white cakes, biscuits, cookies, candies, ice cream, and pies.

Frozen egg yolks are very unstable. Since the yolk is rich in protein it tends to undergo denaturation and the colloidal structure of the fat emulsion in the egg is changed. During the freezing of egg yolk the lecithin content of the yolk tends to separate and co-agulate. This lumpy condition is very undesirable. However, the coagulation of the yolk can be overcome by lowering the freezing point or by adding glycerine, salt, or sugar to the yolk prior to freezing.

Plain, glycerine, or sugar yolks can be used satisfactorily in making biscuits, cookies, dark cake, and doughnuts. Plain and sugared yolks are used in custards and ice cream. Plain yolks are preferred in the making of noodles because processed yolks impart an un-desirable flavor to the finished product.

Schneiter, Batram, and Lepper (1943) concluded that the sanitary practices used in plants during the processing and handling of whole eggs, egg whites and egg yolks prior and during the freezing period very materially alter the quality of the final product. Cracked and overripe eggs obviously contribute to a high microbial content of the egg product.

Milk Products.—The peculiar chemical and physical composition of cream and milk introduces some significant problems when these products are frozen. Freezing changes the colloidal particles so that when the frozen product is thawed out the insoluble fractions separate. This is known as "oiling off." The butterfat separates and rises to the top as a floc. Likewise, the proteins tend to precipitate when the product is held during freezing and storage.

It is well known that high fat creams will "oil off" more readily than a lower fat product. This fact was observed by Bell and Sander (1945). However, if cream is homogenized, which is a physical process, the fat globules are greatly reduced in size so that they are uniformly distributed throughout the product. Consequently, the emulsified fat is partially protected during the freezing and thawing cycle. The work of Trout and Scheid (1943) shows that the addition of sugar will prevent the separation of fat from frozen cream by the formation of small ice crystals. This alteration of the cream lessens the tendency for coalescence of the butterfat particles.

Vitamin Changes in Frozen Foods

It is a general opinion that low temperatures are not effective in the destruction of vitamins in foods. However, during the storage of the foods certain micro-organisms and enzymes may alter the physical characteristics of the food so as to make conditions unfavorable for the retention of certain vitamins.

The following observations have been made regarding long term frozen storage at different temperatures. Foods tend to dry out if not properly packaged, at temperatures ranging from $0°F$ ($-17.8°C$) to $20°F$ ($-6.67°C$). Ascorbic acid content is rapidly lost as the temperature increases. Thiamine in pork is not particularly affected by temperature fluctuations or period of storage in the freezer. However, rancidity usually increases at $0°F$ ($-17.8°C$) or above. Whole eggs or separated yolks must be mixed before freezing to prevent undesirable changes. Most meat and poultry can be frozen raw without any special pretreatment. However, sanitation is highly desirable in order to reduce the contamination by microflora.

Ascorbic Acid Changes.—One way to observe changes in the nutritive value of the food product during cold storage is to study the ascorbic acid (vitamin C) content. Since this vitamin is sensitive to heat and oxidation as well as being soluble in water, it serves as a useful guide in detecting any nutritive changes that may take place in the food.

It has been observed that vitamin C will retard an oxidized flavor in milk. The mechanism of the reactions involved in this process is not well understood. Low storage temperature tends to decrease the disappearance of ascorbic acid normally present in milk. The free oxygen can be removed by spraying the warm milk into a vacuum chamber. The ascorbic acid tends to stabilize the flavor. Therefore, the sooner fresh milk is deaerated, cooled, pasteurized, homogenized, or ascorbic acid added, the better the milk will keep.

The blanching process will destroy some of the vitamin C. Foods naturally high in this vitamin lose a substantial amount during storage, but the remainder is still high enough to supply the normal requirements in a daily diet. Cauliflower has a high vitamin C content, and may retain its value through several months of storage before dropping to about one-half its value at the end of the year. Peas, snap beans, and asparagus are low in ascorbic acid, and the loss of vitamin C is usually small during storage in spite of blanching and storage. Cranberries retain their color and flavor because the skin is tough and serves as a protection against biological changes.

Survival of Micro-organisms in Frozen Meat

There is a voluminous literature on frozen dairy products, fruits, vegetables, and fish, in which a great deal of emphasis is placed on the survival and toxin production by *Clostridium botulinum* and other pathogens.

Fitzgerald (1947) has very effectively summarized this review by stressing the sanitary quality of the foods to be frozen. This depends on the method and rapidity with which the products are handled before freezing and after removal from freezer storage.

Furthermore, he obtained the following data from his studies on frozen pork packaged in various ways and stored at 0°F (−18°C) and 25°F (−4°C) for 12 weeks:

1. Aerobic bacteria counts at 98.5°F (37°C) decreased during the storage period for all samples, regardless of storage temperature and protective methods.

2. Lipase forming micro-organisms were determined at 68°F (20°C) and found to increase during the storage period. Corresponding increases of these organisms were noted for protected samples stored at 25° to 0°F (−4° to −18°C) but were less marked than samples stored at 68°F (20°C).

3. Coliform organisms, as determined by most probable number, showed a marked diminution during storage at 25°F (−4°C). In the protected samples, the coliform count was slightly reduced when stored at 0°F (−18°C). In unprotected samples held at 25°F (−4°C), the counts approached extinction.

The work of Fitzgerald clearly indicates the ability of many bacteria to survive and multiply in meat at freezer temperatures. Likewise, many coliform organisms survived because they were protected in the meat samples stored at 0°F (−18°C).

Obviously, strict sanitation is absolutely necessary for handling meat intended for freezer storage. A low initial bacterial load on the fresh meat is necessary at the time of freezing in order to insure a low microbial count on the product when removed from the freezer. The literature is not very extensive on meat preservation as compared to other food products. The spoilage of meat and meat products depends on the presence and survival of saprophytic organisms including the pathogenic and toxigenic bacteria. Haines (1938) indicated that the growth of Pseudomonas species at sub-freezing temperature played an important role in meat spoilage.

Table 14 shows proper storage period limits for various foods at different temperatures.

TABLE 14

APPROXIMATE NUMBER OF MONTHS OF HIGH QUALITY STORAGE LIFE

Product[1]	Storage Temperature		
	0°F	10°F	20°F
Orange juice (heated)	27	10	4
Peaches	12	<2	6 days
Strawberries	12	2.4	10 days
Cauliflower	12	2.4	10 days
Green beans	11-12	3	1
Green peas	11-12	3	1
Spinach	6-7	<3	$3/_4$
Raw chicken (adequately packaged)	27	$15^1/_2$	<8
Fried chicken	<3	<30 days	<18 days
Turkey pies or dinners	>30	$9^1/_2$	$2^1/_2$
Beef (raw)	13-14	5	<2
Pork (raw)	10	<4	<1.5
Lean fish (raw)	3	$<2^1/_4$	<1.5
Fat fish (raw)	2	$1^1/_2$	0.8

U.S. Dept. Agr. (1960); Van Arsdel (1961).

Effect of Freezing on Flavors in Frozen Foods

The changes in flavor of many vegetables during freezing storage is due to inherent enzymes not appreciably affected by the low temperature or ice formation. Autolytic enzymes are very active in lobsters. Due to their habitat which is usually a cold climate, they have a different enzyme system. Upon death of the animal autolysis sets in very rapidly. This is one reason why they are not frozen. They are kept alive by keeping the lobsters on ice and when served they are cooked alive in order to minimize autolysis.

The work of Morris and Barker (1932) showed that a temperature of −313.6°F did not completely inhibit the action of autolytic enzymes inherent in peas. The off-flavors of raw or underblanched vegetables was also attributed to unknown volatile compounds.

However, the production of off-flavors decreased in proportion to a temperature decrease. Tressler (1938) stated that unblanched vegetables showed marked enzymatic activity in a few weeks at 0°F (−18°C), but if the temperature was lowered to −50°F (−45.6°C) no off-flavors were noticeable in many unblanched vegetables after 6 months' storage.

A good cold storage temperature for many products is $-10°F$ $(-23.3°C)$. It is necessary that all vegetables be treated in order to stop enzyme action that may be involved in the production of off-flavors. It is believed that one or more respiratory enzymes are involved in off-flavors and that these off-flavors are similiar to those produced in plant tissues in which anaerobic respiration[2] is going on.

Causes of Off-Flavors.—According to the findings of Arighi, Joslyn, and Marsh (1936), acetaldehyde was produced in the plant tissue of frozen peas by enzyme activity. This compound served as an index of quality since the quantity decreased with a decrease in catalase activity. It was also noted that acetaldehyde was highest in off-flavored samples and smaller amounts were present in good normal flavored peas. Other vegetables such as artichoke hearts, green beans, asparagus, lima beans, Brussels sprouts, and squash showed considerable variation in their acetaldehyde content. Consequently more work must be done to correlate the amount of this compound present with the flavor and keeping quality of these products.

Effect of Thawing on Quality

Many foods are affected by thawing. In fact some foods should not be thawed out prior to cooking in order not to alter the quality of the product. The rate of thawing and the medium used play an important role in the final quality of the food.

TABLE 15

EFFECT OF THAWING ON THE MICROBIOLOGY OF FROZEN WHOLE EGG MEATS

Method	Hours Required	Per Cent Increase in Microbial Count During Thawing
In air at 80°F (27°C)	23	1,000
In air at 70°F (21°C)	36	750
In air at 45°F (7°C)	63	225
In running water 60°F (16°C)	15	250
In running water 70°F (21°C)	12	300
Agitated water 60°F (16°C)	9	40
Dielectric heat	15 min.	Negligible

In general practice, the faster the food is thawed the more likely

[2] This would mean incomplete oxidation with limited amounts of oxygen from sources other than air.

will be the maximum retention of the quality of the food. However, in foods where there is a leakage of fluid, the slow rate of defrosting is desirable. This procedure will allow the tissue solids to reabsorb some of the fluid which may exist as ice crystals.

It has been found that dielectric (electronic) heating has many advantages over the conventional methods of defrosting foods because heat is generated in the interior of the food. Cathcart (1945) studied the thawing rate of frozen eggs by different methods which are illustrated in Table 15.

The Effect of Refreezing of Thawed Foods

The general practice of refreezing foods should be discouraged because of the presence of micro-organisms which are capable of causing spoilage. However, the microflora of frozen foods is largely made up of soil organisms and these may not be significant from the public health standpoint. In addition to the microflora of the frozen product inherent enzymes are present which may induce undesirable changes in the food.

Enzymes, like micro-organisms, are active at certain temperatures especially when the food is in the process of thawing out. Fellers (1932) shows in Table 16 the microbial content of different foods.

TABLE 16

BACTERIA COUNTS IN VARIOUS FROZEN FOODS AFTER 12 MONTHS STORAGE IN THE FROZEN STATE AND AFTER THAWING 24 HOURS AT 70°F (21.11°C)

| | Bacteria per Gram | |
Product	Frozen	After 24 Hrs. at 70°F
Beef stew	390	1,400,000
Beef steak	390	1,400,000
Carrots scalded	3,000	5,800,000
Eggs (in tin)	190,000	70,000,000
Green beans scalded	1,000	40,000,000
Haddock	38,000	770,000
Oysters	22,000	320,000,000
Peaches, with sugar 3:1	60	700
Peas scalded	1,000	24,000,000
Pork chops	1,300	8,700,000
Raspberries, with sugar 3:1	3,000	8,000
Sour cherries, with sugar 3:1	0	20
Strawberries, with sugar 2:1	200	2,000
Sweet corn scalded	1,500	60,000,000

The Application of Electronic or Dielectric Heat in Cooking and Defrosting Foods

Alternating current of a few megacycles frequency is applied through condenser plates or electrodes between which the food is placed in insulating containers such as glass. The food becomes the dielectric of the capacitor and its dielectric properties are such that strong currents are induced in all parts of the food. This raises the temperature of the food much more quickly than conventional methods which depend on leading heat in from the outside. Little or no heat is generated in anything but the food, hence the method is efficient and economical in the use of power. Precise control which is obviously important is somewhat difficult, however. Because of this problem widespread use of microwaves for thawing has never been adopted but research is continuing on how to thaw food by this method.

There are a few possibilities for the application of electrons in the food industry. The demand for quick service on short orders could be met. For example, consider the possibility of the delivery of hot sandwiches where the meat will heat right in the bun from vending machines. Precooked and frozen meats could be heated in this way, perhaps on airplanes, after the initial weight of the apparatus is greatly reduced. In a matter of seconds, a thick juicy steak can be cooked on a glass plate and the plate removed by hand as no heat has entered the glass. The psychological and advertising value may please customers as they can watch cake rise and bake in paper cups, or see popcorn placed in a sealed bag and then popped to swell the bag to overflowing.

The use of electronic heat in the blanching of vegetables has been tried by Moyer (1945). However, it was found that when sufficient current was applied to raise the temperature of the vegetables rapidly, arcing occurred between the electrodes and the product was burned. However, the burning effect was reduced with an electric field alternating 28 to 29 million times a second.

Experiments have been conducted using microwave heat by Olsen (1965) who observed that *Aspergillus, Rhizopus,* and *Penicillium* sp. on unwrapped bread were reduced after exposure to microwave for two minutes. Copson (1962) reported that use of microwaves for freeze-drying deboned poultry meat resulted in more rapid and uniform removal of water vapor than when conventional units are used. Workers at Litton Food Industries (Anon. 1966), reported the use of a conveyor type microwave oven for precooking chicken parts.

Causey and Fenton (1951) reported that microwave cooking does not eliminate strains of bacilli, staphylococci and clostridia. Lacey *et al.* (1965) reported that microwave exposure for three minutes was an unreliable method of reducing bacterial counts in mashed potatoes. Applegate (1968) reported that Salmonella survived in chicken parts cooked by microwaves.

Storage Life and Micro-organism Population of Frozen Foods

Since frozen foods have come into general use some pertinent questions may be asked. How long should frozen foods be stored in order to maintain their palatability and storage life? The studies of Paul, Wiant, and Robertson (1949) have summarized this as follows. Their studies included 12 fruits, 7 vegetables, whole and separated eggs, and beef roasts. The foods were prepared according to standard recommendations. The freezing temperatures used were 10°, 0°, −20°, −40°, and −60°F and storage periods were 3, 6, 9, and 12 months. The average storage temperature was around 0°F (−18°C). They considered that a freezing temperature of 0°F (−18°C) was satisfactory for most foods. A temperature of 10°F (−12.2°C) or above is not recommended. The storage life of the food product was not acceptable according to standards used.

Sulzbacher (1950) made a comparison on the numbers and groups of micro-organisms surviving in frozen pork packaged in various ways after 12 weeks' storage at different temperatures. He stated that the aerobic counts made at 99°F (37°C) decreased during storage regardless of storage temperature and protective methods. The total aerobic and lipase forming bacteria counts made at 68°F (20°C) showed marked increase. The most probable number of coliform organisms was appreciably reduced during storage at 25°F (−4°C) in protected samples, but was only slightly reduced in unprotected samples stored at 0°F (−18°C).

It appears from this work that many bacteria can multiply in meat at freezing temperatures. Also coliform organisms can survive in adequately protected meat samples stored at 0°F (−18°C).

It is extremely important that good sanitary practices should be observed in handling meat for freezer storage. Hence the adage that any food product stored in a freezer is no better in quality than the condition of the raw product.

The studies of Gunderson and Rose (1947) on the survival of bacteria in precooked fresh-frozen food are interesting. These authors studied the death rate of six strains of *Salmonella* stored in sterile chicken chow mein at −14°F (−25.5°C) and found no appreciable reduction in the viability of the test organisms during the early stages of storage. A large number of *Salmonella typhimurium* survived after 9 months in storage. Also five of the eight samples of chicken salad examined showed potential food poisoning hemolytic *Staphylococcus aureus*.

Public Health Aspects of Frozen Foods

There is a voluminous literature on the public health aspects of frozen foods. It is apparent that the presence of active acid producing types of bacteria may suppress the toxigenic or pathogenic bacteria during the stages of spoilage of the food. However, this viewpoint is open for discussion when one considers the possibilities of contamination of frozen foods by *Clostridium botulinum*, *Staphylococcus aureus*, the *Enterococci*, and *Salmonella*. The possibility exists that pathogenic bacteria may survive the freezing storage treatment and still remain viable to cause infectious diseases. The ever increasing use of fruits and vegetables in raw salads could be another important source of infections.

The bacteriologists do not have good reliable methods to detect toxigenic or pathogenic strains of organisms that may be potentially dangerous to man. The human is the only reliable test animal. Naturally this method has its limitations and disadvantages.

Perhaps the greatest assurance that the consumer may have in the use of frozen foods is that a constant vigil is kept by public health authorities on the sanitary practices used in handling the raw product, and the processing, distribution, and storage of the food.

BIBLIOGRAPHY

Anon. 1961. Proceedings Low Temperature Microbiology Symposium, Campbell Soup Co., Camden, N. J.

Anon. 1966. Microwave cooking of chicken broilers. Food Process. Marketing 27, No. 4, 92–96, 100.

Anon. 1967. Handbook of Fundamentals, Heating, Refrigerating, Ventilating and Air Cond. Am. Soc. Heating, Refrig., and Air Cond. Engrs., New York.

Applegate, K. L. 1968. Relationship of thermal characteristics and temperature changes to the survival of *Salmonella senftenberg* 775w and *Salmonella typhimurium* TM-1 in chicken meat exposed to microwaves. M.S. Thesis, Ohio State University, Columbus.

Arighi, A. L., Joslyn, M. A., and Marsh, G. L. 1936. Enzyme activity in frozen vegetables. Ind. Eng. Chem. 28, 595–598.

Bell, R. W., and Sander, C. F. 1945. The influence of milk fat globule size and cream temperatures on the stability of the frozen cream emulsion. J. Dairy Sci. 28, 581–589.

Brown, H. D., Kunkle, L. E., and Winter, A. R. 1946. Frozen Foods, Processing and Handling. Hinkle and Sons. Ashville, Ohio.

Cathcart, W. H. 1945. High speed defrosting of frozen eggs by applying broadcast heat. Western Frozen Foods 6, 8.

Causey, K., and Fenton, F. 1951. Effect of reheating on palatability, nutritive value, and bacterial count of frozen cooked foods (1) vegetables, (2) meat dishes. J. Am., Dietet. Assoc. 27, 390, 491.

Copson, D. A. 1962. Microwave Heating in Freezedrying, Electronic Ovens, and Other Applications. Avi Publ., Co., Westport, Conn.

Diehl, H. C., Campbell, H., and Berry, J. A. 1936. Some observations on the freezing preservation of Alderman peas. Food Research 1, 61–71.

Elliott, R. P., and Michener, H. O. 1965. Factors Affecting the Growth of Psychrophilic Micro-organisms in Foods. U. S. Dept. Agr. Tech. Bull. 1320.

Esselen, W. B., Fellers, C. R., and McConnell, J. E. W. 1949. Frozen apples and apple products. Food Technol. 3, No. 4, 121–126.
Fellers, C. R. 1930. Pasteurized dried fruits. Am. J. Public Health 20, 175–118.
Fellers, C. R. 1932. Public health aspects of frozen foods. Am. J. Public Health 22, 601–611.
Fitzgerald, G. A. 1947. Are frozen foods a public health problem? Am. J. Public Health 37, 695–701.
Gunderson, M. F., and Rose, K. D. 1947. Survival of bacteria in a precooked fresh frozen food. Food Research 13, 254–263.
Haines, R. B. 1938. The effect of freezing on bacteria. Proc. Royal Soc. London 124, 451–463.
Hepburn, H. 1950. Biochem. Bull. 4, 136–150.
Jacobs, M. B. 1951. Heat removal. In The Chemistry and Technology of Food and Food Products. Interscience Publishers, New York.
Jones, A. H., and Lochhead, A. G. 1939. A study of micrococci surviving in frozen pack vegetables and their enterotoxic properties. Food Research 4, 203–216.
Joslyn, M. A., and Marsh, G. L. 1933. The role of peroxidase in the deterioration of frozen fruits and vegetables. Science 78, 174–175.
Kennedy, L., and Weiser, H. H. 1950. Some observations on bacteria isolated from milk that grow within a psychrophilic temperature range. J. Milk Food Technol. 13, No. 6. 353–357.
Kiser, J. S., and Beckwith, T. D. 1942. Effect of fast freezing upon bacterial flora of mackerel. Food Research 7, 255–259.
Kopeloff, L. M., Etchells, S. J., and Kopeloff, N. 1934. Bacteriological changes in acidophilus milk at room and ice box temperatures. J. Bacteriol. 28, 489–500.
Lacey, B. A., Winner, H. I., McLellan, M. E., and Bogshawe, K. D. 1965. The effects of microwave cookery on bacterial counts of food. J. Appl. Bacteriol 28, No. 2, 331–335.
McCallum, J., and Kirkpatrick, C. A. 1934. Survival of tuberculosis organisms in cow's milk frozen at various intervals. Cited by E. C. McCullough. 1945. Disinfection and Sterilization, 2nd ed. Lea and Febiger Co., Philadelphia.
McCoy, D. C. 1963. Refrigeration in Food Processing. In Food Processing Operations, Vol. 1. J. L. Heid, and M. A. Joslyn (Editors). Avi Publ. Co., Westport, Conn.
McCullough, E. C. 1945. Disinfection and Sterilization, 2nd ed. Lea and Febiger Co., Philadelphia.
Morris, C. B., and Barker, E. L. 1932. Low temperature on autolytic enzymes. J. Brit. Dept. Sci. Ind. Research 23, 129–133.
Mountney, G. J. 1966. Poultry Products Technology. Avi Publ. Co., Westport, Conn.
Moyer, E. 1945. Electronics in the service of food technology. Farm Research 11, No. 4.
Olsen, C. M. 1965. Microwave inhibits bread mold. Food Eng. 37, No. 7, 51–53.
Paul, C., Wiant, D. E., and Robertson, W. F. 1949. Freezing temperature and length of frozen storage for foods frozen in household freezers. Mich. State College, Agr. Expt. Sta., Bull. 213.
Schneiter, R., Batram, M. T., and Lepper, H. A. 1943. Bacteriological and physical changes occurring in frozen eggs. J. Assoc. Official Agr. Chemists 26, 172–182.
Smart, H. F. 1939. Microbiological studies on commercial packs of frozen fruits and vegetables. Food Res. 4, 293–298.
Smart, H. F., and Brunstetter, B. C. 1937. Spinach and kale in frozen pack. Food Research 2, 151–163.
Sulzbacher, W. L. 1950. Survival of micro-organisms in frozen meat. Food Technol. 4, 386–390.
Swift, H. F. 1937. A simple method for preserving bacterial cultures by freezing and drying. J. Bacteriol. 33, 411–421.
Tanner, F. W., and Oglesby, E. W. 1936. Influence of temperature on growth and toxin production of Clostridium botulinum. Food Research 1, 481–484.
Tressler, D. K. 1938. Bacteria, enzymes, and vitamins: indices of quality in frozen vegetables. Refrig. Eng. 36, 319–321.
Tressler, D. K., Van Arsdel, W. B., and Copley, M. J. (Editors). 1968. The Freezing

Preservation of Foods, Vol. 2.   Factors Affecting Quality in Frozen Foods.   Avi Publ. Co., Westport, Conn.

Trout, G. M., and Scheid, M. V.   1943.   The stability of the fat emulsion of cream.   J. Dairy Sci. 26, 619–624.

U. S. Dept. of Agr.   1960.   Conference on Freezer Food Quality.   U. S. Dept. Agr., Agr. Res. Serv. 74–21.

Van Arsdel, W. B.   1961.   Alignment chart speeds computation of quality changes in frozen foods.   Food Process. Dec., 1961.

Wiant, D. E., Griswold, R. M., Barrons, K. C., and Blakeslee, L. H.   1946.   Planning for frozen foods.   Michigan State College, Agr. Expt. Sta.   Circular Bull. 198, 1–38.

Wrinkle, C., Weiser, H. H., and Winter, A. R.   1950.   Bacterial flora of frozen egg products.   Food Research 15, 91–98.

CHAPTER 8

Inherent and Biological Acidity in Foods

Effect of Inherent Acidity in Foods Upon the Growth of Micro-organisms

$$\frac{0 \qquad\qquad pH \quad 7.0 \qquad\qquad 14}{3.5 \qquad\qquad\qquad 11.0}$$

The optimum pH for nearly all micro-organisms is near the neutral point or pH 7.0. Acid tolerant organisms have an advantage in an acid medium over other organisms inhibited by acid. Molds and yeasts as a rule are acid tolerant. This is one reason why these organisms are usually associated with acid foods, especially fruits. Many kinds of bacteria are not acid tolerant and, therefore, seldom found in normal healthy fruit.

The bacteriologist usually takes advantage of the acid tolerant characteristic of micro-organisms in obtaining pure cultures from a mixture of bacteria, molds, and yeasts. Various kinds of selective culture media are available for this purpose.

There are a few species of acid tolerant bacteria that are important in food products. Such organisms as *Lactobacillus* and *Streptococcus* are capable of producing various acids in milk. However, their survival in an acid environment is usually of short duration. These organisms are highly desirable in the production of cheeses, fermented milks, and butter. Tomato juice is an acid food product and is subject to one type of food spoilage when contaminated with *Bacillus thermoacidurans*.

A few varieties of molds are capable of utilizing the acids present in food products as a source of energy. Thus the acidity is reduced or neutralized by the basic end products due to the metabolism of the mold. Yeasts and most bacteria as a rule do not utilize inherent acidity as a source of food.

Germicidal Properties of Acids in Foods

Most acid foods owe their germicidal properties to the fact that the acids inhibit the growth of microorganisms. As mentioned above molds and yeasts are not affected by an acid medium as much as bacteria.

Fresh raw milk may owe some of its bactericidal properties to a substance called "lactenin." This inhibitor has been dialyzed,

118

concentrated, and desiccated. It has been kept for three months with no apparent loss of activity. The dry preparation was 200 times as active as the original milk when tested with selected varieties of *Streptococcus*.

Fresh eggs likewise possess bactericidal properties. It has been shown that egg white contains an inhibitory substance called lysozyme. When diluted 50,000,000 times it was active against several kinds of bacteria. Egg yolk does not possess any appreciable active inhibitory powers.

The sterility of fruits and vegetables during the ripening period is probably due to certain inhibitory substances.

In general, it can be assumed that all foods possess varying degrees of germicidal substances. This is nature's way of protecting foods from premature spoilage. In fact, all living tissues and juices, including the gastric juice, saliva, tears, and blood, have inhibitory powers.

BIOLOGICAL ACIDITY

This is the acidity formed by the activity of micro-organisms utilizing the different constituents in the food. A few examples of biological acids are given as follows:

Kind of Acid	Volatile or Non-volatile	Substrate
Lactic $H-\overset{\overset{\displaystyle H}{\vert}}{C}-\overset{\overset{\displaystyle H}{\vert}}{\underset{\underset{\displaystyle OH}{\vert}}{C}}-C\overset{\displaystyle O}{\underset{\displaystyle OH}{}}$	Non-volatile	Lactose
Succinic $\overset{O}{\underset{HO}{}}C-\overset{\overset{\displaystyle H}{\vert}}{\underset{\underset{\displaystyle H}{\vert}}{C}}-\overset{\overset{\displaystyle H}{\vert}}{\underset{\underset{\displaystyle H}{\vert}}{C}}-C\overset{\displaystyle O}{\underset{\displaystyle OH}{}}$	Non-volatile	Protein
Pyruvic $H-\overset{\overset{\displaystyle H}{\vert}}{\underset{\underset{\displaystyle H}{\vert}}{C}}-\overset{\displaystyle O}{\overset{\Vert}{C}}-C\overset{\displaystyle O}{\underset{\displaystyle OH}{}}$	Non-volatile	Lactose
Butyric $H-\overset{\overset{\displaystyle H}{\vert}}{\underset{\underset{\displaystyle H}{\vert}}{C}}-\overset{\overset{\displaystyle H}{\vert}}{\underset{\underset{\displaystyle H}{\vert}}{C}}-\overset{\overset{\displaystyle H}{\vert}}{\underset{\underset{\displaystyle H}{\vert}}{C}}-C\overset{\displaystyle O}{\underset{\displaystyle OH}{}}$	Volatile	Fats and proteins
Acetic $H-\overset{\overset{\displaystyle H}{\vert}}{\underset{\underset{\displaystyle H}{\vert}}{C}}-C\overset{\displaystyle O}{\underset{\displaystyle OH}{}}$	Volatile	Proteins, fats, carbohydrates

Propionic $H-C-C-C$ Volatile   Amino acids, carbohydrates and fats

The production of biological acidity or fermentation has many commercial uses in the food industry. Perhaps the few examples, shown in Table 17, will demonstrate the practical significance of acid formation in foods.

TABLE 17

MOISTURE CONTENT AND PH OF A FEW SELECTED COMMERCIALLY CANNED FOODS; ALSO OTHER MISCELLANEOUS PRODUCTS

Kind of Food	pH Ranges	Percentage of Moisture
Apples (whole)	3.4–3.5	..
Apple (juice)	3.3–3.5	..
Apricots (dried)	3.6–3.4	..
Asparagus (green)	5.0–5.8	..
Beans		
Baked	4.8–5.5	..
Green	4.9–5.5	95.1
Lima	5.4–6.3	80.7
Soy	6.0–6.6	..
With pork	5.1–5.8	..
Beef (corned, hash)	5.5–6.0	55.6
Beef (stew)	5.6–6.2	72.6
Beef (dried)	5.5–6.8	59.3
Beets (whole)	4.9–5.6	85.4
Blackberries	3.0–4.2	..
Blueberries	3.2–3.6	87.9
Boysenberries	3.0–3.3	..
Bread		
White	5.0–6.0	..
Date and nut	5.1–5.6	..
Broccoli	5.2–6.0	..
Carrots (chopped)	5.3–5.6	91.0
Carrot (juice)	5.2–5.8	..
Cheese		
Parmesan	5.2–5.3	..
Roquefort	4.7–4.8	..
Cherry (juice)	3.4–3.6	82.0
Chicken (roast)	6.2–6.4	47.2
Chicken (with noodles)	6.2–6.7	..
Chop suey	5.4–5.6	..
Cider	2.9–3.3	..
Clams	5.9–7.1	83.7
Cat fish	.....	81.2
Cod fish	6.0–6.1	82.6
Corn-on-the-cob	6.5–6.6	76.0
Corn		
Cream style	5.9–6.5	..
Whole grain		
Brine packed	5.8–6.5	..
Vacuum packed	6.0–6.4	..
Crab apples (spiced)	3.3–3.7	..

Kind of Food	pH Ranges	Percentage of Moisture
Cranberry		
Juice	2.5–2.7	
Sauce	2.3–2.3	62.1
Crackers	7.0–8.5	..
Currant (juice)	3.0–3.0	..
Dates	6.2–6.4	..
Duck (roast)	6.0–6.1	46.2
Figs	4.9–5.0	87.4
Flour	6.0–6.5	..
Frankfurters	6.2–6.2	..
Fruit cocktail	3.6–4.0	..
Goose (roast)	.....	57.5
Gooseberries	2.8–3.1	..
Grapefruit		
Juice	3.0–3.3	..
Pulp	3.4–3.4	..
Sections	3.0–3.5	..
Grapes	3.5–4.5	..
Ham (spiced)	6.0–6.2	..
Herring	.....	68.3
Hominy (lye)	6.9–7.9	82.6
Huckleberries	2.8–2.9	90.4
Jams (fruit)	3.5–4.0	..
Jellies (fruit)	3.0–3.5	..
Kidney (beef)	.....	76.0
Lamb (cutlets)	.....	65.3
Lemons	2.2–2.6	..
Lemon (juice)	2.2–2.4	..
Liver (calf)	.....	66.8
Loganberries	2.7–3.3	..
Mackerel	5.9–6.2	70.1
Milk		
Cow	6.4–6.8	87.0
Evaporated	5.9–6.3	..
Molasses	5.0–5.4	..
Mushrooms	6.0–6.5	92.4
Olives (ripe)	5.9–7.3	78.0
Orange (juice)	3.0–4.0	..
Oysters	6.3–6.7	..
Peaches	3.4–4.2	88.0
Pears (Bartlett)	3.8–4.6	88.0
Peas	5.6–6.5	82.9
Pheasant (baked)	.....	51.5
Pickles		
Dill	2.6–3.8	..
Sour	3.0–3.5	..
Sweet	2.5–3.0	..
Pimento	4.7–5.2	..
Pineapple		
Crushed	3.2–4.0	80.0
Sliced	3.5–4.1	..
Juice	3.4–3.7	..
Plums	2.8–3.0	..
Pork (leg)	.....	53.7
Potatoes		
White	5.4–5.9	..
Mashed	5.1–5.1	..
Potato Salad	3.9–4.6	..
Prune (juice)	3.7–4.3	..

Kind of Food	pH Ranges	Percentage of Moisture
Pumpkin	5.2–5.5	..
Rabbit	.....	75.0
Raspberries	3.2–3.7	..
Rhubarb	2.9–3.3	94.8
Salmon	6.1–6.3	72.0
Sardines	5.7–6.6	53.6
Sauerkraut	3.1–3.7	93.2
Juice	3.3–3.4	..
Shrimp	6.8–7.0	59.4
Soups		
Bean	5.7–5.8	..
Beef broth	6.0–6.2	..
Chicken noodle	5.6–5.8	..
Clam chowder	5.6–5.9	..
Duck	5.0–5.7	..
Mushroom	6.3–6.7	..
Noodle	5.6–5.8	..
Oyster	6.5–6.9	..
Pea	5.7–6.2	..
Tomato	4.2–5.2	..
Turtle	5.2–5.3	..
Vegetable	4.7–5.6	..
Spinach	5.1–5.8	92.1
Squash	5.0–5.3	..
Strawberries	3.1–3.5	..
Sweet potatoes	5.3–5.6	66.7
Tomatoes	4.1–4.4	..
Juice	3.9–4.4	..
Tuna	5.9–6.1	54.1
Turnip greens	5.4–5.6	80.0
Veal	.....	75.0
Vegetable		
Juice	3.9–4.3	..
Mixed	5.4–5.6	..
Vinegar	2.4–3.4	..
Youngberries ·	3.0–3.7	..
Other miscellaneous products:		
Beers	4.0–5.0	..
Ginger ale	2.0–4.0	..
Human		
Blood plasma	7.3–7.5	..
Duodenal content	4.8–8.2	..
Feces	4.6–8.4	..
Gastric content	1.0–3.0	..
Milk	6.6–7.6	..
Saliva	6.0–7.6	..
Spinal fluid	7.3–7.5	..
Urine	4.8–8.4	..
Magnesia, milk of	10.0–10.5	..
Water		
Distilled CO_2 free	6.8–7.0	..
Mineral	6.2–9.4	..
Sea	8.0–8.4	..
Wines	2.3–3.8	..

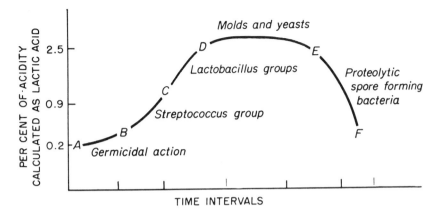

FIG. 23. SEQUENCE OF BIOCHEMICAL CHANGES IN MILK
Their relation to acid concentration.

Sequence in Milk Fermentation

Raw milk is not free of micro-organisms. The animal may contribute organisms during the formation of milk in the mammary gland, but the greatest source of micro-organisms in milk is external contamination. Obviously a heterogenous microflora exists in the raw milk. If the milk is allowed to undergo a normal fermentation, a sequence of biochemical changes may be evident. Fig. 23 illustrates these changes.

A similar comparison can be made with other food products.

Growth Phases and Acidity.—The phase represented from A to B is the lag phase in which the total numbers of microflora are destroyed or unable to multiply. *Streptococcus lactis*, usually present in all raw milk, grows and produces acid up to approximately 0.9 per cent as shown in B to C. Eventually the acid restricts the growth of these organisms and then the Lactobacillus group occupies a prominent place, C to D. They are normally present in the milk. Being more acid tolerant than the Streptococcus they are able to survive the acidity already produced and in turn produce more acid up to 3.5 to 4.0 per cent. The Lactobacillus like the Streptococcus cannot survive in an acid environment for a great length of time. Gradually they are eliminated in this high acid milk, and the way is paved for typical acid tolerant organisms, molds, and yeasts, as shown in D to E. The molds play an important role in that they can utilize the acid as a source of energy to produce several kinds of basic compounds which tend to neutralize the remaining acidity in the milk   A change from a high acid product to one that is basic then takes place. Proteolytic bacteria as represented in E to F become the predominant organisms. They cannot survive in an acid medium, hence they must wait until conditions in the milk are favorable for them. These organisms, like the molds, produce basic products and, as a result, the milk becomes extremely alkaline or approximately a pH range from 8 to 10.

The Survival of Organisms in Fermented Foods

The presence and survival of pathogenic bacteria in certain acid foods has been of interest for a long time in relation to public health. Such foods as milk, cheese, and sauerkraut produce biological acidity by means of desirable and selected organisms. The term fermented foods has been selected in order to differentiate this class of foods from those having an inherent acidity. The latter are often called "acid foods."

The organisms responsible for the acid formation in certain foods may survive for long periods in the acid environment they have created. Maybe the acid tolerant characteristics of these organisms are responsible for their prolonged survival and the amount of acids formed is another factor. In the case of certain kinds of fermented milks produced by members of the Lactobacillus group of bacteria, a pH of 3.0 or 3.5 may be reached which is comparable to a titratable acidity of around 3.5 to 4 per cent as lactic acid. However, the acid tolerance of these organisms will not insure their continued survival indefinitely. Eventually the milk will be sterile as a result of the high acid content.

The acid tolerance of organisms, normally associated with sauerkraut making, silage fermentation, pickle production, and butter making, may allow them to be present throughout the life of the product. Perhaps there are many biological conditions present in these food products, such as a buffer system, type of processing, temperature, or environmental factors that favor the survival of desirable organisms while undesirable ones find unfavorable conditions for growth.

The survival of *Salmonella typhi, Salmonella paratyphi,* and *Shigella dysenteriae* has been studied by the author when these organisms were inoculated into fermented milk. Likewise these test bacteria were added to sterile skim milk acidified with lactic acid comparable to pH values obtained by the growth of lactic acid in milk. The following conclusions were made regarding this study:

1. The test organisms were destroyed more easily in acidified milk than in milk in which biological acidity was formed.
2. The acidity of fermented milks is not sufficient to completely

destroy the pathogenic bacteria. It was found that pathogens survive from 7 to 10 days in acid milk having a titratable acidity ranging from 0.95 to 1.20 per cent or a comparable pH range from 3.9 to 4.5. When the acidity of the milk ranged from 0.5 to 0.9 per cent (pH 4.2 to 5.0), the test organisms survived from 3 to 10 weeks.

3. More pathogens survived in the milk when the acidity increased slowly. This is probably due to the presence of acid tolerant strains of these organisms.

4. There was a wide fluctuation in the acidity values of the milk due to variations in the metabolism of the lactic acid bacteria.

It has been proposed by public health interests that laws be enacted requiring that all dairy products be made from pasteurized milk. This proposal would affect the cheese industry since many types of cheeses are made from raw milk. Although the milk is heated during the process of cheesemaking, the temperature is not comparable to regular pasteurization requirements. Moreover, there is the age old question of how long pathogens survive in cheese, due to normal acidity formed by desirable organisms.

Biological and Inherent Acidity and the Survival of Micro-organisms.—Inherent acid in foods tends to destroy micro-organisms by creating an unfavorable pH, since most organisms grow very abundantly in a neutral environment or a pH of 7. However, if acid fruit juice is kept cold, its bactericidal properties are greatly restricted.

McClesky and Christopher (1941) tested strawberries which were inoculated with suspensions of different pathogenic bacteria before quick freezing in cardboard containers and holding at 66°F (18.69°C). *Salmonella typhi* survived for 6 months in sliced sweetened berries, *Staphylococcus aureus* for 5 months, *Salmonella aertrycke* for one month and *S. paratyphi* was not recovered at any time after freezing. In sweetened berries, *S. typhi* survived for 14 months. By comparison, when *S. typhi* was added to sliced sweetened berries and held at 40° to 41°F (4.44° to 5°C), 98 per cent of the test organisms were killed in one day and sterility was reached in 8 days. Similarily, when the storage temperature was 72° to 81°F (22° to 27°C), no *S. typhi* survived after 6 hours.

Apparently the inherent acidity of strawberries and the dissolved sugar were responsible for the death of *S. typhi* within a few hours at room temperature. Temperatures above freezing required a few days and at 65°F (18.3°C), very little effect upon the survival of the organisms was noted. The greatest benefits will be derived if food is handled and processed under strict sanitary conditions. Washing berries at the patch with unclean water could be a public health hazard.

Fermented Milks

The souring of milk is well known. The use of sour or fermented milks goes back beyond the pages of recorded history. Metchnikoff, in his book, "The Prolongation of Life," describes the therapeutic value of fermented milks, especially acidophilus milk. All of these milks are prepared by growing selected lactic acid organisms in the milk either as one pure culture or a mixture of these organisms.

At the present time the consumption of fermented milk drinks has increased, particularly in the warm climates. Fermented milks are now recognized as important products of the dairy industry.

The fermented product is largely consumed in the U.S. in the form of ripened skim milk, although the composition of the fermented milk will vary with the type of culture used and modification of the milk. The average composition of skim milk is: water 90.35, protein 3.72, fat 0.15, lactose 4.98, and ash 0.80 per cent. During the fermentation process a small portion of the lactose in the milk is converted to lactic acid. In some instances, 1 to 2 per cent butterfat is added to improve the body and flavor of the product. It is a common belief that the nutritional value of fermented milk is comparable to whole milk in many respects, since 40 per cent of the proteins remain, approximately 50 per cent of the lactose and practically all the minerals are present.

The therapeutic value of fermented milks has been greatly exaggerated. The underlying principle is based upon the ability of the organisms to perpetuate themselves in the intestinal tract, thereby creating an unfavorable environment for many kinds of undersirable bacteria that may be present. The diet that one eats will tend to influence the type of microflora that will predominate in the intestine. A high protein intake will favor proteolytic organisms. Early scientists believed that toxic byproducts resulting from the growth of putrefactive bacteria in the intestinal tract were responsible for the so-called "auto-intoxication" or other intestinal disturbances. However, when aciduric organisms were present in the alimentary tract sufficient acid was found to prevent the growth of large numbers of proteolytic organisms. Perhaps this is nature's way of controlling and maintaining a biological balance in a microbial world.

Bulgaricus Milk.—Bulgarian milk resembles cultured buttermilk in most respects. It has a more acid flavor due to the high acidity produced by the culture. *Lactobacillus bulgaricus* is the starter organism used in the preparation of the product. Sterile skim milk is used because of the high temperature of incubation, namely 90° to 100°F (32.2° to 37.8°C); this temperature is also favorable for the growth of undesirable organisms resisting pasteurization. This organism often grows in milk with a two to three per cent acid content. The high acidity produced is not always acceptable to the consuming public although the addition of whole sweet milk aids in masking the acid flavor and thus makes a good refreshing milk beverage.

One part of cultured buttermilk to one part of Bulgarian milk produces a fine flavored product that has the desirable characteristics of each. However, the growth features of each fermented milk are different so they must be prepared separately and then mixed at the time of consumption for the best results.

Acidophilus Milk.—Acidophilus milk is comparable to Bulgarian milk in the acid produced and general growth requirements for the culture. *Lactobacillus acidophilus* is the organism used in the preparation of acidophilus milk.

The therapeutic value of this product is of general interest because *L. acidophilus* has the ability to.grow in the intestinal tract provided the proper carbohydrates are present. Other types of fermented milks do not have this characteristic of surviving for any length of time in the intestinal tract. This is of fundamental importance in treating certain intestinal disorders. *Lactobacillus acidophilus* produces sufficient acid in the alimentary tract to suppress many types of undesirable organisms.

The preparation of acidophilus milk is very difficult, as is that of *L. bulgaricus* milk because the temperatures used also favor many other varieties of bacteria that are not important in the production of acidophilus milk.

Usually sterile skim milk is used. About 1 to 2 per cent inoculum is recommended. The culture should be freshly isolated from the intestinal tract of man or other animals for the best results. Cultures carried in skim milk for a short time tend to lose their ability to establish themselves in the intestinal tract.

The relatively high acidity produced by *L. acidophilus* makes it an unpopular fermented drink. However, there are many ways to modify the product and still receive the beneficial results. Usually the addition of small amounts of whole milk to acidophilus milk at the time of consumption makes the product more palatable. The viability of the organisms tends to decrease rapidly as the milk is stored in the refrigerator. However, one week is a safe period for storage, if one wishes to receive the most beneficial results.

Yogurt Milk.—Yogurt is another popular fermented milk especially in the Balkan countries. The product is made from either cow, goat, sheep, or buffalo milk.

Preparation of yogurt.—Fresh raw milk can be inoculated with an active fermenting batch of yogurt, or from the dried preparation. The milk culture is incubated at 100° to 115°F (37.8° to 46.1°C) until a thick curd develops, or until the titratable acidity reaches sharp acid flavor, and a distinctive aroma.

Yogurt starters.—The principal organisms are *Streptococcus thermophilus* and *Lactobacillus bulgaricus*. The high acidity during the fermentation yields an acid curd.

Preparation of yogurt milk.—The milk batch is sterilized much like milk for acidophilus. Usually one per cent of starter organisms is added. It is incubated at 98.6° to 100°F (37° to 37.18°C) for 10 to 12 hours. The finished product can be placed in suitable retail containers and held at 50°F (10°C) until it is consumed.

Taette.—The principal organism involved in the fermentation of Taette is *Streptococcus lactis* var. *hollandicus*. Usually cow's milk is inoculated with a small amount from a previous batch. Pasteurization of the milk is highly desirable to prevent the growth of other undesirable organisms. The culture mixture should be incubated around 70°F (21°C) for 24 to 36 hours. The fermented milk becomes viscous or stringy, with a mild acid flavor. The acidity may reach one per cent lactic acid. Taette is a delicacy in the Scandinavian countries. It is used as a "spread" for bread and other pastry products.

Kumiss.—The product is native to Russia. It is usually prepared from mare's milk. The wandering tribes of European Russia were great horsemen and by a process of selection they developed a hardy breed of horses which gave large amounts of milk.

Kumiss is a lactic acid fermentation in which *Streptococcus lactis* and *Lactobacillus bulgaricus* play an important role. A lactose fermenting yeast is also necessary in order that variable amounts of alcohol are produced.

The native method of inoculation of the milk is the addition of some fermenting or decayed matter, such as a piece of flesh, tendon, or vegetable matter. Usually the lactic acid bacteria and yeast are able to compete with other organisms and thus establish themselves as the predominant microflora in the milk.

The temperature of incubation may vary from 75° to 86°F (24° to 30.4°C) for 12 to 72 hours. About 1 per cent acid and 2 per cent alcohol are formed during this period. In some cases the product is distilled to increase the alcohol content of part of it.

Kefir Milk.—Kefir milk is perhaps one of the oldest and most interesting of the fermented milks. It was prepared by the people of southern Russia, Turkey, and the Balkan countries. The product can be prepared from milk from cows, goats, and sheep. The word Kefir goes under varying names as "hippe," "kepi," and "kaphir"— all of which come from a common root meaning a pleasant or agreeable taste.

A preliminary treatment of the culture is necessary in order to get an active fermentation. The dry Kefir grains should be soaked in lukewarm water for 3 hours and then placed in 1 per cent sodium bicarbonate solution for 3 hours. The grains after this treatment should be swollen and then rinsed in cold water. The culture is ready to be added to fresh pasteurized skim milk and incubated at 70° to 80°F (21.1° to 26.6°C) for 24 hours until the milk curdles. Daily transfers to fresh pasteurized skim milk are absolutely essential so the grains will increase in size and will rise to the surface during the fermentation.

The final product is prepared by adding one pint of Kefir grains to 3 parts of pasteurized whole or skim milk. The milk culture should be incubated at 57° to 61°F (13.9° to 16.1°C) for 8 to 10 hours with frequent stirring. The container should be loosely stoppered. The Kefir grains are removed by straining the fermented milk through coarse cheese cloth. The grains are washed with lukewarm water and preserved for subsequent batches of kefir milk. The fermented kefir milk is usually transferred to clean milk bottles, stoppered securely and incubated at 57° to 60°F (13.9° to 15.5°C) for 24 hours, then placed in the refrigerator until used.

Lactic acid is formed, ranging from 0.5 to 1.0 per cent; carbon dioxide and alcohol also appear, the latter ranging from 0.3 to 1.0 per cent after 3 to 5 days' incubation.

The Kefir grains resemble grains of popcorn. The fermenting organisms are *Streptococcus lactis, Lactobacillus bulgaricus,* and lactose fermenting yeasts. These organisms exhibit a symbiotic relationship. No doubt during the active fermentation of the milk a synergistic action takes place which may account for the characteristic flavor and aroma associated with Kefir milk.

Rogers and Albus in 1928 suggested a procedure for preparing a substitute for Kefir. It involves adding from 2 to 4 teaspoons of sucrose to a pint of cultured buttermilk and a small amount of "Red Star" or Fleischmann's prepared yeast. The yeast can be obtained at most food markets. The milk mixture is incubated for 3 to 4 days at 65° to 70°F (18.3° to 21.1°C). The fermentation should be carried out in heavy bottles and rubber stoppers securely fastened because a strong gas pressure is built up. The Kefir substitute can be kept in the household refrigerator for several days providing the containers are tightly stoppered to prevent a loss of carbon dioxide.

Production and Importance of Lactic Acid Produced in Food by Microorganisms.—The production of lactic acid by certain groups of organisms is important in many desirable food fermentations. Lactic acid or α hydroxy propionic acid is widely distributed in nature. It occurs in sour milk, beer, bread, and in muscle tissue. It is one of the important organic acids in the soil.

Any compound to be optically active must have an asymmetric "C" atom. Lactic acid has one which permits two types of the acid or three modifications according to action on polarized light.

Based on Van Hoff's theory of optically active bodies, the following forms exist:

$$
\begin{array}{ccc}
\text{CH}_3 & & \text{CH}_3 \\
| & & | \\
\text{H---C---OH} & & \text{HO---C---H} \\
| & & | \\
\text{COOH} & & \text{COOH} \\
(d) & & (l)
\end{array}
$$

Dextrorotatory is *d* form (rotating light to right). Levorotatory is *l* form (rotating light to left). Racemic or inactive is a mixture of "*d*" and "*l*" forms, hence no rotation.

The significance of the different types of lactic acid involves the stability and amount of lactic acid produced. For instance, *Streptococcus lactis* invariably produces "*d*" form of lactic acid, while *Lactobacillus bulgaricus* varies from "*d*" to "*l*" forms. The latter organism is used as one of the starter organisms in the production of Swiss cheese. Frequently *L. bulgaricus* produces "*l*" lactic acid which means less acid, in terms of titratable acidity and is undesirable as a good active starter.[1]

Lactic Acid

In 1780 Scheele isolated and identified lactic acid (hydroxypropionic acid) in sour milk. Storch in Denmark and Conn in the United States in 1890 were among the first scientists to use lactic acid cultures to add flavor and aroma to butter. They obtained these natural cultures from

---

[1] When this organism produces the "*l*" lactic acid, it is observed to lack vitality for some reason, hence, less acid is produced.

ripened or sour cream or buttermilk. The introduction of pasteurization to cream destroyed many organisms that caused defects in the butter and inhibited the bacteria that caused natural souring. To take the place of natural souring the cultures were added to pasteurized cream and allowed to develop prior to the churning process.

As acid increases in milk, the casein will precipitate. Precipitation usually occurs when the pH reaches 4.6 to 4.8. Acidity will continue to increase, even after coagulation of casein, until the acid prevents further growth.

Although milk contains about 5.1% lactose, it is the limiting factor in acid production. When fresh milk is inoculated with S. lactis and A. aerogenes and incubated at room temperature for 60 hours, 22% of the lactose disappears and 88% is converted to lactic acid. As acid is produced, it combines with free casein forming a casein salt which is called the curd.

Lactic acid, formed by micro-organisms, usually prevents the growth of putrefactive bacteria because they are not acid tolerant. However molds can utilize the acid as a source of energy, thus decreasing the acid concentration which creates a more favorable environment for acid sensitive bacteria to grow and break down the casein.

Lactic Acid Cultures.—The production of lactic acid in different fermented foods is highly desirable. It is one of the important fermentations in the food industry, especially in the production of certain dairy products.,

There are many varieties of lactic acid bacteria. However our discussion will be confined to butter cultures, commonly called "starters," since the other lactic acid organisms will be considered in connection with their role in other foods. The principal use of "starters" is in the manufacturing of butter, many kinds of cheese, cultured buttermilk, and in the production of oleomargarine.

There are three types of streptococci associated in a good butter culture. The organisms are: Streptococcus lactis, S. citrovorus, or (Leuconostoc citrovorum) and S. paracitrovorus or (L. dextranicum). Streptococcus lactis is often called the sour milk organism because it is normally associated with raw milk and grows very rapidly in milk when conditions are favorable with the formation of lactic acid. The associates, sometimes called citric acid fermenters, namely S. citrovorus and S. dextranicum are largely responsible for the characteristic flavor and aroma imparted to the product. For instance the fine flavor of butter is due to diacetyl produced by the associate organisms.

Streptococcus lactis produces the "d" form of lactic acid ranging from

0.65 to 1.00 per cent calculated as titratable lactic acid (pH 4.3 to 4.7). Lactic acid is odorless; it definitely contributes to the flavor because of its acid taste. *Streptococcus citrovorus* produces very little acid; in fact the acid formed cannot be detected when the organism is growing in a tube of litmus milk. However, *S. paracitrovorus* produces enough acid in litmus milk to change the litmus to red but usually insufficient acid to coagulate the milk.

An active butter culture produces appreciable amounts of volatile acids. Acetic and propionic acids are produced during an active fermentation. These volatile acids give a distinct flavor and aroma to the product, and these acids can be increased by adding small amounts of citric acid to the milk, hence the name citric acid fermenting bacteria. The addition of acid also enhances the production of acetylmethyl-carbinol and diacetyl; these compounds greatly intensify the aroma and flavor in butter.

Cultured buttermilk is prepared by inoculating pasteurized skim milk with a good active butter culture. The milk should be heated at 180° to 190°F (82.2° to 87.8°C) for at least 30 minutes. Sufficient starter should be added to give an acidity in the milk of around 0.75 to 0.90 per cent in 12 to 16 hours. Usually an active starter will produce this level in 12 hours using 0.5 to 1 per cent inoculum.

Butter cultures are sensitive to any marked changes in temperature. Therefore, the optimum temperature of 68° to 72°F (20° to 22.2°C) should be maintained.

Dairy Starter Cultures

Cultures of lactic acid producing organisms may be purchased from commercial laboratories for use as an inoculum. Although lyophilized cultures are sometimes available as a source of inoculum for making butter and cheese, frozen concentrated cultures are more widely used. They have the advantage of being easier to prepare and they are carried by more commercial laboratories in this form than in the lyophilized state.

Bacteriophages and Bacterial Inhibitors

Bacteriophages are viruses that can inhibit the metabolic activity of lactic acid producing organisms used in the food industry. As such, they prevent or slow down the production of lactic acid in butter and cheese by lactic acid producing organisms. The problem can be reduced by selecting cultures for use that are resistant to bacteriophages. Although the problem of bacteriophages is mainly concerned with cultures used in the dairy industry, bacteriophages can also present difficulties in the production of streptomycin, acetone, and butyl alcohol.

Some micro-organisms also produce substances which can inhibit the growth of other micro-organisms which are inoculated or cultured in foods for the purpose of bringing about specific reactions or conditions. In some cases, certain compounds are deliberately added to foods to prevent growth of micro-organisms. The addition of propionates to bread is an example. In other cases, the additives are unintentional. For example, antibiotics are used to control mastitis in dairy cattle. If some of the antibiotic residues contaminate the cows milk, growth of desirable micro-organisms, such as lactic acid producing bacteria, may be inhibited and limit the desired production of lactic acid. To overcome this problem the enzyme penicillinase can be added to the milk to destroy the inhibitory action of the penicillin.

The Utilization of Citric Acid

The biochemistry of butter cultures is interesting from the standpoint of adding desirable and characteristic flavors to different food products. The general scheme of the breakdown of citric acid by the flavor organisms with the formation of many intermediate products has been suggested by Hammer and Babel (1957).

$$COOH.CH_2.\underset{\underset{\text{citric acid}}{|}}{\overset{\overset{OH}{|}}{C}}.CH_2.COOH + 2H \xrightarrow{\text{reduction}} \underset{\text{acetyl methyl carbinol}}{CH_3.CHOH.CO.CH_3 + 2CO_2 + HOH}$$

$$\underset{\text{acetyl methyl carbinol}}{CH_3.CHOH.CO.CH_3} + 2O \xrightarrow{\text{oxidation}} \underset{\text{acetic acid}}{2CH_3.COOH}$$

$$\underset{\text{acetyl methyl carbinol}}{CH_3.CHOH.CO.CH_3} + 2H \xrightarrow{\text{reduction}} \underset{\text{2,3-butylene glycol}}{CH_3.CHOH.CHOH.CH_3}$$

Another suggested mechanism of fermentation and formation of aroma and flavor compounds is indicated below:

$$\underset{\text{lactose}}{C_{12}H_{22}O_{11}} + HOH \xrightarrow{\text{hydration}} \underset{\text{glucose}}{C_6H_{12}O_6} + \underset{\text{galactose}}{C_6H_{12}O_6}$$

$$\underset{\text{galactose}}{C_6H_{12}O_6} \xrightarrow{\text{dehydration}} \underset{\text{methyl glyoxal}}{2CH_3.CO.CHO} + 2HOH$$

$$\underset{\text{methyl glyoxal}}{CH_3.CO.CHO} + HOH \xrightarrow{\text{hydration}} \underset{\text{methyl glyoxal hydrate}}{CH_3.CO.CH(OH)_2}$$

$$\underset{\text{methyl glyoxal hydrate}}{CH_3.CO.CH(OH)_2} \xrightarrow{\text{glyoxalase}} \underset{\text{lactic acid}}{CH_3.CHOH.COOH}$$

$$CH_3.CHOH.COOH + 2H \xrightarrow{\text{reduction}} CH_3.CH_2.COOH + HOH$$

lactic acid → propionic acid

Or, with H acceptor, methyl glyoxal yields

$$CH_3.CO.CHO + HOH \xrightarrow{\text{oxidation}} CH_3.CO.COOH + 2H$$

methyl glyoxal → pyruvic acid

$$CH_3.CO.COOH + 2H \xrightarrow{\text{reduction}} CH_3.CHOH.COOH$$

pyruvic acid → lactic acid

$$CH_3.CO.COOH \xrightarrow{\text{decarboxylation}} CH_3.CHO + CO_2$$

pyruvic acid → acetaldehyde

$$2CH_3.CHO + 2H \xrightarrow{\text{reduction}} CH_3.CHOH.CHOH.CH_3$$

acetaldehyde → 2,3-butylene glycol

$$CH_3.CHOH.CHOH.CH_3 + O \xrightarrow[\text{oxidation}]{\text{partial}} CH_3.CHOH.CO.CH_3 + HOH$$

2,3-butylene glycol → acetyl methyl carbinol

$$CH_3.CHOH.CO.CH_3 + O \xrightarrow[\text{oxidation}]{\text{further}} CH_3.CO.CO.CH_3 + HOH$$

acetyl methyl carbinol → diacetyl

When *S. lactis*, *S. citrovorus*, and *S. paracitrovorus* are grown in pure culture, each culture produces very small amounts of flavor compounds. However, when they are grown in a mixture or as they normally occur in a good active starter, these compounds appear in appreciable quantities. A symbiotic relationship seems to exist in which these organisms are mutually beneficial to each other and it is only under these environmental conditions that the flavor compounds are formed.

Butter cultures are not used to any great extent at the present time, because good reliable results are not always obtained. Perhaps the fault may be the human element. If butter cultures are not properly handled and transferred regularly poor results in the manufacture of butter can be expected. Recently the use of starter distillate has come into general use in buttermaking. The distillate is prepared by steam distilling a good active butter culture so that the volatile compounds are not lost. It is prepared commercially, standardized, and sold to the dairy industry as "starter distillate." It can be added to butter directly just before it is removed from the churn.

The oleomargarine industry still uses butter culture to ripen the milk in which the vegetable fats are churned. Obviously this product acquires the delicate flavor of butter from the fermented milk. In fact, oleomargarine manufacturers are more concerned about maintaining good active butter cultures than the butter industry because of the satisfactory use of starter distillate in buttermaking. Starter distillate cannot be used satisfactorily in the manufacture of oleomargarine to obtain the flavor compounds due to some unexplained chemical reaction between the vegetable fats and the distillate which gives a marked off-flavor to the product. However, some of the recently developed flavor preparations are giving very good results.

Although starter organisms play an important role in cheese ripening, the existence of many varieties of cheese depends very largely on the processing techniques employed, the temperature of storage, and the kinds of organisms added to the cheese during its manufacture.

The mother substrate and the mechanism by which acetylmethylcarbinol and diacetyl are formed by the butter culture organisms are not very well understood. It has been suggested that the compounds may be formed from the citric acid in the milk by a series of oxidation and reduction reactions, or they may be formed from the lactose.

Cheese Production

The commercial varieties of cheese may be divided into the following classifications:

Class of Cheese	Variety of Cheese	Ripening Organisms
Hard	Cheddar	Bacteria with or without eye
	Swiss	forming bacteria
Semi-hard	Brick	Bacteria
	Blue	Mold
	Roquefort	Mold
	Gorgonzola	Mold
Soft	Limberger	Bacteria
	Camembert	Mold
	Cottage	Unripened by bacteria
	Cream	,, ,, ,,
	Neufchatel	,, ,, ,,

Cheese ripening is a complex microbiological process. It is very difficult to appraise the exact role of the different kinds of organisms present in the milk and in the cheese during the processing. No one knows the role of the initial microflora in the raw milk and the complex enzymes that are also present. These biological agents are important in the ripening of cheese in addition to the role of starters that are added to the milk. When milk is thoroughly cooked, many of these biological agents are destroyed and under these conditions it is very difficult to manufacture certain varieties of cheese regardless of the activity of desirable starters.

The general use of antibiotics for the treatment of mastitis and other diseases in dairy cows has presented a serious problem in the manufacture of certain varieties of cheese. Many of the well known antibiotics such as penicillin and terramycin have a marked inhibition on the organisms involved in a desirable fermentation, particularly the starter cultures that are used to ripen the milk for the various varieties of cheeses. A cow treated with penicillin by injection of the wonder drug into the teat canal will eventually build up a penicillin residue in the milk. While the concentration may be very small there is enough to alter the metabolic activities of many desirable bacteria. It has been reported that many cheesemakers object to the use of antibiotics in treating dairy cows unless the treatment is conducted by a veterinarian. It has been recommended that milk from cows treated with antibiotics should be retained on the farm from 3 to 10 days before the milk is permitted to be delivered to the cheese factory. This procedure seems to be satisfactory but is very difficult to enforce so as to insure a milk supply that is free of antibiotics.

The manner in which the curd is formed is the principal step in cheesemaking regardless of the variety. In one case the curd is produced through the action of rennet, and in another case it is formed by lactic acid.

Many varieties of cheese are produced through the action of rennet upon milk. Differences among these varieties are due to many factors such as kind of milk used, amount of moisture retained in the curd, amount of salt added, size of finished cheese, temperature and conditions of ripening, length of ripening period, kinds of microorganisms used as starters and the general microbial content of the raw milk.

The biochemical changes that take place during cheese ripening are not thoroughly understood, although many investigators have contributed a great deal of information in regard to cheese ripening, especially in the use of selected organisms, commonly known as "starters."

Since acid development by organisms is important in cheese ripening a few advantages are listed to emphasize the function of acid formation.

The presence of acid helps to control many putrefactive types of bacteria which may alter the quality of the cheese.

The production of lactic acid from lactose in the milk begins early in the cheesemaking process and will continue as long as lactose is available. Cheese has a high buffering capacity in relation to the sugar content, therefore, the high pH does not seriously inhibit the growth of lactic acid producing bacteria.

Lactic acid favors curdling of the milk with rennet. Apparently this enzyme is more active in the presence of certain concentrations of acid.

Acid production favors expulsion of the whey from the curd. Too much moisture may be retained in the curd and this interferes with normal biochemical changes.

The fusion of curd particles is very necessary if the cheese is to have the proper body. A lack of acid formation will cause the cheese to crumble instead of having a smooth firm mass.

Spoilage of Milk and Dairy Products

A natural souring of the milk will take place by *Streptococcus lactis* and *Lactobacillus sp.* which is undesirable in market milk. However, souring is desirable in fermented milk and cheese production.

Gas production by coliform organisms and members of the Clostridium group is undesirable, causing a "stormy fermentation" of milk. Lactose fermenting yeasts may play a role in gas production especially in gassiness in cream. The souring of the cream greatly favors these yeasts.

There are two types of coagulation in milk, acid and enzyme forms. Acid proteolysis is usually accompanied by acid formation. Micrococcus in the udder of the cow produces acid proteolysis; also, *Streptococcus faecalis* acts in the same manner. *Bacillus cereus*, a spore forming organism which survives pasteurization, causes acid proteolysis.

Streptococcus liquefaciens coagulates milk by producing a rennet-like enzyme followed by acid production. However, proteolysis is much in evidence.

Alcaligenes, Pseudomonas, Achromobacter, Micrococcus, and *Proteus* are genera capable of growing at low temperatures and causing proteolysis. A bitter flavor in milk is usually associated with these organisms.

Alcaligenes viscosus is responsible for ropiness in milk held at 10°C (50°F). The ropiness is due to the formation of gums and mucins. There are other organisms which may cause a fake type of ropiness such as coliforms and *Streptococcus lactis* var. *hollandicus* which causes ropiness in butter cultures, thus reducing the acid production of the starter culture.

Certain organisms in raw milk produce the fat splitting enzyme lipase which, regardless of its source, can break down fats by hydrolyzing the butter fat to fatty acids and glycerin. *Achromobacter, Alcaligenes, Proteus* and *Pseudomonas* are genera of bacteria capable of producing lipase. Some varieties of molds are lipolytic. This may be desirable in mold ripened cheese such as Blue cheese ripened by *Penicillium roqueforti.*

Milk is very susceptible to flavor changes. The cow may be responsible for off-flavors because of feed, green grass vs. dry roughage, mastitis, and stage of lactation.

Acid flavors are due to lactic organisms which may produce volatile fatty acids such as acetic or butryic which are produced by coliform bacteria.

Bitterness may result from lipolysis or the stage of lactation of the cow. *Actinomycetes* if present in large numbers produce a musty-flat flavor.

Strepotococcus lactis var. maltigenes is responsible for a cooked or caramel flavor in milk and cream. Pasteurization will not remove the malt-like flavor.

Red milk may be due to *Serratia marcescens* pigment, while *Torula glutinis* may cause red or pink colonies on the surface of sour cream or milk. Bovine mastitis results in a red coloration of the milk.

Clostridium sporogenes may cause a swelling of the cans in evaporated milk due to gas formation. The spores survive the heat process and reproduce in the can under anaerobic conditions to produce gas, coagulation of the milk, and a bitter flavor. *Bacillus calidolactis*, a typical thermophile, may produce similar conditions to those produced by the Clostridium, providing a small amount of air is available in the can.

An unsealed can may result in swelling and bitterness in the product; coliforms and certain yeasts may be largely involved.

Undesirable flavors in butter may come from absorbed volatile compounds in the air, but micro-organisms are largely responsible for most of the off-flavors. Surface taint, caused by *Pseudomonas putrefaciens*, comes from wash water and equipment. Fishiness may be due to *P. ichthyosmia*. Rancid, esterlike flavors come from *P. fragi.*

Chemical reactions independent of microbial activity may be characterized by tallowiness due to oxidation of unsaturated fats or exposure to copper in the equipment. Lecithin may form trimethyl amine giving a characteristic fishy odor.

Members of the anaerobic group such as *Clostridium sporogenes* and *C. tyrobutyricum* produce foul smelling compounds in Swiss cheese. Coliforms, micrococci, and yeasts may contribute their share of proteolysis causing off flavors.

Oospora lactis, a typical dairy mold, may be present in soft cheeses; the mold may cause some proteolysis thus making a soft mushy cheese. Species of *Penicillium* may produce green spots in cracks or trier holes of Cheddar and other cheeses. *Monilia nigra* produces black spots on the surface of hard cheeses.

Microbiology of Sauerkraut

The word sauerkraut means "acid cabbage." A sequence of desirable organisms play a major role in transforming the fresh cabbage tissues into a fermented product called sauerkraut. The maker creates and selects the most favorable environmental conditions for the maximum growth of the desirable organisms. Consequently, due to a series of complex biochemical changes, initiated by certain types of bacteria, the cabbage undergoes a fermentation process. Even at the present time some of the steps in this complicated fermentation process are not well understood.

In normal cabbage fermentation the process is a spontaneous one in which the bacteria attack the inherent sugars present in the cabbage and convert them into acids, alcohol, and carbon dioxide. At the same time the proteins of the cabbage undergo biochemical changes. The bacteria involved in the normal fermentation are classified into three general groups. The end-products, as the result of the growth of these organisms, are largely lactic acid and a mixture of other acids in lesser amounts. These organisms are frequently referred to as the lactic acid producing bacteria.

a. *Leuconostoc mesenteroides* is an acid and gas producing coccus.

b. *Lactobacillus plantarum* and *L. cucumeris* are bacilli which produce acid and a very slight amount of gas.

c. *Lactobacillus pentoaceticus* and *L. brevis* are acid and gas producing bacilli.

These are the three groups of bacteria that play a major role in sauerkraut fermentation.

In addition to the desirable bacteria in kraut fermentation there are many kinds of micro-organisms present on the cabbage that may interfere or alter the course of fermentation.

The quality of the kraut will depend very largely on how well these bacteria are held in check during the normal fermentation. Spoilage bacteria are typical soil organisms; they attack the protein and to a lesser extent the sugars producing undesirable substances thus affecting the quality of the sauerkraut. Fortunately the growth of these organisms is inhibited in normal kraut fermentation. Yeasts are also present on the cabbage but they seldom develop early enough in the fermentation to do any particular damage. However these organisms are not affected by the acidity formed and may in turn utilize the acid as a source of energy thus reducing the acidity or neutralizing it by the end-products resulting from their metabolism. Molds and transitional fungi are troublesome organisms. They, like the yeasts, can utilize the biological acidity and may seriously alter the quality of the kraut.

Biochemical Changes in Sauerkraut Fermentation.—After the shredded cabbage is placed in a suitable jar, salt and mechanical pressure are applied to expel the juice from the cabbage. This is accomplished by the osmotic pressure of the salt together with the mechanical pressure applied. The cabbage juice contains the inherent fermentable sugars and other nutrients suitable for microbial activity.

Within a period of hours after the cabbage is placed in the jar biological acids begin to form due to the activity of the gas producing cocci. When the acidity reaches 0.25 to 0.3 per cent (calculated as lactic acid) the cocci begin to slow down and gradually disappear although their enzymes continue to function. When the acidity reaches 0.7 to 1 per cent the majority of the cocci have disappeared. However, the two types of lactobacilli are active in increasing the acidity up to

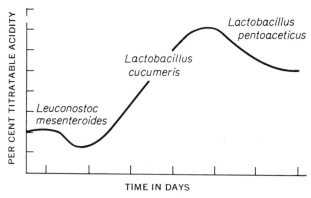

FIG. 24.   ACID PRODUCTION IN SAUERKRAUT

1.5 to 2 per cent in spite of the inhibitory effect of the salt and low temperature. Finally the third group of lactobacilli, namely *L. pento-*

aceticus, are left to complete the fermentation, thus bringing the acidity up to 2 and sometimes 2.5 per cent acid.   Fig. 24 shows the acid formation during normal fermentation.

End-products Formed During the Normal Fermentation.—During fermentation appreciable amounts of lactic acid (non-volatile) together with acetic and propionic acids (volatile); a mixture of gases, of which CO_2 is the principal one; also small amounts of alcohol; and finally a mixture of aromatic esters are formed.   The acids in combination with the alcohol form esters which contribute to the characteristic flavor of good kraut.   Also the acidity thus formed by the desirable bacteria helps to govern the course of the fermentation by stopping putrefactive changes in the cabbage.   Moreover, fermented kraut owes its keeping qualities to the acids formed.

The final or completed kraut contains only traces of sugar;   the lactic acid content is high, while acetic acid and alcohol have not increased much beyond the amounts formed by the first type of bacteria, the cocci.   Hence the main part of lactic acid fermentation is carried on by the non-gas producing bacilli.   Any disturbance in the sequence of the order of desirable bacteria will change the flavor and quality of the kraut.

Effect of Temperature on the Fermentation of Kraut.—The optimum temperature for good fermentation is around 70°F (21°C); a variation of a few degrees from this temperature will alter the activity of the microbial process, thus affecting the quality of the finished product.   Therefore, temperature is one of the most important factors in kraut fermentation.   A temperature range from 65° to 72°F (18° to 22°C) is most desirable for initiating the fermentation process.   The *Leuconostoc* group of bacteria are the first organisms to start the fermentation and they are rather sensitive to temperature changes.   Temperatures above 72°F (22°C) favor the growth of the Lactobacilli.   Although it is desirable that they complete the fermentation, an early growth thus replacing the *Leuconostoc* group will produce harmful effects.   In good kraut fermentation it is imperative that members of the Leuconostoc group of bacteria initiate the fermentation and temperature is one of the factors that will largely control the sequence of organisms in normal fermentation.   A low temperature will cause the Leuconostoc bacteria to produce about 1 per cent acid;   this amount of acid is undesirable at this phase of the process.   The fermentation virtually ceases and the kraut will lack flavor and will also be of poor quality.   A higher temperature will favor the growth of lactobacilli, although this group of organisms is important but not in the early stages of fermentation.

Function of Salt.—Salt plays an important role in starting the desirable fermentation process and in the final product. The addition of too much salt tends to inhibit the desirable bacteria although it may contribute to the firmness of the kraut. The principal function of the salt is to withdraw the juice from the cabbage thus making a more favorable medium for the proper kind of bacteria to develop. Usually from 2.0 to 2.5 per cent salt is the most widely accepted amount to add to cabbage. Even this percentage of salt is slightly inhibitory to the lactobacilli but does not affect the cocci. The concentration of salt actually has a greater inhibitory effect on the desirable fermenting bacteria than the organisms responsible for spoilage in kraut. The latter organisms are not inhibited in a salt concentration less than 5 to 7 per cent. The biological acidity thus formed is chiefly responsible for controlling spoilage organisms and not the salt.

Methods of Salting.—In acid fermentation of various vegetables two methods are generally used (a) dry salting is used at the rate of 2 to 3 lbs. per 100 and (b) brine is used for vegetables with low water content. The latter method is not recommended in sauerkraut making.

The relation of salt concentration to the texture of kraut has been shown by Pederson (1938):

Per Cent	Texture
2.8–3.4	Soft to medium
2.2–2.5	Medium to very firm
1.8–2.1	Medium to firm
0.7–1.7	Soft

Only pure salt should be used in kraut making. Special salts containing alkali should never be used because the alkali tends to neutralize the acids formed. The amount added should be weighed rather than measured by means of a bucket, since difference in texture of salts may decidedly alter the total percentage added.

The Use of Starters or Pure Cultures in Sauerkraut.—Various individuals have occasionally recommended that starters similar to those used in the dairy industry be used in making sauerkraut. Starters have been used to some extent in Europe but have not been used on a large scale in the U.S.

The one beneficial effect derived from the use of starters is that they are acid, and thereby slightly acidify cabbage, causing undesirable soil bacteria to be inhibited. Kraut produced by addition of starters prepared from sour milk, such as *Streptococcus lactis*, is usually of good quality, but the flavor is no better than that of a normal spontaneous fermentation. Since sour milk organisms grow only for a short time in the kraut, they do not disturb the natural sequence of bacterial growth which takes place in a typical fermentation. Starters prepared from other types of bacteria that do not grow in kraut have the same effect as do starters prepared from the sour milk organisms. The use of *Leuconostoc mesenteroides* found in the early stages of kraut fermentation gives a good flavor to the final product, but apparently alters the sequence of growth since the final product is not as completely fermented as normal kraut. The addition of gas producing rod types such as *L. brevis* (formerly *L. pentoaceticus*) gives an abnormal kraut. More acetic and less lactic acid are produced, hence the fermentation never reaches completion. When lactic acid, non-gas-producing (*L. cucumeris*) rods are used as starters, the resulting kraut is not completely fermented; it is often bitter, and apparently more readily attacked by yeasts.

Use of kraut juice as a starter.—The effect of addition of juice from other normal kraut depends to a great extent upon the types of organisms present in the juice. This can be determined by the acidity of the juice. If starter juice has an acidity of 0.3 per cent or more, the kraut produced is of poorer quality than normal kraut. Obviously the cocci which normally initiate the fermentation are suppressed so that the bacilli carry on the biochemical changes. Such starter juice is comparable to a pure culture of *Leuconostoc*, which predominates in kraut juice at this stage.

If starter juice has an acidity of 0.25 per cent or less, the kraut produced is normal, but no definitely beneficial effects are shown. Usually the organisms present in old kraut juice have a detrimental effect upon the normal fermentation of the cabbage. The presence of bacilli in large numbers which adhere to the fermentation vat occurs under commercial conditions, especially during the rush season, when tanks of kraut are emptied and immediately refilled with very little attempt to clean the vats. Ordinarily the bacilli are the desirable types and are associated with the cocci in normal fermentation but their presence in large numbers may alter the normal fermentation of the succeeding vats of kraut. This is especially true in warm weather because the growth of bacilli are favored by warm temperature.

Spoilage of Sauerkraut.—Sauerkraut spoilage is due very largely to soil micro-organisms. As a rule they are aerobic; they do not attack the inherent sugars to any extent, but they act on the protein and thus produce undesirable changes. Fortunately their growth and biochemical activity are quickly inhibited by a normal fermentation.

Yeasts are not affected to any appreciable extent by acids, but seldom develop early enough in the fermentation process to do damage.

Molds and transitional fungi require air and cannot grow in covered vats. They metabolize acids.

Mycoderm, a false yeast, grows very readily on the surface of the kraut and can utilize the acids present, thus altering the normal fermentation process.

Rotted kraut.—This defect is usually caused by bacteria, molds, and yeasts resulting from unsanitary conditions in harvesting and processing the kraut subsequent to fermentation.

Slimy kraut.—This type of spoilage is not too common. The flavor and odor of the kraut are not seriously impaired. The product is edible but the consumer does not like it. As a rule cooking or canning will cause the sliminess to disappear. Slimy kraut is not harmful to the consumer.

The usual cause is due to a slimy capsular material formed by certain kinds of bacteria. A high temperature during the fermentation process is most favorable for the development of these undesirable bacteria.

Soft kraut.—Several causes may be responsible for this condition, such as large amounts of air, poor salting procedure, varying temperatures, and other factors favorable for undesirable fermentation.

The growth of the desirable bacteria not in their normal sequence will invariably produce soft kraut. The lactobacilli seem to have greater ability to break down the plant tissue of the cabbage as compared to the cocci, thus contributing to this defect. Again a high temperature and a lowered salt content will favor the lactobacilli. Since these organisms are sensitive to certain concentrations of salt such a condition will favor their development. Whereas the cocci are more salt tolerant than the lactobacilli, the latter tend to grow and upset the normal sequence of the fermentation.

The continuous use of the same vat during the kraut season without periodic cleaning will cause the succeeding batches of kraut to have a soft texture.

Dark kraut.—Dark kraut is one of the common types of spoilage, and it is very difficult to determine the cause due to a variety of reasons. A few causes are listed. An uneven distribution of the salt will tend to inhibit the desirable organisms in these areas, but allows the rotting types of micro-organisms to grow, because many of them are salt tolerant. The cabbage juice may aid in dissolving the salt patches thus distributing the salt more uniformly.

If insufficient juice is present to cover the kraut, due primarily to lack of sufficient weights, certain undesirable aerobic bacteria and yeasts will grow on the surface of the kraut and cause darkening as well as off-flavors.

Too high a fermentation temperature permits undesirable microflora to grow. This may cause a darkening of the kraut.

An even distribution of kraut juice is essential to inhibit undesirable micro-organisms. Thus repacking of kraut in barrels for shipping may result in unequal distribution of the juice which may lead to spoilage in some barrels.

Sometimes barrels are used for packing kraut that have had pickles in them. The pickles, together with the tannin from the wood or spices, may act on iron or rust and cause a darkening of the product.

Pink kraut.—Pink kraut is due to the growth of certain types of yeasts of which *Torula glutinis* produces an intense red pigment in the kraut juice and on the surface. Usually an uneven distribution of salt or too high a salt content are conditions favorable for the development of these yeasts. A chemical analysis of pink kraut often shows an increase in the alcoholic content and a slight diminution of the acid. Conditions that are favorable for a good normal fermentation will usually suppress the activities of these forms of yeast.

Microbiology of Pickle Fermentation

Cucumber pickles are produced by a fermentation process comparable to that used in making sauerkraut.

Cucumber pickles should be mature, and in harvesting approximately $1/8$ in. of the stem should be retained. Because cucumbers grow on vines and in close contact with the soil they should be thoroughly washed before being placed in brine.

The next step in the process is to place the pickles in large tanks or barrels and add 15 to 20 per cent salt brine. In this concentration many of the cucumbers will float and some provision must be made to keep them submerged, otherwise the pickles will spoil. Usually board lids weighed down with stone or brick are used.

Function of the Brine.—The strong brine draws the sugar out of the cucumber which slowly transforms into a pickle. Since the cucumber contains about 90 per cent water, the salt concentration is quickly reduced and more salt must be added. As the osmotic action and fermentation process proceed, the brine becomes diluted with cucumber juice. The concentration of salt should never fall below 12 per cent or putrefaction or softening of the pickles will occur. In practice, the concentration is gradually raised to 15 to 18 per cent by adding salt slowly, thus insuring a brine of uniform strength. Usually the addition of 1 lb. of salt per 15 gal. of brine each week for 5 consecutive weeks will be satisfactory.

A spontaneous fermentation usually takes place within a few days after the cucumbers have been placed in the brine. The evidence of vigorous boiling indicates fermentation is going on followed by the formation of acids which tend to inhibit many undesirable micro-organisms which may initiate spoilage.

During the fermentation process, certain visible changes are taking place which are important criteria in judging the progress of the curing of the pickles. Certain normal physical changes become apparent. They are:

1. Change from a bright green to a dark olive green. This is probably due to the action of the acid on the chlorophyll.

2. Change in the appearance of the cross section of the cucumber from a snow white to a waxy transparent color. This color change is due primarily to a large amount of air in the cucumber which initially imparts this white appearance and which is driven out later.

3. An increase in the specific gravity of the cucumbers takes place. At first they float on the surface, later the diffusion of salt increases the weight and the cucumber no longer floats. This process is called plasmolysis, and it is accompanied by swelling. The salt content in the interior of the pickle may be sufficient to inhibit the undesirable biochemical activity of many kinds of micro-organisms. Fortunately the desirable organisms involved in the fermentation process are not appreciably affected by the salt. In fact, they are slightly salt tolerant. The studies of Fabian, Bryan, and Etchells (1932) amply support this observation. They state that undesirable proteolytic bacteria are more numerous than the desirable acid forming organisms. However, they are gradually destroyed by the brine before any marked defect becomes apparent in the finished product.

Micro-organisms in Pickle Fermentation.—*Leuconostoc mesenteroides*, a gram-positive coccus, usually predominates during the first stages of the fermentation. The organisms are resistant to temperature changes as compared with other bacteria involved in this fermentation and are more salt tolerant than other organisms associated with them in this process. Then *Lactobacillus cucumeris* or other closely related gram-positive bacilli follow the sequence of fermentation.

The active stage of fermentation continues from 10 to 30 days, depending very largely upon the temperature employed. The most favorable temperature range for *L. cucumeris* is 85° to 90°F (29° to 32°C). During this interval the total acidity increases to around 2 per cent.

Strong acid producing types of bacteria reach their maximum growth during this period of the fermentation. The addition of sugar or small amounts of acetic acid to the fermenting mixture will help the production of acid.

Precautions in Cucumber Fermentation.—If excessive amounts of acidity are formed during the fermentation, the acid will tend to cause a shriveling of the pickles. Moreover, stirring of the brine may introduce air bubbles and thus make conditions more favorable for the growth of spoilage bacteria.

Factors in Abnormal Fermentation.—Soft or shriveled pickles sometimes are the result of excessive acid formation by members of the *Leuconostoc mesenteroides* group. Due to the relatively high salt tolerance of these organisms, they are able to produce appreciable amounts of acid. The *Mycoderm* group is also troublesome. They utilize the biological acids as a source of energy and at the same time neutralize the acid by alkaline waste products resulting from their metabolism.

However, if the pickles are well covered with brine, and the salt concentration is uniformly maintained and the proper temperature regulated, a good quality product can be expected which can be held for a year or longer.

Processing of Sweet and Sour Pickles.—In the preparation of sweet or sour pickles the cucumbers undergo essentially a normal lactic acid fermentation. The subsequent pickling operations consist of leaching out the excess salt in warm water, firming the flesh or outer coating of the cucumber with a dilute solution of alum and impregnating the fermented product with plain, spiced, or sweetened vinegar. The final treatment of the fermented cucumbers is the addition of a mixture of vinegar and sugar.

Processing of Dill Pickles.—The preparation of dill pickles is essentially the same process as cucumber fermentation. The cucumbers are fermented in 10 to 12 per cent salt brine in closed barrels fitted with small holes for the escape of gas during the fermentation. Dill and other herbs and spices are added to the brine with the cucumbers before the fermentation process starts. If conditions are favorable for the fermentation, appreciable amounts of lactic and other acids will be produced. The acids will preserve the pickles for a long period of time providing air is excluded.

The finished product can be pasteurized very easily because the acidity will supplement the short heating time and thus give the product a longer shelf life.

Microbiology of Vinegar

Vinegar is one of the oldest fermentation products used by man. Vinegar literally means sour wine (French vinaigre = vin "wine," plus aigre "sour" or sharp). Any fermentable carbohydrate in the food may serve as raw material. However, the sequence of fermentation follows a definite course of action. Fruits of various kinds serve as excellent material for spontaneous fermentation. Apples are usually the most widely used raw material for making vinegar.

Raw Material for Vinegar Making.—Any raw product that will yield an alcoholic fermentation is acceptable for the production of vinegar. Such materials as apples, grapes, pears, peaches, plums, figs, oranges, berries, honey, sugar, syrups, hydrolyzed starchy materials, beer, and wine may be used. Wine and cider are the best raw materials for vinegar production. Malt is widely used in England, wine in France, Italy, and Spain, and cider in the United States.

In order to produce a high grade product the raw material should be clean, sound, and mature. If wine is used it should be clean and free from preservatives.

Preparation of Fruit.—It is a common practice to use apples for vinegar making that have been rejected as a No. 1 grade, bruised, small size, and partially spoiled fruits. A high grade vinegar can only be made from good sound fruit. The apples are mechanically crushed, and then pressed. The apple juice is sweet due to inherent carbohydrates present, particularly dextrose. The juice is placed in large containers called fermenters. A spontaneous fermentation takes place in a very short time due to transient micro-organisms which are normally present in the product.

Biochemical Changes in the Fresh Fruit Juice.—The fermentation process is usually initiated by certain varieties of yeast of which *Saccharomyces cerevisiae* is one of the desirable types. The following reactions are typical in vinegar-making.

$$C_6H_{12}O_6 \xrightarrow{\text{yeast}} 2C_2H_5OH \quad + \quad 2CO_2$$

Dextrose   Ethyl alcohol   Carbon dioxide

The alcohol is oxidized by Acetobacter bacteria to form acetic acid.

$$C_2H_5OH + O_2 = \quad CH_3COOH + HOH$$

Alcohol   Acetic acid or vinegar

The yeasts and bacteria exist in a form known as commensalism. The Acetobacter are dependent upon the yeasts to produce an easily oxidizable substance. Vinegar could not be produced by the activity of one kind of organism.

Alcohol Content of the Fermenting Medium.—A concentration from 10 to 13 per cent of alcohol is necessary for good fermentation. If the alcohol content is much higher than 13 per cent, the alcohol is incompletely oxidized to acetic acid. Likewise, too low concentrations result in the loss of vinegar due to the oxidation of esters and acetic acid. Carbon dioxide and water are formed from acetic acid.

$$CH_3COOH + 2O_2 \rightarrow 2CO_2 + 2HOH$$

However, there are other organic acids formed in addition to the acetic. From this mixture of acids esters are formed which contribute to the characteristic odor, flavor, and color of vinegar.

Acetic Acid Fermentation and Yield.—Acetaldehyde is an intermediate product in the transformation of the reducing sugar in the fruit juice to acetic acid or vinegar.

According to the Cannizzaro reaction one molecule of ethanol and one molecule of acetic acid are produced from two molecules of acetaldehyde.

Butlin (1936) believes that acetaldehyde is dehydrogenated to acetic acid. Oxygen acts as the hydrogen acceptor in converting alcohol to acetaldehyde.

$$CH_3{-}\overset{\displaystyle OH}{\underset{\displaystyle H}{C}}{-}H + \tfrac{1}{2}O_2 \rightarrow CH_3{-}\overset{\displaystyle O}{C}{-}H + HOH$$

Ethanol   Acetaldehyde

$$CH_3{-}\overset{\displaystyle O}{C}{-}H + HOH \rightarrow CH_3{-}\overset{\displaystyle OH}{\underset{\displaystyle H}{C}}{-}OH$$

Acetaldehyde   Hydrated acetaldehyde

Two hydrogen atoms of the hydrated acetaldehyde are activated and attached to oxygen, the hydrogen acceptor.

$$CH_3{-}\overset{\displaystyle OH}{\underset{\displaystyle H}{C}}{-}OH + \tfrac{1}{2}O_2 \rightarrow CH_3{-}\overset{\displaystyle OH}{C}{=}O + HOH$$

Hydrated acetaldehyde   Acetic acid

Generally, 100 parts of sugar will produce from 50 to 55 parts of acetic acid which is a yield of about 1.2 gm. of acetic acid from 1.0 gm. of ethanol. Since part of the acetic acid and alcohol are lost by evaporation and some of the sugar is used as food for yeasts, the yield is less than 100 per cent.

$$\underset{\text{Glucose}}{\underset{(180)}{C_6H_{12}O_6}} \rightarrow \underset{\text{Ethanol}}{\underset{(2 \times 46)}{2C_2H_5OH}} + \underset{\text{Carbon dioxide}}{\underset{(2 \times 44)}{2CO_2}}$$

1.

$$\underset{\text{Ethanol}}{\underset{(2 \times 46)}{2C_2H_5OH}} + \underset{\text{Oxygen}}{\underset{(2 \times 32)}{2O_2}} \rightarrow \underset{\text{Acetic acid}}{\underset{(2 \times 60)}{2CH_3COOH}} + HOH$$

2.

Therefore 1 gm.-mol. of glucose (180 gm.) should yield 2 gm.-mols., or 120 gm. of acetic acid, representing 2 parts of acetic acid from 3 parts of glucose.

If both reactions are 90 per cent efficient then the yield of acetic acid should be 66.7 × 0.9 × 0.9 = 54.0 gm., which shows a yield of 54 parts of acetic acid from 100 parts of glucose.

Methods of Processing Vinegar

I. Home Process.—Vinegar can be made at home by simply providing an air supply and allowing barrels of cider or wine to ferment spontaneously. This does not always produce a high-grade product.

Air is admitted to the barrels through holes—one usually at each end of the barrel, which is placed on its side—above the level of the vinegar medium. These holes are at least one in. in diameter and screened to prevent the entrance of insects. Air may also be admitted through a top bunghole likewise screened. The acetic acid bacteria form a thin film on the surface of the solution, and this film later becomes quite thick and gelatinous. This gelatinous zoogleal mat, which contains very large numbers of bacteria, is known as the "mother of vinegar." Eventually, unless supported on a "raft" or framework, it will sink to the bottom of the barrel and a new film will form.

Although vinegar of high grade is produced by this method, it is a slow and costly process that involves much attention. The films are easily disturbed by the addition of the alcoholic medium and the withdrawal of vinegar.

II. Orleans Process.—The oldest and also the best of the slow processes for the production of table vinegars is considered to be the Orleans or "French method." To produce vinegar by this process, barrels of approximately 200 liters (52.8 gal.) capacity are used for containers. To initiate the process, each barrel is filled with about 65–70 liters of a high grade vinegar and 10–15 liters of wine. The vinegar serves as the starter culture. At weekly intervals during the next four weeks approximately 10–15 liters of wine are added. Thereafter about 10–15 liters of vinegar are withdrawn each week and the same amount of wine is added to replace the vinegar, thus forming a slow but continuous process.

III. Modification of the Orleans Process.—Although there are other slow methods of making vinegar, most of them are merely modifications of the Orleans process. A problem commonly encountered with these methods is how to add liquids without disturbing the floating bacterial film or zoogloeal mat. One of the two methods is generally used. Wood shavings which float are sometimes added to help support the mat or a glass tube is inserted in the top of the barrel so that it reaches almost to the bottom. This tube is then used to add additional solutions so that the zoogloeal mat is not disturbed. A glass tube can also be attached to the bottom of the barrel to serve as a gauge for measuring the level of vinegar in the barrel.

IV. The Quick Vinegar Method or German Process.—In this method the vinegar maker has done what he can to help the micro-organism work at a rapid pace. The apparatus used is called a generator. It is an upright cylindrical tank filled with beechwood shavings, or similar materials. This tank is fitted with devices for allowing the alcoholic solution to trickle slowly down through the shavings on which the acetic acid bacteria are living. The tank is not allowed to fill, for that would keep out the oxygen. Near the bottom of the generator are holes for allowing air to be drawn in; the air rises through the generator and is used by the acetic acid bacteria for oxidizing the alcohol. In many respects the generator is like a furnace. Both are contrivances in which active combustion takes place. Coal is added to the furnace to be chemically oxidized. Alcohol is added to the vinegar generator to be oxidized by bacterial enzymes. Both yield large amounts of heat (see Table 3). In the furnace the heat is desired; in the vinegar generator too much heat must be avoided and careful attention is necessary to prevent the temperature from rising too high and destroying the bacteria.

V. The Fringe Method.—Fringe and his associates from Bonn, Germany were able to produce vinegar by submerged fermentation. Their apparatus is called an acetator and it consists of a tank constructed of stainless steel, wood and accessory equipment and controls. It is possible to convert 150–200 gallons of alcohol per day into 100 grain vinegar. Because of the higher oxidation rate of the submerged process, it is necessary to maintain a residue of alcohol in order to preserve the vitality of acetic acid bacteria. The acid and alcohol mixture can be automatically controlled.

The generator consists of an air tight tank located at the bottom of the apparatus, a collection chamber constructed of stainless steel inside a 1 ½ inch copper tube water jacket and above the collection chamber an air intake where oxidation of the vinegar takes place. Above this area is a pile of 10 to 15 feet of wood shavings packed into the generator and on top of the generator is a stainless steel spray in which a rubber tube feed line and automatic controls are located.

Oxygen flow is controlled by a damper located on top of the generator. Air enters the generator through several intakes installed at intervals around the tank near the wooden grate. The incoming air is filtered by special screens.

Vents serve to remove the heat, otherwise the high temperature would inhibit the growth of acetic acid bacteria. As an acid alcohol mixture passes through the cooling coils the temperature is controlled. The cycling of the acetic acid mixture proceeds until the desired acetic acid strength is reached. This may require 8 to 12 days.

The Fringe method has certain advantages over the other generators. It is very economical, requires very little space, losses by evaporation by fumes are reduced to a minimum, and because it is a continuous process very little slime forms in the generator.

VI. Synthetic Acetic Acid.—Crude acetic acid or "pyroligneous acid" is the principal source of commercial acid and acetate. It is produced by dry distillation of selected varieties of hardwoods. This is purely a chemical process and no micro-organisms are involved in this type of acetic acid production.

Starter Organisms in Vinegar Making.—The organisms involved in the production of acetic acid usually grow at the top of the substrate in a thick jelly-like mass, commonly known as "mother of vinegar." In many respects these organisms are comparable to cultures used in the dairy industry. The "mother" floats on top of the acetifying medium. It is composed of both acetobacter and yeasts which work together harmoniously. *Acetobacter acetic, A. xylinum*, and *A. ascendens* are the principal species of the acetic acid-producing bacteria. *Saccharomyces ellipsoideus* is one of the varieties of yeasts involved in the alcohol production from the fermentable substrate.

Importance of Acidification.—The maintenance of the initial acidification in the production of vinegar is important in order to suppress undesirable organisms and on the other hand to encourage the presence of desirable acetic acid-producing bacteria. Ordinarily

10 to 25 per cent by volume of strong vinegar is added to the alcoholic medium to attain the desirable fermentation.

The alcoholic fermentation should be allowed to go to completion before acidification, otherwise the sugar in the medium would not be converted to alcohol after the addition of acetic acid. Incomplete fermented juices are usually low in acetic acid. The acetic acid strength of good vinegar should be around 6 per cent.

Temperature for Acetic Acid Fermentation.—The optimum temperature will vary with the organisms and the process being used. Ordinarily a temperature range of 80° to 85°F (26.7° to 29.4°C) is the most favorable. Too low a temperature favors a slow fermentation; a high one accelerates the evaporation of alcohol, acetic acid, and volatile substances that contribute to the characteristic flavor and aroma of the vinegar.

Factors in Maintaining a High Quality Vinegar.

Storage.—Acetic acid fermentation should be allowed to reach approximately 6 per cent. After the final stage of fermentation, the acetic acid bacteria will tend to destroy the vinegar by oxidation unless oxygen is excluded. Therefore, during storage the containers should be completely filled and sealed to prevent access of air to the vinegar.

Aging.—This is an important process because aging improves the flavor and clarifies the product. During aging many biochemical changes take place in the vinegar such as the formation of esters which contribute to the fine flavor and odor of the final product. Aging for one year or longer produces a good high grade vinegar. However, alcoholic vinegars, which contain *dilute* acetic acid solutions are not improved by aging.

Treatment of Vinegar for Merchandising.

Clarification.—Sometimes vinegar is bottled without further treatment, but clarification should be done in most cases. This is done by filtration, using filter aids or by fining.[1]

Bottling.—Only clear and aged vinegar should be bottled. The containers should be completely filled and tightly capped using treated corks to prevent access of air.

Pasteurization.—Vinegars may be pasteurized in the bottles at a temperature ranging from 60° to 66°C (140° to 150°F) for 30 minutes. Sometimes vinegar is pasteurized in bulk, cooled to 21.1°C (70°F) and then bottled.

---

[1] "Fining" is clarification by the addition of bentonite or Spanish clay, settling, and decantation.

Antiseptic Substances.—Several unsuccessful attempts have been made to produce certain germicidal or antiseptic substances in the vinegar by passing an electric current between two silver electrodes immersed in the vinegar.

Causes of Vinegar Spoilage.—*Vinegar eels or nematode worms,* may cause trouble in the commercial production of vinegar. Unsanitary practices, soil from plants, and insects may be the principal sources of these organisms. Eels have no public health significance in the vinegar. Indirectly they reflect the general sanitary conditions in the factory, and their presence in the product is objectionable.

They may be controlled by strict sanitary practices in every phase of vinegar production. Sterilization of vinegar barrels will destroy these organisms; since they are susceptible to steam or chemical agents, their removal is not a difficult problem. Pasteurizing the vinegar to a temperature of 130°F (54°C), or filtration, using Filter-Cel will control the organisms.

Mites entering through the air hole in the barrel are sometimes troublesome. Moisture and warm temperatures favor the growth of mites. Control practices are comparable to those used for vinegar eels.

Vinegar flies.—Decayed fruit, spoiled fruit juices, and vinegar are good breeding places for these flies. Clean sanitary practices along with screens over windows will help to control vinegar flies.

Wine flowers.—The term denotes a whitish film on the surface of the liquid. The film is sometimes called *Mycoderma vini* and is composed of yeast-like organisms. These micro-organisms grow aerobically, and will oxidize the carbon containing constituents to carbon dioxide and water. Hence the flavor and alcohol content is altered. This defect may be controlled by adding 1 part vinegar to 3 parts of the alcoholic solution or storing the alcoholic liquid in filled and closed containers.

Darkening of vinegar.—This is due primarily to iron and tannin or an oxidase. The iron comes from pipe lines, etc., while tannin may come from new barrels. Aeration of the solution helps to remove the darkening caused by iron and tannin. However, if oxidase producing organisms are present, pasteurization of the vinegar is strongly recommended.

Olive Industry

The industry started in California in 1869 from seeds brought from Mexico. Varieties for canning and fermentation are:

Variety	Native
Mission	U.S.
Sevellano	Spain
Ascolano	Italy
Mazanillo	Spain
Barocini	Italy

Olives are harvested in California around September 25. They are usually harvested when green.

Green and Ripe Olive Fermentation.

Green Olives.—Green olives are a fermented product preserved by biological acidity formed during the pickling process.

The processing usually involves the following steps:

a. The green olives are placed in a 2 per cent NaOH (lye) solution, at a temperature range from 70° to 75°F (21.1° to 23.8°C), until the lye has penetrated the flesh or outer tissue of the fruit.

b. The lye is removed by adding cold water thus diluting the mixture until the fruit is practically free of lye.

The lye treatment of olives is necessary because the outer coating or tissues contain a bitter glucoside ($C_{20}H_{27}NO_{11} + 3H_2O$) which is highly bactericidal. This glucoside associated with green olives is called oleuropein. The compound must be removed because it will retard or alter the course of a normal fermentation of the olives.

Removal of the glucoside can be accomplished by:

1. Dry oxidation.

2. Aeration, which involves washing the olives 4 or 5 times, then heating the olive mixture in a retort at 242°F (117°C) for 60 minutes.

3. Enzyme process. Certain enzymes are capable of destroying or altering the bactericidal properties of the glucosides. An enzyme obtained from burdock has this property but other disadvantages outweigh the desirable properties of this enzyme.

Steps in the processing of olives.—After the removal of the glucosides, the olives are placed in barrels with 7 to 10 per cent salt brine and allowed to undergo a spontaneous fermentation. The most favorable temperature is around 75°F (24°C) for maximum activity of the desirable bacteria. Naturally, a heterogenous microflora exists in the raw product but the salt concentration will suppress the undesirable organisms and thus favor the lactic acid bacteria. Usually 2 to 3 months are required for the completion of a normal fermentation of the green olives. Since air is practically excluded; the growth of many undesirable acid destroying organisms is retarded. The exclusion of air will also minimize oxidation reactions which tend to change the green olive to a dirty brown color.

The finished product is packed in jars and sterilized. This procedure insures a good quality product for a long time.

Ripe olives.—Ripe olives are light brown in color in contrast to the immature green olives. However, the ripe olives are placed in 5 to 7 per cent brine to soften the outer tissue before they are exposed to the lye solution. This pretreatment in brine allows the lye to penetrate into the fruit more easily. Apparently the germicidal substance is more concentrated in the interior of the fruit. The concentration of lye usually ranges from 0.7 to 2.0 per cent. The treated product is washed free of lye, packed in barrels with 2 to 5 per cent brine and allowed to undergo normal fermentation, usually from 2 to 6 weeks depending upon the temperature, etc. During the fermentation the ripe olives are exposed to air in contrast to the green olives where air is practically excluded. The air in the presence of slight amounts of NaOH left on the fruit will oxidize the polyphenols of the olive tissue to a black color. Hence the characteristic color of ripe olives. The finished product is usually packed in cans, with 3 to 5 per cent salt brine and then sterilized. This procedure renders a good finished product that will keep for a long time.

Organisms involved in the normal fermentation are:

1. *Leuconostoc mesenteroides.*
2. *Lactobacillus plantarum.*

The environmental factors are practically the same as in pickle fermentation.

Spoilage of Olives.—*Aerobacter aerogenes* may be involved in gas formation in green olives, and *Clostridium* species may cause gas pockets, also bad odors and flavors formed by an abnormal fermentation. The production of butyric acid by *Cl. butyricum* may cause putrefactive odors.

In ripe olives, pectolytic enzymes produced by *Bacillus subtilis* may cause a mushy or soft product. If the wash water used for removing the lye is below 140°F (60°C) many varieties of bacteria may survive and cause a poor quality product.

Citric Acid Fermentation

The commercial production of citric acid is accomplished by employing some of the common molds for fermentation. The principal

mold used in this fermentation is *Aspergillus niger*, although *Penicillium luterim* and *Mucor pyriformis* may be used, but not as efficiently as *A. niger.*
Many carbohydrate sources may be used in the production of citric acid. Low quality molasses is a cheap source of raw material. Also cane blackstrap molasses, or solutions of glucose or sucrose may be used provided some sources of nitrogen and mineral salts are available. Conditions most favorable for the growth of mycelium tend to increase oxalic acid productions, while a decrease in the mycelium growth will increase the citric acid production. Therefore there is a problem in controlling the growth of the mold in order to harvest the maximum amount of citric acid. The presence of oxalic acid necessitates procedures for separating citric and oxalic acids.
Modern methods of citric acid production utilize solutions with sugar concentrations between 10 and 20 per cent, a pH around 6.0, and a temperature range of incubation around 77° to 86°F (25° to 30°C) for 7 to 12 days for the surface method.
Citric acid has many uses in the food industry. It is used in candies, flavoring extracts, and soft drinks. Citric acid is sometimes used to preserve fish and other marine foods, and to prevent discoloration of crab meat and browning of sliced peaches.

BIBLIOGRAPHY

Anon. 1928. Fundamentals of Dairy Science. The Chemical Catalog Co., New York.
Anon. 1949. Canned Food Reference Manual, 3rd ed. The American Can Co., New York.
Butlin, K. R. 1936. The Biochemical Activities of the Acetic Acid Bacteria. Chemistry Research Special Report 2. H. M. Stationery Office. London.
Fabian, F. W., Bryan, C. S., and Etchells, J. L. 1932. Experimental work on cucumber fermentation. Michigan Agr. Exp. Sta. Tech. Bull. *126.*·
Foster, E. M., Nelson, F. E., Speck, W. L., Doetsch, R. N., and Olsen, J. C. 1957. Dairy Bacteriology. Prentice-Hall, Inc., Englewood Cliffs, N. J.
Frazier, W. C. 1967. Food Microbiology, 2nd ed. McGraw-Hill Book Co., New York.
Hammer, B. W., and Babel, F. J. 1957. Dairy Bacteriology, 4th ed. John Wiley & Sons, New York.
Kopeloff, N. 1926. *Lactobacillus Acidophilus.* Williams & Wilkins Co., Baltimore.
McClesky, C. S., and Christopher, W. N. 1941. The longevity of certain pathogenic bacteria in strawberries. Abstr. J. Bacteriol. *41*, 98.
Pederson, C. S. 1938. The gas producing species of the Genus *Lactobacillus.* J. Bacteriol, *35*, 95–108.
Pelczar, M. J., and Reid, R. D. 1967. Microbiology, 2nd ed. McGraw-Hill Book Co., New York.
Peppler, H. J. 1967. Microbial Technology. Reinhold Publ. Co., New York.
Prescott, S. C., and Dunn, C. G. 1959. Industrial Microbiology, 3rd ed. McGraw-Hill Book Co., New York.
Tanner F. W. 1944. Microbiology of Foods, 2nd ed. Garrard Press, Champaign, Ill.

CHAPTER 9

Microbiology of Eggs and Egg Products

A number of egg characteristics influence penetration, growth and spoilage by micro-organisms, as well as the transmission of human pathogens. These characteristics include the following:

(1) Eggs are produced in a shell which offers limited protection from bacterial penetration. (2) The egg and the shell just before they are expelled by the hen pass through the end of the intestinal tract, and thus are subjected to all microflora therein. (3) Abuses from improper handling of eggs so contaminated can result in penetration of the shell and growth of these organisms in the egg where they cause spoilage or harbor organisms pathogenic to humans. (4) Eggs are an excellent food for humans and micro-organisms; in fact, they are sometimes used in culture media for micro-organisms. (5) Egg white contains several bacteriostatic substances; therefore, the egg is considered a semi-perishable commodity. (6) Chickens have a species affinity for harboring *Salmonella* organisms. (7) Eggs are often consumed uncooked in meringues or egg nog or partially cooked in forms such as in scrambled eggs. (8) Eggs are frequently used in therapeutic diets for high risk populations. (9) Despite all of the above hazards fresh, high quality normal sound shelled eggs are not considered a hazardous food.

As a result of the above conditions, the microbiological content of an egg may vary from a few organisms to several million. A review of the physiology of the hen and of egg formation may help to explain how the egg may become contaminated.

PHYSIOLOGY OF THE EGG

The yolk is the first part of the egg to develop and this takes place in the ovary. There are numerous small yolks (ova), each contained in a separate sac. As the yolk develops in the vitelline membrane, it passes through the oviduct. It is here that the egg may be fertilized. As the yolk passes along the oviduct, albumen is added; a little further along the shell membrane is added and more albumen. The egg finally reaches the uterus where the final shell membrane is added. Then, before it is expelled from the cloaca, it receives a wax-like coating on the shell. This substance aids in protecting the egg from external contamination, see Fig. 25.

It is possible for hens harboring certain bacterial infections to contaminate the egg in the process of formation. It is also possible for the egg during the process of formation to pick up organisms such as *Salmonella pullorum*, the causative agent of pullorum in chicks.

In a normal, newly laid egg, the white or albumen appears to be composed of two distinct parts: the thick viscous portion surround-

158

ing the yolk and a thinner portion. Actually, however, there are four parts or layers of white. The innermost, or chalaziferous, layer immediately surrounds the yolk and ends in twisted strands of thick white resembling cords. These cords are called chalazae. There are usually two of them, one on each side of the yolk. They provide an axis upon which the yolk may rotate but serve to restrict the movement of the yolk away from the center of the egg.

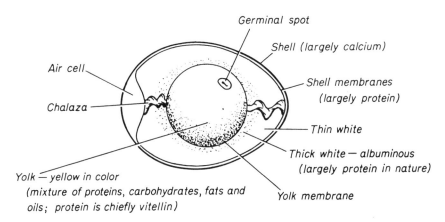

FIG. 25.   STRUCTURE OF HEN EGG

Next to this layer is one of thin white which is contained within the next surrounding layer, or envelope, of thick white. The remaining layer is thin white and it fills the space between the thick white and the shell membrane. Except for the chalazae, all layers of white are generally clear or transparent. In newly laid eggs, however, and in older eggs under certain conditions, the white may be slightly cloudy. Also certain types of deterioration or certain feeds may cause the egg white to be discolored.

The yolk of the egg is suspended in the white at approximately the center of the egg and is contained by the yolk (vitelline) membrane. On the surface of the yolk, and usually on its upper side when the egg is broken out, is the germ spot or germinal disc. The germ spot in a fertile egg, under proper temperature conditions, develops into the embryo. The size of the germ spot in the fertile egg, therefore, varies, depending on the degree to which this development has taken place. As the egg ages, the yolk tends to take up water, and becomes larger, and the yolk membrane weakens, thus giving the yolk a more flattened or spread-out shape.

When an egg is first laid the contents entirely fill the shell. As the egg loses the body temperature the contents shrink and air is drawn through the pores of the shell. This causes a small air cell to form between the two shell membranes usually at the large end of the egg where these membranes separate most easily. Some loss of water from the contents takes place with the aging of the egg, and the air cell gradually grows larger.

Blood spots on the surface of the yolk or suspended in the white lower the grade of the egg. The spots are caused by rupture of blood vessels in the yolk follicle (sac-like membrane) during ovulation. Some spots degenerate and change in color to reddish brown, tan, or white. They are called meat spots. Heredity and breed seemingly are factors associated with blood spots.

Eggs in which the blood has diffused throughout the albumen are known as bloody whites. They may be caused by a blood clot breaking and spreading throughout the white as the egg passes down the oviduct. Eggs with bloody whites are classed as inedible.

Microbial Content of Shell Eggs

Several genera of molds have been isolated from shell eggs. They are *Alternaria, Cladosporium, Mucor, Penicillium,* and *Thamnidium.* Spoilage is due to the mycelium of the mold entering through cracks or pores in the egg.

"Whiskers" is a form of fungal spoilage which covers the surface of the egg shell, especially when the eggs are stored in high humidity.

Different molds cause spots of different colors. Penicillium causes blue to green spots in the egg white. *Cladosporium herbarum* is one of the common molds causing spoilage of eggs. It produces black spots on eggs and it may be present in other foods. The yolk is ruptured by the hyphae, thus releasing an abundance of food for more mold growth. Age, moisture, temperature, general sanitation under which the hens are kept, and the condition of the storage facilities are important factors that will determine the general microflora of shell eggs. Mallman and Michael (1940) believe that mold infection originates from handling and packing after the eggs have reached the storage plant. They isolated several genera from packing material, although not all the molds studied penetrated the egg during the cold storage.

In the trade spoiled eggs are classified according to the color of the rots they produce. Winter (1942) made an exhaustive study of the microflora in black rot eggs. It appears that *Alcaligenes, Escherichia,* and *Proteus* genera were the predominant organisms in black rot eggs and that *Alcaligenes* and *Proteus* groups of bacteria produced this defect

Courtesy Hy-Line Poultry Farms

FIG. 25A.   PHOTOMICROGRAPH OF AN EGG SHELL

very quickly in fresh eggs. Moreover, these genera are widely distributed in feces, soil, and water. Their presence on dirty eggs is not uncommon. The best way to control black rot in eggs is to produce clean eggs and then handle them in accordance with accepted sanitary practices. Green rot is caused by some organisms in the genus *Pseudomonas*, red rots by the genus *Serratia*, pink rots under some conditions by *Pseudomonas* and white rots with thread-like white areas by *Pseudomonas*. With the exception of green rots other types of spoilage are rare in normal trade channels. Eggs are not held long enough for organisms to multiply sufficiently to cause spoilage even though such organisms are on the surface of the shell.

Yeasts are rarely found in shell eggs probably because the size of yeast cells makes their penetration through the shell difficult. At least one virus which causes a form of avian leukosis can be transmitted through the egg.

Penetration of Microorganisms Through the Shell

In general there is agreement that over 95 per cent of chicken eggs are sterile inside when they are produced. Most contamination occurs after the egg is laid. Salmonella organisms are sometimes found inside the eggs from hens infected with this organism.

Egg shells contain from 7,000 to 17,000 pores. Many of these do not go completely through the shell. At the time of laying the egg is coated with a mucous-like material which dries immediately. It is called the cuticle or bloom. In addition to acting as a coating it plugs the pores partially and acts as a mechanical barrier to microbial invaders.

The cuticle degenerates with conditions of storage making it easier for microorganisms to penetrate the shell. Microorganisms do penetrate egg shells even though the eggs receive good treatment. Proper handling, however, can reduce spoilage. Generally in industry all eggs are washed. Improper washing is the most common source of contamination.

The most common means of contamination is by immersing warm eggs in cold contaminated water. The egg is immersed in the water, the interior contents contract, and contaminated water is aspirated through shell pores into the white. Haines (1940) demonstrated this phenomena by placing freshly laid eggs in a cold suspension of bacteria and as the eggs cooled, the egg meats contracted thus drawing the bacteria through the shell. He also inoculated fresh eggs with some of the test organisms and was able to produce black rot in the eggs within 14 days.

The following factors influence the number of eggs which will become contaminated: (1) porosity of the egg shell; (2) the temperature differential between the water and the egg (the greater the differential the more contamination); (3) the length of time of immersion; (4) the concentration of cells in the water; and (5) the age and condition of the interior quality of the egg.

TABLE 18

BACTERIA ISOLATED FROM BLACK ROT EGGS AND THEIR ABILITY TO REPRODUCE THE DEFECT IN FRESH EGGS

Kind of Bacteria	No. of Lots Found in	No. Eggs Found in	No. Eggs Inoculated	No. Eggs Developing Rot
Aerobacter aerogenes	5	10	39	2
Alcaligenes bookeri	3	20	24	13
Alcaligenes fecalis	2	8	8	5
Alcaligenes recti	3	12	22	17
Eberthella oedematiens	2	5	4	4
Eberthella pyogenes	1	1	6	0
Escherichia coli	5	16	88	21
Escherichia freundii	2	3	27	0
Micrococcus epidermidis	1	3	4	0
Micrococcus varians	1	1	4	4
Proteus ichthyosmus	4	20	39	28
Proteus vulgaris	1	1	4	4
Serratia marcescens	2	2	18	18
Salmonella pullorum	1	1	4	0

The Effect of Mycostatic Agents Upon the Mold Growth in Shell Eggs.—Mallman and Michael (1940) tested the mycostatic effect of different compounds on pure cultures of molds from eggs, fillers, flats and cases. Sodium 2, 4, 5 trichlorophenate (Dowicide B), sodium 2, 4, 5, 6, tetrachlorophenate (Dowicide F), and sodium pentachlorophenate (Dowicide G) were most effective in preventing the development of molds.

Enzymes in Fresh Hen Eggs

The works of Lineweaver, Morris, Kline, and Bean (1948) show only small amounts of a few enzymes in eggs. The low enzyme content of hen eggs is comparable to that found in dormant seeds. It is reasonable to assume that developing embryos control the enzyme activity of the egg or seed and that the fresh egg or dormant seed would, therefore, possess very little enzyme activity.

These authors conclude that the deterioration of processed eggs, frozen or dried, is not caused by inherent enzymes. Moreover, autolipolysis of egg yolk reported by Koga and Wohlgemuth (1923) occurs only in the presence of contaminating micro-organisms. Tributyrinase occurs in both yolk and white. However, the yolk contains much larger quantities. Esterases are present in the livetin fraction of the yolk and are capable of hydrolyzing methylbutyrate, benzyl-butyrate, acetylcholine, benzylcholine, acetyl-β-methylcholine, triacetin, tripropionin, and tributyrin. Amylase is usually associated with the livetin fraction which occurs in the yolk. Peptidase is present in small amounts in both white and yolk. Likewise, phosphatase is present in the yolk, while catalase more often occurs in the white. Lipase, capable of attacking fatty acids with six or more carbons, phenol oxidase, cytochrome oxidase, and peroxidase could not be detected by these investigators. They conclude that it is extremely doubtful that inherent egg enzymes play an important role in egg deterioration.

However, other investigators believe that there are several inherent enzymes associated with normal eggs and that their activity will vary with the state of maturity and general conditions under which the eggs are stored. Such enzymes as pepsin, trypsin, lipase, catalase, and reductase have been demonstrated in eggs. Lipase will vary from a little in a fresh egg to a considerable amount in a stale egg. The catalase content varies very widely in a fresh egg and apparently occurs in equal amounts in the whites and yolks. In a putrid egg this enzyme is present in large amounts. No doubt the enzyme systems will vary in eggs from different species of birds. Geese and duck eggs have a pronounced flavor and odor and some workers claim this is due to the variation of the enzymes present. It appears that very little work has been done with respect to enzymes in eggs other than hen's eggs.

Lysozyme Activity in Shell Eggs

There are several bacteriostatic substances in eggs. The defenses of the egg against microbial invasion may be classified as physical and chemical. The shell, shell membranes, conalbumin, lysozyme, avidin, ovomucoid, and high pH levels are all known to have inhibitory action on micro-organisms. Many investigators believe that lysozyme plays an important role in deterioration of quality of eggs during storage.

The work of Kraft and Bryant (1956) showed that lysozyme activity in shell eggs increased during storage at 78°F (25°C) and then gradually declined. Lysozyme was not related to the incidence of bacterial infection of shell eggs stored at specified temperatures, or to the pH of the albumen. These authors observed that *Pseudomonas* bacteria responsible for green fluorescence in shell eggs were not lysed or inhibited in growth by either lysozyme or egg albumen. Apparently the pH of the albumen did not affect the percentage of shell eggs infected during storage regardless of the temperatures used.

TABLE 18A

ANTIBACTERIAL SUBSTANCES IN EGGS

Substance	Action
Lysozyme	Lysis of cell walls of gram + bacteria Flocculation of bacterial cells
Conalbumin	Chelation of iron
Ovomucoid	Inhibits trypsin
Avidin	Inhibits biotin
Riboflavin	Chelation of cations
Other uncharacterized proteins	Inhibit trypsin, chymotrypsin, fungal protease or combine with riboflavin or B_6

Board (1966).

Antibacterial Substances in Eggs

Freshly-laid eggs are normally low in bacterial content. A number of investigators report evidence of the presence of a germicidal substance in the fresh egg. Although there is conflicting evidence relative to this point, it has long been established that healthy tissues in any animal exert a germicidal effect upon invading micro-organisms. Analogously, it would appear reasonable to expect that freshly laid eggs, like freshly drawn milk, possess at least a transitory germicidal action. It has been found recently that the hydroxyl ion concentration within the egg tends to enhance this germicidal property. The hydroxyl ions increase during the first few days after the egg is laid when stored in a ventilated room. This increase in hydroxyl ions means greater alkalinity, which in turn means a greater inhibitory effect upon the micro-organisms.

Since many workers found very few, if any, bacteria in the egg white, they concluded that this portion of the egg had some bactericidal properties. Haines and Moran (1940) claimed that 98 per cent of the egg whites examined were sterile. Hadley and Caldwell showed that egg white contains bacteriolytic, bactericidal, and bacterio-inhibiting substances which they called lysozyme. When this substance was diluted 50,000,000 times, it showed marked lytic power on a susceptible test organism. Likewise it varied with different species of birds. The egg yolk showed much weaker bactericidal power.

Egg white showed a definite lethal or lytic effect on *Staphylococcus, Streptococcus, Meningococcus, Salmonella typhi,* and *Bacillus anthracis.* Egg white added to blood *in vitro* maintained its anti-bacterial activity and when injected into the blood stream of small animals, the blood had marked antibacterial powers which were evident for several hours.

Factors That May Influence the Microflora of Eggs

Eggs, like milk, are a food originating from animals. Eggs occupy an important place in the diet of man. Nature has very wisely protected the egg with a natural covering, the shell. Since the composition of the egg offers ample opportunity for biological processes to take place, the shell plays an important role in retarding these changes. Although there are many microbiological problems associated with eggs, the greatest of them is spoilage due to bacterial activity. The danger in eating eggs is not a major public health problem at the present time. In a few instances eggs have been thought to be the source of organisms causing intestinal disturbances. For example, it has been found that soft boiling, coddling, or frying on one side did not always render an egg free from *Salmonella*. Eggs artifically infected with *Salmonella pullorum* required five minutes boiling period to kill all of the test organisms. Van Oijen and Wedeman (1940) recommended that duck eggs be boiled ten minutes before use or the broken out liquid be heated at 149°F (65°C) for 20 minues to destroy *Salmonella enteritidis* and *Salmonella paratyphi* which are sometimes present. Bringing custard to a second boil, after adding a little thickening, was found to render it free from *S. enteritidis.* Gibbons and Moore (1944) used reconstituted egg powders heavily contaminated with several species of *Salmonella* in the preparation of scrambled eggs, omelettes, sponge cakes, custards, and muffins. They were unable to detect any viable *Salmonella* in these cooked foods.

Sources of Micro-organisms in Eggs

As already mentioned, a laying hen infected with *Salmonella pullorum* may transmit the causative agent to the egg and then to the chick. This is a common way in which young chicks acquire the disease known as pullorum, which can cause serious economic losses in the hatchery and in farm flocks. Other pathogens may be transmitted through the egg from an infected hen. Fortunately none of these pathogens have been reported to be significant in man. Current investigations are attempting to relate the pathogenicity of certain organisms responsible for diseases in poultry and in man.

Contamination of eggs from various external sources plays an important role in prolonging the keeping quality of eggs. The entrance of micro-organisms through the shell after the egg is laid is possible. The shell is porous in order to permit an exchange of gases within the egg during the development of the embryo.

The membrane lining on the inside of the shell is likewise semi-permeable and permits the entrance of micro-organisms from the exterior. Some workers maintain that the shell membrane offers very little resistance to organisms. It is the opinion of a few investigators that bacteria do not enter the egg until the natural resistance is broken down with age. The author doubts this viewpoint. Decayed or spoiled eggs placed next to fresh eggs will cause them to be more susceptible to the invasion of micro-organisms. The author has placed fresh eggs in broth cultures of several different kinds of bacteria. After a few days the several types of organisms were recognized in the egg.

According to Haines and Moran (1940) the egg shell is porous and bacteria can enter through it very easily. A difference in the temperature of the egg and the surrounding medium may account for the bacteria entering the egg by the process of suction.

Moisture apparently plays an important part in the transmission of micro-organisms through the shell. Excessive moisture facilitates the passage of micro-organisms, while the lack of moisture retards their passage. Clean, dry eggs are essential to the production and maintenance of good quality.

A deficiency of shell-forming food in the diet of the hen results in thin, defective shells which are more permeable to micro-organisms. Eggs laid under unsanitary conditions or improperly handled are quite certain to show greater contamination. The temperature at which eggs are stored is very important. Since the egg is a living cell with a complex enzyme system all its own, a favorable temperature favors the growth of organisms already present in the egg and also activates the inherent enzymes, all of which materially influence the quality of the egg. Cracked and dirty eggs are invariably high in organisms. The season may influence the microbial content based on the sanitary conditions under which the hens are kept. The author obtained a lower count on eggs from hens housed on winter range under average conditions. The range of organisms was 500 to 12,000 per ml. of mixed egg content, while under summer range the count was 1500 to 350,000 per ml.

The Influence of Changes in the Egg on Quality

The studies of Swenson, Slocum, and James (1936) attribute the loss in quality to a decrease of moisture, the absorption of off-odors, a continuous loss of carbon dioxide which increases the alkalinity of the egg white and finally the decrease in hydrogen ion concentration due to the loss of carbon dioxide. The latter factor greatly favors the activity of proteolytic enzymes present in the thick white. Moreover there is a diffusion of the water from the white through the yolk membrane to the yolk thus raising the pH of the yolk. Egg white usually has a pH from 7.4 to 7.6 when it is laid. At room temperature it may reach 9.4 or 9.5 within a week. In cold storage temperatures with little or no ventilation the pH may reach 8.8 or 9 in 3 months. According to Sharp and Powell (1927) any procedure which will stop or slow down chemical and physical changes in the egg will help to maintain its quality.

Shell Treatment

Shell treatment with oil in some form to control microbial invasion and to decrease the loss of moisture and carbon dioxide is not new. In fact Dutch farmers early in the 19th century preserved eggs for the winter season by dipping them in linseed oil.

Evans and Carver (1942) maintain that oiling eggs as soon as they are gathered improves the quality. Eggs must be oil treated before too much carbon dioxide escapes from the egg.

The success of oil treatment of eggs on the farm depends on dipping the eggs shortly after they are laid. A light paraffin oil (viscosity 50–60) is sprayed on the eggs with a hand paint or aerosol sprayer after they have been collected or packed in filler flats.

Heat Treating Shell Eggs.—The pasteurization process has been applied to many foods, especially dairy products. Consequently, this method has been applied to shell eggs to inactivate the inherent enzymes, destroy the bacteria present on the shell, in the shell, and shell membrane, as well as in the albumen and yolk of shell eggs.

There is a critical temperature range at which coagulation of the albumen occurs if either or both time or temperature are increased. The point at which coagulation begins is considered the upper limit for satisfactory results. Obviously several factors must be considered such as temperature of eggs before pasteurization, size, age, grade, and type of heating medium. The best results have been obtained by adjusting the eggs to room temperature around 75°F (23.89°C) before immersing and rotating them in oil. The temperature of the oil is held at 140°F (60°C) and the eggs rotate for ten minutes.

The above process is primarily of academic interest only, since it is no longer practiced in the trade.

Salmonella

Organisms of the genus *Salmonella* have been a particular and peculiar problem in eggs. The situation has been brought under control by an intensive campaign by the industry itself, more stringent federal and local regulations, pasteurization, and a better knowledge of the sources of contamination.

Surveys have implicated feedstuffs, particularly meat scrap and fish meal, as one of the sources of *Salmonella*. A typical case history involving menhaden fish meal illustrates the chain of contamination. The fish caught in the ocean are unloaded at the dock. After unloading, the hold and decks of the ship where the fish are held are washed down with water pumped from the harbor. The water is contaminated with *Salmonella*, which contaminates the hold which contaminates the next load of fish.

After unloading the fish are processed by cooking at times and temperatures which destroy all *Salmonella*, but the cooked meal is dumped out on the same area where the uncooked fish were held prior to cooking, thus recontaminating the cooked meal. This cooked meal which contains *Salmonella* organisms eventually is mixed with other feedstuffs and fed to poultry. A few birds become infected with *Salmonella* organisms and spread the disease throughout the flock. Finally the birds begin to lay occasional eggs contaminated with *Salmonella*. These eggs are generally of poor quality because the infection also affects the hens' reproductive organs. Eventually such birds stop laying altogether.

The cycle can be stopped at this point if the eggs go to a breaking plant and are pasteurized. If they are marketed as shell eggs, only clean, normal, sound shelled eggs should be sold since it has been established that the risk of high quality eggs as a source of *Salmonella* is almost nonexistent.

Other sources of contamination are from contaminated poultry flocks, wild birds, insects, soil, and water.

Pasteurization of Liquid Egg Products

Eggs are pasteurized primarily to eliminate *Salmonella* but the reduction in other microflora is also of considerable value. The temperature at which egg white proteins are denatured is very close to the temperature required to kill *Salmonella*. For that reason accurate temperature regulation is essential to prevent the loss of functional properties in the white. To help solve this problem several different methods of pasteurization have been developed. Table 18B shows the typical time-temperature schedules for ordinary heat treatment of the various types of liquid eggs. Other methods are referred to as the Western Regional Research Laboratory method, the Armour method, and the Ballas method.

To pasteurize eggs by the Western Regional Research Laboratory method, egg whites are acidulated with lactic acid to pH 6.8–7.3, and then aluminum sulfate is added to prevent damage by heat to the egg whites. After this treatment the eggs can be pasteurized at 140°F (60°C) for the usual 3.5 minutes.

In a process patented by Armour and Co., egg whites are heated to 125°F (51.7°C) for 1.5 minutes to inactivate the enzyme catalase. Then hydrogen peroxide is added and the pasteurization process continues at 125°F (51.7°C) for two more minutes. After cooling, the enzyme catalase is again added to remove the hydrogen peroxide.

A process where the white can be heated to 134°F (56.7°C) for 3.5 minutes under vacuum has been developed by the Ballas Egg Products Co.

TABLE 18B

PROPOSED TEMPERATURE FOR PASTEURIZATION IN 3.5 MINUTES

Product	Calculated (°F)	Proposed (°F)
Whole egg	140.0	140.0
Yolk plain	141.6	142.0
+10% sugar	148.3	146.0
+10% salt	148.7	146.0
Whites		
pH 7	138.0	140.0
pH 9	133.0	134.0

Anon. (1967).

Heat Treatment of Whole Egg Powder

The heat treatment involved in the production of dried whole egg powder does not produce a sterile product. The author has isolated many enteric organisms from the finished product. Obviously many heat resistant and typical thermophilic organisms are present usually as the result of unsanitary practices in the egg drying plant. The U.S. government specifies that the bacterial content of dried whole egg meats shall not be over 100,000 per gram and the moisture content must be five per cent or lower.

According to Hartsell (1944) the microflora of spray-dried egg powder is raised markedly at first when the product is stored at high temperatures. However, as the storage time is increased, the total microflora is decreased. Conversely when the temperature is lowered higher counts are obtained and a more diversified bacterial flora can be detected. The genus *Bacillus* seems to be the predominant microflora in spray-dried egg powder when held for three months regardless of the temperature of storage. Likewise the storage of spray-dried, whole egg powder in tin cans or greaseproof cartons does not affect the total bacterial count or the type of bacterial flora.

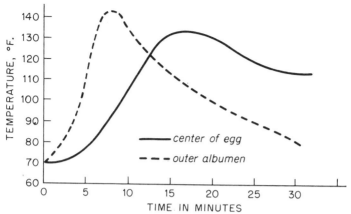

Fig. 26. Temperatures of a Shell Egg During Pasteurization

The Influence of Processing on the Microbial Content of Eggs

Liquid and Frozen Eggs.—The sequence of operations for freezing and drying eggs is as follows: (1) candling eggs to remove cracked and inedible ones; (2) washing eggs (no quaternary sanitizers permitted); (3) churning and/or milling, pressure filtration; (4) clarifying or filtering; (5) cooling to 40°F (4.4°C) (heat exchanger can be used); (6) fermentation to remove sugars (whites for dehydration only); (7) pasteurization; (8) processing (adjust pH, additives, etc.); (9) packaging for freezing or; (10) dehydrating; and (11) packaging of egg solids.

Dried Eggs.—This phase of the egg industry reached large proportions during the war. It was estimated that one of every three eggs was dried. Two types of product are obtained from eggs. Dried whole eggs have the shells removed and the egg meats are collected for drying. The following steps are employed in drying whole egg meats.

1. Shell eggs are stored at 40°F (4.4°C) for at least 72 hours prior to breaking.

2. Federal requirements specify that the broken egg meats shall not be over 60°F (15.5°C).

3. Egg meats are thoroughly mixed in a paddle churn.

4. Clarification to remove extraneous matter and particles of egg shell.

5. Eggs are held in a holding vat comparable to a milk pasteur-

izer, at 40°F (4.4°C) for not longer than 48 hours.   If they are held beyond 48 hours they must be frozen.

6. Eggs are pumped to the drier by a high pressure pump at a pressure of around 3,000 lbs.

7. Egg from the pump is broken up into a fine spray as a result of passing through special spray nozzles.

8. The drying temperature is 340°F (171°C).

9. Powdered eggs are collected at the bottom of the sprayer and passed through a system of cooling coils, resulting in a temperature of the powder around 90°F (32.2°C) or less.

10. Whole egg powder is packed in barrels or 14 lb. cartons and stored at 50°F (10°C).

BIOLOGICAL PROCESSES INVOLVED IN EGG DRYING

Fermentation of Egg Whites

The first egg drying in China, about 45 years ago, consisted of placing cracked eggs in shallow pans and exposing them to the sun. The white separates from the yolk.   Then the white is allowed to ferment, liquefying the thick white.   During the fermentation carbon dioxide is formed and ammonia is produced by deaminating enzymes. The egg white then becomes alkaline—bacteria then grow and break down the proteins and carbohydrates.   This fermentation is allowed to continue from 30 to 60 hours at 70°F (21.1°C).   A scum rises to the top and a sludge settles to the bottom of the vat.   Both are discarded as unfit for drying and make up about eight per cent of the total.   At the present time commercial enzyme preparations are used to accelerate this fermentation, then at the proper stage the fermentation is stopped by adding NH_4OH and C_2H_5OH to the mixture.

Advantages in the Use of Trypsin.—It is possible to regulate the time required for thinning the white by the amount of trypsin added and by the temperature at which the enzyme is allowed to act.   A temperature of 40° to 43°F (4.4° to 6.1°C) retards bacterial development.

Egg white hydrolyzed by trypsin resembles thin white more closely than does "fermented" white.   Bacterial growth during a fermentation treatment produces changes in the white besides breaking down the water insoluble proteins.   Furthermore, a uniform standard product can be produced over a long period of time.

Trypsin hydrolyzed white tends to darken at room temperature and must be stored at low temperatures as it is difficult to control the activity of the enzyme.   The enzyme glucose-oxidase is also used.

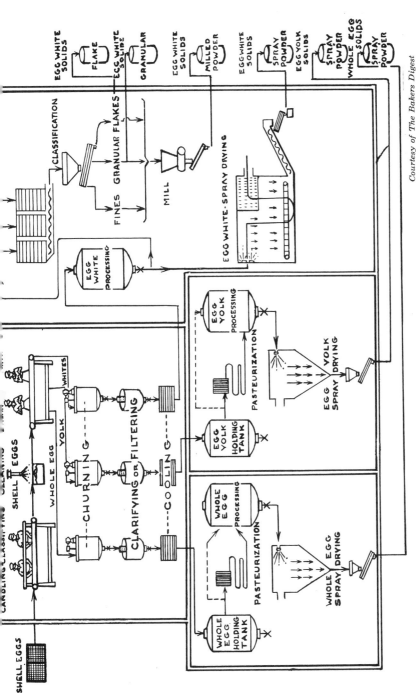

Courtesy of The Bakers Digest

FIG. 26A. SCHEMATIC OUTLINE SHOWING THE VARIOUS PROCESSING STEPS INVOLVED IN THE PRODUCTION OF WHOLE EGG, EGG YOLK, AND EGG WHITE SOLIDS

Method of Drying Egg Albumen

The fermented liquor is drawn off into pans about 12 in. in diameter and 1.5 in. deep. Pans are placed on racks in the drying room at a temperature of 120°F for 20 hours, then raised to 140°F (60°C) for 48 hours. The albumen is removed from the pan and allowed to cure for 24 hours, then it is packed.

At the present time some plants are using the spray method. The liquid egg is forced through nozzles under 1,500 to 3,000 lbs. of pressure. The yield is not good with the spray method.

Salmonella in Egg Albumen.—Duck eggs in the past have been involved in food poisoning. Such outbreaks were associated with custards in which infected duck eggs were used. There is a voluminous amount of material on this subject which indicates that various types of *Salmonella* infections are due to infected duck eggs. In Germany where lots of ducks are raised, laws have been passed which compel prominent labeling of duck eggs offered for sale.

Destruction of Salmonella in Egg Albumen.—Ayres and Slosberg (1949) studied three methods applicable for the destruction of members of the Salmonella group of organisms and found all three processes were satisfactory. The two methods were concerned with the destruction of the pathogens in the fermented liquor albumen prior to drying. The other method involved the storage of the dried albumen for controlled periods of time.

The authors concluded that vat pasteurization at 139°F on a commercial scale destroyed Salmonella. In the second method, hydrogen peroxide at levels of 0.1 and 0.2 per cent followed by the removal of the residual H_2O_2 with excess catalase destroyed the test organisms, but produced an excess of foam. The storage of dried fermented albumen at room temperature was the least successful in destroying the organisms.

Storage at 120°, 130°, and 135°F for 20, 8, and 4 days, respectively, destroyed the potential enteric pathogens. Likewise increasing the storage temperature of the dried, fermented albumen eliminates the danger of recontamination during the drying process encountered when liquid albumen is sterilized.

BIBLIOGRAPHY

Anon. 1967. Egg Pasteurization Manual. U.S. Dept. Agr. Western Utiliz. Res. Dev. Div., Albany, Calif.
Ayres, J. C., and Slosberg, H. M. 1949. Destruction of salmonella in egg albumen. Food Technol. *3*, 180–183.
Barott, H. G., and McNally, E. H. 1943. Heat treating shell egg. U.S. Egg and Poultry Mag. *49*, 320–322.

Board, R. G. 1966. Microbiology of the hen's egg. J. Appl. Bacteriol. 29, 319–341.

Evans, R. J., and Carver, J. S. 1942. Shell treatment of eggs by oiling. U.S. Egg and Poultry Mag. 48, 546–549.

Funk, E. M. 1943. Pasteurization of shell eggs. Missouri Agr. Exp. Sta. Research Bull. 364.

Gibbons, N. E., and Moore, R. L. 1944. Dried whole egg powder. Can. J. Research 22F, 48.

Hadley, P. B., and Caldwell, D. W. 1916. The bacterial infection of fresh eggs. Rhode Island Agr. Exp. Sta. Bull. 164.

Haines, R. B., and Moran, T. 1940. Porosity of and bacterial invasion through the shell of the hen's egg. Hygeia 40, 453–461.

Hartsell, S. E. 1944. Studies on the bacteriology of stored dried egg powder. Food Research 9, 505–511.

Koga, T. 1923. Enzyme activity in hen eggs. Arch. Biochem. 141, 430–466.

Kraft, A. A., and Bryant, A. W. 1956. The influence of environment on the lysozyme activity in shell eggs. Food Technol. 10, 45–47.

Lineweaver, H., Morris, H. J., Kline, L., and Bean, R. S. 1948. Enzymes of fresh hen eggs. Archives of Biochem. 16, 443–472.

Mallmann, W. L., and Michael, C. E. 1940. The development of mold on cold storage eggs and methods of control. Mich. Agr. Exp. Sta. Tech. Bull. 174.

Romanoff, A. L. 1943. Study of the various factors affecting permeability of bird's egg shell. Food Research 8, 212–223.

Sharp, P.F., and Powell, C. K. 1927. Physio-chemical factors influencing the keeping quality of hen's eggs in storage. World's Poultry Congress Proceedings, 399–402.

Swensen, T. L., Slocum, R. R., and James, L. H. 1936. The use of cold oil at ordinary temperatures. U.S. Egg and Poultry Mag. 42, 297–311.

Tanner, F. W. 1944. The Microbiology of Foods, 2nd ed. Garrard Press, Champaign, Ill.

Van Oijen, C. F., and Wedeman, G. 1940. Salmonella infektie in Endeneieren. M. Tydsehr. V. Dergeneesh., 67–280.

Winter, A. R., and Stewart, G. F. 1946. Pasteurization of liquid egg products. Am. J. Public Health 36, 451–460.

Winter, A. R., Greco, P. A., and Stewart, G. F. 1946. Pasteurization of liquid egg products. Food Research 11, 229–245.

Winter, A. R. 1942. Black rot in fresh shell eggs. U.S. Egg and Poultry Mag. 48, 506–509, 520.

Wrinkle, C., Weiser, H. H., and Winter, A. R. 1950. Bacterial flora of frozen egg products. Food Research 15, 91–98.

CHAPTER 10

9   # Microbiology of Meats

INTRODUCTION

Meat and meat products have been a constant food for man as far back as there has been any evidence of civilization on the face of the earth. Prehistoric man's crude hunting and eating implements which have come to light are evidence that he must have consumed his share of dinosaur and other forms of flesh. Ancient drawings and records on rock and in the caves of the primitive people further substantiate this fact.

General Factors Associated with the Microflora of Meat

In general the microflora of meat will be that of the barnyard or feed-lot. Micro-organisms from soil, water, air and manure make up the predominant flora. During slaughter these organisms, which are on the external surface of the animal, contaminate the meat by direct contact, through air and water, and on the hands and tools of workers. In addition the microflora of the slaughtering area, which includes contaminants from previously slaughtered animals, contribute to the overall load.

Unhealthy animals are generally removed at *ante mortem* inspection but the remaining animals with no visual signs of disease are slaughtered and processed in the plant. A few of these animals are diseased and may contribute to the general microflora of the plant. Healthy animals can also carry pathogens without having the disease itself. For example, contamination of meat with *Salmonella* organisms is a problem. Fortunately these organisms are killed by thorough cooking before consumption by the consumer. Unfortunately some of these organisms can contaminate areas in the kitchen and thus inoculate other foods in the home.

Specific conditions which influence microbial contamination are: (1) Bacterial load in the gut. Withholding feed for 24 hours before slaughter is recommended to empty the digestive tract. (2) Physiological changes. For example, evidence suggests that when animals are excited or fatigued, bacteria enter the tissues easier. Fatigued animals use up muscle glycogen which forms lactic acid and changes the pH of the meat tissue. (3) The method used for killing and bleeding. (4) The rate at which the carcass is cooled. (5) Whether the meat is ground or not.

Other factors which are believed to influence the numbers and types of micro-organisms on the animal are age of the animal, type of rations, method of slaughter, and conditions of storage.

Animals have a number of defensive mechanisms which prevent invasion of tissues. These are the skin and mucous membranes, hair and cilia, gastric juices, digestion in the intestines, and urine. Other defenses are inflammatory processes and humoral antibodies.

Sometimes the bung and esophagus are tied off during processing to avoid contamination.

Bacteria Generally Found in Meat

Examples of pathogenic micro-organisms found in meat as a result of infection of the animal prior to slaughter or as a result of cross contamination are those from the genera *Brucella, Salmonella, Streptococcus,* and *Mycobacterium*, especially *Mycobacterium tuberculosis*, as well as some anaerobic bacteria such as the clostridia. The two spoilage producing psychrophiles, *Achromobacter* and *Pseudomonas* often make up the predominant microflora, especially after storage. Bacilli and staphylococci are also present frequently and may contribute to the slime which forms on the surface of spoiled meats.

Achromobacter and some yeasts can produce lipases which cause rancidity.

Molds

Molds cause considerable trouble in the meat packing industry, especially with different kinds of preserved meats. For example, although the growth of molds on hams may not cause any pronounced decomposition, their presence still represents an economic loss because some of the meat must be trimmed.

Lack of proper handling and sanitary practices and excessive humidity in storage rooms all contribute to the growth of molds. Pickling vats also provide an especially favorable environment for the growth of yeasts and molds, especially when good sanitation practices are not used.

Aspergillus, Mucor, Penicillium, Alternaria, Monilia, and *Rhizopus* are the principal genera associated with meats.

Growth of Micro-organisms on Meat

The same conditions for growth of micro-organisms—moisture, nutrients, pH, time and temperature of storage, oxidation-reduction potential, level and types of contamination, surface area and inhibitors—required for other foods also apply to meats. Since meat is an excellent source of nutrients, micro-organisms given the other conditions required for growth multiply rapidly and cause spoilage in a short time. In fact, meat is often used as part of the cultural media used to grow micro-organisms.

Frazier (1958) described a number of different types of spoilage caused by micro-organisms on meat. (1) Surface slime is characterized by a shiny, viscous, moist covering on the surface of the meat. It is generally caused by micro-organisms of the genus *Pseudomonas, Achromobacter, Streptococcus, Leuconostoc, Bacillus* and *Micrococcus.* Some lactobacilli can also produce slime. (2) Some species of the genus *Lactobacillus* and *Leuconostoc* cause a green discoloration of meat such as the "greening of sausage" when nitrite is part of the curing ingredients. (3) Some lipolytic species such as *Pseudomonas* and *Achromobacter* as well as yeasts cause rancidity with resultant off flavors in fats. (4) *Photobacterium* and some *Pseudomonas* organisms cause a condition known as phosphorescence on meat. (5) Certain micro-organisms under some conditions will produce pigments which are visible on the surface of the meat. Examples of this condition are the "red spot" condition caused by *Serratia marcescens* and the blue color caused by *Pseudomonas syncynea.* Other pigmenters are *Micrococcus* and *Chromobacterium.* (7) All micro-organisms if they are present in large enough numbers can cause off-odors such as souring, rancidity, and foul odors.

Molds cause stickiness, a white fuzzy growth called whiskers, black spot, white spot, green patches, and off-odors and off-flavors depending upon the types of molds present.

Anaerobic organisms cause souring, putrefaction, and "bone taint."

Microbial Content of Meat and Meat Products

Obviously, the number of organisms will vary widely due to external contamination of the carcass. The counts may range from 100 to 100,000 per gram of beef and 5,000 to 1,000,000 per gram of swine. The samples were taken from the surface of the animal which accounts for the wide variation in counts.

Chopped meat (hamburger) was examined by the author and showed a wide variation in counts ranging from 5,000,000 to 10,000,000 per gram of sample.

Minced or spiced meats showed a relatively low bacterial count due to the preserving action of heating during processing. The microflora in smoked or dried meats is usually very low due primarily to chemical and physical environmental conditions which are detrimental to the growth of the organisms. Salting or brining of meats has about the same effect as smoking on the number of micro-organisms present in the meat. However, halophilic (salt tolerant) bacteria may be able to thrive in a salt environment. Canned meats are as a rule sterile. Meats held in cold storage temperatures may be of good quality after a long storage period providing the product has been properly chilled and handled prior to freezing. Cold temperatures are not an effective means for destroying organisms. They merely delay metabolism and reproduction of the organism. However, the bacteria tend to die off slowly during the storage period. Psychrophilic bacteria are able to survive in cold storage temperatures for relatively long periods of time.

Bacon is susceptible to certain microbial contamination. Lipolytic bacteria may cause rancidity when the bacon is held in storage. Also sulfide forming bacteria may alter the color and produce an oxidized flavor. The presence of high concentrations of nitrite may cause undesirable color changes.

Molds such as *Aspergillus*, *Alternaria*, *Monilia*, *Mucor*, *Rhizopus*, and *Penicillium* are encountered in fresh beef, pork sausage, wieners and dried beef when temperature, storage and humidity are favorable for their growth.

Microbiology of Frozen Meat

Because of the general use of frozen food lockers, a very large amount of meat is frozen. The so-called quick freezing tends to minimize "drip" after the meat is thawed. During the slow method of freezing the free water forms large ice crystals throughout the meat, and many of the soluble nutrients would be lost during thawing. Obviously such a condition would degrade the meat in taste and in physical appearance.

There is agreement among microbiologists that freezing is not an effective means of destroying organisms. On the contrary, bacteria may survive for long periods of time in various food products. The colloidal system occurring in meats, fish and poultry serves also to protect many kinds of micro-organisms.

In many instances cold storage meats are covered with molds. Again, molds are not destroyed any more readily than bacteria under similar conditions. If mold or bacterial spores are present on the surface of the meat prior to its entrance into cold storage, they may germinate, although the rate of multiplication would be very slow. The work of Chadat (1897) shows how resistant spores can be in cold temperatures. He kept mold spores frozen in his laboratory for three years after which the spores were viable.

Trichinella spiralis, a worm which lives endoparasitically in the muscle tissue of swine, can be a health hazard when raw pork is eaten. Augustine (1933) claims that quick freezing at 30°F (−1.1°C) followed by 24 hour storage at zero will destroy the larvae. Federal regulations in general require refrigeration below 5°F (−15°C) for 20 days to destroy the parasite. However, these conditions vary with the size of the cut. This parasite is also destroyed by cooking at 137°F (58.33°C).

Mechanism of Microbial Spoilage in Ham.—How do spoilage organisms enter into the hams and other tissues of the carcass? This is a debatable question. Several investigators, Topley and Wilson (1938), Arnold (1928), and Burns (1934) claim that tissues are not always free of organisms, yet most of the early reports suggest that tissues of normal healthy food animals are sterile. A voluminous review of the literature offers ample support for both viewpoints. Let us assume that contamination of the carcass is quite logical during the slaughtering and dressing process.

According to Jensen (1954) ham sours may be grouped into 6 classes:

1. Shank sours occur in the tibial bone marrow and are due to bacterial growth, particularly those that can grow at 38°F.

2. Body sours or "loin sours." These signify souring of the meat.

3. Aitchbone sours due to portions of the ospubis remaining on the ham.

4. Stifle-joint sours. This is the articulation of femur and fibula-tibia.

5. Body-bone sours (femur marrow).

6. Butt sours (butt between aitchbone and muscle).

The term sour refers to putrefaction of the muscle and not the formation of acid. Ham sours are rare.

Jensen (1954) has very clearly summarized the current theories regarding the causes of ham sours as follows:

1. Faulty exsanguination of the animal.
   a. Not bled properly.
   b. Severing of juglar vein too small to bleed out rapidly.
   c. Too large an incision.
2. Improper chilling.
   a. Frozen shanks cannot be properly pickled.
   b. Slow chilling of the carcass.
3. Contaminated salt used in pickling.
4. Previously used contaminated brines.
5. Excessive mechanical injury by dehairing machine.
6. Injury or bruises during processing of hams.
7. Holding carcass too long at high temperatures.
8. Failure of salt to penetrate into marrows.
9. Insufficient salt used to inhibit bacterial growth.
10. Poor quality hogs.

Table 19 shows the effect of temperature on the rate of growth of micro-organisms.

TABLE 19

GROWTH OF MICRO-ORGANISMS IN MEAT AT DIFFERENT TEMPERATURES

Temperature, Degrees F	Per Cent Increase of Microflora Over the Initial Count at the End of Each Period ————————Hours———————			
	24	48	72	96
35	2	4	8	9
40	3	7	10	20
45	8	20	25	30
50	20	30	40	45
55	25	40	45	60

TABLE 19A

SOME SOURCES OF BACTERIAL CONTAMINATION IN SAUSAGE MANUFACTURE

Ingredient	% of Raw Emulsion	Count per Gram	Approx. Load Contributed
Bull beef	41.20	1,590,000	656,000
Ground pork	13.75	88,500,000	12,170,000
Pork jowls	13.75	193,000	26,560
Ice	21.30	28	6
Dried milk	3.30	88,000	2,900
Corn sugar	1.65	595	10
Seasoning mix	.34	260	0
Rework (cooked)	1.37	190,000	2,600
Rework (raw)	1.37	8,150,000	111,700
Total	98.03		12,969,776 or Approx. 13 million

Source: Price (1965).

Spoilage of Sausage

Although microorganisms grow on the surface of sausage, most spoilage is caused by growth of organisms inside the casing. For example, some lactic acid producing bacteria can multiply to the point where lactic acid is produced. This is a form of spoilage except when fermented sausages are desired. In such cases the sausage is deliberately inoculated with a culture of lactic acid producing organisms.

Some of these same organisms can cause a green discoloration on the surface or in the core of the sausage when nitrites are present. This condition is caused by growth of these micro-organisms and production of a heat-stable peroxide before smoking and cooking. Apparently the heating and smoking complete the process and the green discoloration appears. *Lactobacillus viridescens* and certain *Leuconostoc* species seem to be the principal offenders.

Spoilage of Cured Meats

Salt, sodium nitrate and/or nitrite, sugars, spices and smoke all influence the growth of micro-organisms. Consequently the microflora of cured meats are different from that of uncured meat. Smoke contains many antibacterial substances such as creosols, aldehydes, ketones and acids. Nitrates and nitrites can actually be used by some micro-organisms as a source of nitrogen. Salt inhibits the growth of many micro-organisms but, in inhibiting bacteria it also removes competition for salt tolerant organisms.

Several other types of spoilage or quality defects occur in meat. One problem of particular concern is "soft-watery pork." It consists of an extremely pale watery condition of the muscles. The functional properties such as water holding capacity are adversely affected.

"Boar odor" is the "perspirative" or "urine-like" odor from the meat of uncastrated, sexually mature, male pigs.

Nitrate or nitrite discoloration, which results in pink meat after cooking, although not harmful is objectionable to consumers.

Tenderization of Meat

Meat becomes tender as a result of several conditions. Age, sex, and treatments during production, such as feeding hormones or castration of males, influence the tenderness of meat.

Post-mortem tenderization occurs as a result of (1) autolysis where the enzymes in the cells literally digest the cell tissues (2) treatment with proteolytic enzymes which break down the tissues and (3) cooking which coagulates protein, melts fat, and hydrolyzes collagen.

Generally beef is held for about 10 days at 36°–38°F (2.2°–3.3°C) after slaughter. This treatment permits autolysis to proceed at a slow rate and the low temperature retards the growth of micro-organisms. During this holding or ripening period, mold growth may appear on the cut surfaces of the meat, unless some precautions are taken to minimize it. Improved sanitation practices in processing plants have reduced the problem of mold and bacterial growth on carcasses.

In addition to molds there are several genera of psychrophilic bacteria that are capable of growing very slowly on meat at refrigerator temperatures. *Achromobacter, Pseudomonas,* and *Proteus* are the principal genera present. There is some evidence to suggest that these bacteria may play an important role in the flavor development of beef.

When beef carcasses are aged by the "Tenderay" process, ultraviolet lights are used in coolers to reduce the rate of growth of micro-organisms. As a result, the storage temperature can be increased, enzyme action is accelerated, and the aging period for tenderization is reduced.

Commercial Enzyme Preparations.—A few enzymes have been prepared as tenderizers for meat.

Macin—An enzyme obtained from osage orange.
Asclipian—An enzyme obtained from milkweed.
Unknown enzyme like the above substances obtained from edible mushrooms.
Ficin—An enzyme obtained from figs.
Enzyme-like substance obtained from *Aspergillus*.
Papain—An enzyme obtained from the papaya fruit.
Bromelin—An enzyme obtained from the juice of fresh pineapple.

The latter two enzymes have shown the greatest promise as far as commercial enzyme preparations go.

Recently a new process has been developed in which proteolytic enzymes are injected into an artery of the animal at the time of slaughter. This process tends to distribute the enzyme throughout the meat and results in a better and more uniform tenderization.

The control of enzyme action is very important. An ideal enzyme is one that can be inactivated during cooking. If the enzyme is not inactivated, the meat tends to become mushy during the heating or cooking.

Enzymes are not generally used in tenderizing hams or in the preparation of ready-to-eat hams. These hams are cooked and tenderized in the smoke house to an inside temperature of 137°F (58.3°C) or higher.

Action of Enzymes on Meat.—There are two kinds of enzyme reactions that may occur in meats: inherent enzymes and those produced by micro-organisms associated with meats. Likewise undesirable flavors may be developed by microbial enzymes which act on amino acids and their derivatives, converting them into highly odorous substances such as amines, mercaptans, and skatole.

It is interesting to note that enzyme action comes to a halt when the water content of the meat is dropped to 2 or 3 per cent. This is the active principle involved in the preservation of dried meats of various kinds.

Biological and Physical Changes in Meat During Cold Storage

Various kinds of meat tend to dry out during storage. The thin moisture film on the surface of the meat is removed by natural desiccation, the fat is exposed to oxidation and ultimately rancidity will develop, according to Dubois and Tressler (1943). Desiccation is speeded up if large amounts of salt are present in the product. It is known that seasoned sausage develops rancid odors and flavors and even loses color when stored at 0°F (-18°C), whereas ground pork can be stored at a comparable temperature for several months with no noticeable change in the product. Cooking the sausage will destroy the inherent enzymes.

Microbiology of Poultry Meat

The sources of contamination and microflora of poultry and poultry meat are similar to red meats. In the past poultry and eggs have served as a reservoir for *Salmonella.* Some workers are of the opinion that poultry have a species affinity for *Salmonella.* More recent investigations, however, suggest that the reason for the high incidence of *Salmonella* infection in poultry is caused by contaminated feed ingredients, especially meat scrap and fish meal.

Walker and Ayres (1956) in a study of micro-organisms found on poultry in six Iowa processing plants reported that live poultry generally had from 600 to 8100 organisms per square centimeter of skin area. After processing and eviscerating, these numbers increased to a range between 11,000 and 93,000.

Pseudomonas, Micrococcus, Achromobacter, Flavobacterium, Alcaligenes, Proteus, Bacillus, Sarcina, Streptococcus, Eberthella, Salmonella, Escherichia, Aerobacter, Streptomyces, Penicillin, Oospora, Cryptococcus, and *Rhodotorula* are the principal genera found on cut-up poultry.

The Preservation of Fish

There are numerous methods employed in the preservation of fish. However, only a few procedures will be discussed because the others do not have many practical and economical advantages. The basic principle in the preservation of fish is to prolong the quality of the product so that there is little change in appearance and flavor.

The icing of fish is a well established method of preservation. However, ice may carry many kinds of micro-organisms. Even ice produced artificially is not sterile although the microbial content may be much lower than ice harvested from streams, lakes, and ponds.

The storing of fish in several atmospheres of carbon dioxide has been very successful. Watson (1934) working in the laboratory of the Canadian Fisheries has stated that a 0.02 per cent concentration of refined sodium nitrite proved very effective as a curing agent for meats and fish. When hydrochloric acid and sulfur dioxide were used the product developed an unpleasant odor, flavor, and appearance probably due to a reaction between the acid and the oil of the fish.

Salt is an old standby in preserving fish, usually the immersion of the fresh gutted fish in a 20 per cent salt brine for 30 minutes prolongs the keeping quality of the fish. Fortunately most pathogenic bacteria are not salt tolerant and thereby many of the organisms are destroyed, but of course there are several exceptions.

Smoked Fish.—Smoke as a means of curing and preserving meat has been well established. Hence the application of smoke to fish preservation is not new. Dehydration of the fish during the smoking process is one factor in controlling microbial growth. The formation of certain chemical compounds such as formaldehyde, resulting in a chemical reaction between the constituents in the smoke and the food material, produces a chemical inhibiting agent for most organisms. Moreover, the formation of certain flavor characteristics in the product are usually desirable from a consumer acceptance standpoint. Smoking of fish is limited in use and applies only to certain varieties of fish.

Freezing of Fish.—Freezing fish is one of the common methods employed to get fish to distant points of consumption. However, the freezing of the fish involves considerable loss of water so that when they are thawed out much of the flavor is lost. Ice glazing of fish is one method that will minimize dehydration. A thin coating of ice around the product is very effective in controlling microbial spoilage. The method has not been used very extensively for economical reasons.

Canning of Fish.—Fish preserved by canning are heat treated prior to the canning or are sterilized in the container and sealed. The problems involved in canning fish are about the same as with other canned foods. The keeping quality of the product is entirely dependent upon the efficiency of the heat treatment.

Microbiology of Fish, Shellfish Meats, and Shellfish Meat Products

Fish, like other animal tissue, is not free of micro-organisms. Fish muscle is readily susceptible to enzyme action and decomposition by bacteria. Therefore, the problem of preservation is important. It is a common practice to eviscerate the fish after catching and then ice the edible portion. Obviously, surface contamination and sealing depends upon the degree to which sanitary practices are employed. The addition of chlorine and calcium hypochlorite has been recommended as a means of keeping the wash water sterile. The use of ice containing calcium or sodium hypochlorite has given satisfactory results and prolongs the keeping quality of the fish packed in ice.

Canada now permits the addition of chlortetracycline (Aureomycin) to ice in order to preserve fish during the transportation to the harbor.

Many investigations indicate that all kinds of edible fish carry a varied microflora in the intestinal tract and the organisms will vary according to the food and the water from which the fish are taken. Both aerobic and anaerobic organisms have been isolated from the intestinal contents of fish. Obviously, many of these micro-organisms can be associated with spoilage of the fish. Good sanitary practices in handling, processing, and storage of fish are a major factor in preserving the quality of the product.

Sewage polluted waters from which fish may be taken are often a significant public health problem. Studies have been made that indicate the survival of many enteric bacteria in the gut of fish. This observation should not be overlooked and unless steps are taken to destroy these organisms, fish may be a menace to public health.

Fish that are preserved by canning may present problems of spoilage. However, like all food products that are preserved in closed containers, fish should remain sterile and keep for long periods. Subsequent treatment, sanitary practices employed, and efficiency of the heat treatment will largely determine the shelf life of these products.

An interesting observation was made by Lang (1935) regarding the presence of *Clostridium botulinum*. He found this organism in the slime of tuna. Type A toxin was found in cultures from fish slime and cleaned fish just prior to canning. The observer also found *Cl. botulinum* in the washings from empty sardine cans. He studied the heat resistance of this organism when packed in different oils and sauces. The results are reported in Table 20.

TABLE 20

HEAT RESISTANCE *Cl. botulinum* IN OILS AND SAUCES

Product	Lethal Heat Treatment Necessary at 250°F (121.1°C) in Minutes
Abalone	1.57
Kamaboko	8.97
Mackerel in brine	2.44
Sardines in brine	2.34
Sardines in mustard sauce	6.55
Sardines in oil	8.00
Sardines in tomato sauce	3.66
Shad	1.58
Shad roe	5.61
Squid in ink	0.69
Tempera	6.17
Tuna in oil	6.95

Apparently the rate of heat penetration into oils is low as compared to that of moisture alone. Sauces and oil served to protect *Cl. botulinum*.

Recently an attempt has been made to preserve fish in vinegar sweetened with sugar. The fish are prepared by removing all inedible portions including the scales. They are thoroughly washed in water and then placed in 6 per cent vinegar pickle with 10 per cent salt. The product remains in the vinegar brine for 4 days. The fish are then packed in sterilized cartons with the addition of mustard seeds and peppercorns between the layers. Lastly, about 2 or 3 per cent vinegar containing sugar is added and the cans immediately sealed.

Swelled cans which were examined showed only acetic acid bacteria with no evidence of sporeformers or putrefactive bacteria. Usually the swells resulted from the action of acid on the metal of the container.

The microbiology of mussels, lobsters, and crabs is comparable in that all of them live and feed on marine life.

Mussels are widely used as a meat product. Acute toxemia has been attributed to mussels when they have been harvested from polluted water. The California State Department of Health has repeatedly warned the public of the danger from eating mussels obtained along the coast. Sanitarians have reported many cases of "mussel poisoning" due primarily to *Salmonella typhi*. This pathogenic organism has been known to survive for long periods of time in the mussel flesh. The public health aspect of mussels is comparable to that of oysters or any other marine food used for human consumption. Again, the quality of marine foods is no better than the environment in which these products grow.

The two methods available at the present time to insure their freedom from enteric organisms are self purification in clean unpolluted water and, then, thorough cooking of the meats before eating them. These suggestions will guarantee the safety of these marine foods except paralytic shellfish poisoning.

Lobsters constitute an important delicacy in the American diet. There are a few interesting observations in regard to the microbiology of lobsters. Several investigators claim that freshly caught lobsters are not free of bacteria and that these organisms are always present in the digestive glands and intestinal tract. Just what role these organisms may play in spoilage is not known.

The harvesting of lobsters at different times during the year reveals a marked change in the chemical composition of the meat. In canning, the liberation of hydrogen sulfide from the meat reacts with the iron in the can to cause iron sulfide discoloration. Bacteriological studies seem to indicate that several species of bacteria are capable of producing hydrogen sulfide in the live lobster. A change in pH values is correlated with the season of the year. A high pH value seems to accelerate the black discoloration of the lobster meat. It may be possible that an acidic pH level favors the growth of the H_2S forming bacteria.

Lobster meat contains a very active autolytic enzyme system. The enzymes are not active as long as the lobster remains in its natural environment and alive. When the lobsters are caught and packed in ice these enzymes seem to be activated and the meat undergoes marked changes. This is one reason why lobsters are kept alive until they are cooked.

Recently lobster meat has been canned. The keeping quality has been good. Again the processing has reached the place where the enzymes are inactivated and thereby not actively involved in spoilage.

Crabs, clams, and winkles are additional examples of marine food for man. In general, they are subject to the same degree of contamination from polluted waters. The same sanitary precautions apply to these foods as to oysters, lobsters, crabs, and mussels.

Microbiology of Oysters and Shellfish

To understand properly the bacteriological problems of the oyster industry, it is first necessary to have a clear conception of all the processes and conditions involved, from the very beginning of the seed oyster through its growth, harvesting, and final preparation for sale.

Sources and Control of Oyster Production.—Centuries ago, man had a plentiful supply of oysters in the natural oyster beds that abounded on almost all the coasts. However, with increased facilities to remove the oysters it soon became evident that if such wholesale ravaging continued unchecked, they might easily meet a fate identical with the passenger pigeon and other resources which have been so ruthlessly and wantonly destroyed or wasted. It was at this point that the state governments took measures to protect the natural oyster beds by declaring all of them the property of the state. Louisiana, as an example, claimed as property of the state "all beds and bottoms of river, streams, bayous, lagoons, lakes, bays, sounds, and inlets connecting with the Gulf of Mexico, within the territorial jurisdiction, including all oysters and shell fish."

Methods of production.—In the United States oyster production varied slightly with the different regions and the different kinds of oyster. The following methods may be classified as follows: (1) Natural propagation; it is possible at the direction of state commissions for one to secure seed oysters from natural beds. This will involve bringing large numbers of oysters to the surface, keeping the seed and throwing the large ones and shells back into the water. When the seed oysters have been gathered they are then taken to pools leased for the purpose. Several factors determine the usefulness of these pools for oyster beds. These are: the presence and prevalence of pathogenic micro-organisms, the population of the surrounding cities, the amount of industrial wastes draining into the area, as well as the size of the drainage area. Bacteriological tests for the presence of *Escherichia coli* in the water and oysters, as well as chemical tests for oxygen availability should be made. Such a survey results in a clear condemnation of certain waters as well as an explanation why in these waters no attempt should be made to raise oysters because of excessive factory wastes.

As has already been mentioned, oysters present a dangerous problem in public health work because they are eaten raw or nearly raw most of the time. Some outbreaks of hepatitis can be traced directly to contaminated water. There arises the question as to the purification of polluted oysters by allowing the oysters to purify themselves.

Inspection of Oysters for Harmful Organisms.—Oysters are commonly shucked on the coast and then shipped inland in buckets or containers. It is obvious that clean oysters, handled improperly, may become so contaminated as to be unfit for eating. Oysters in the beginning, if dredged, should be cleaned before bringing them into the shucking house. After shucking oysters they are always washed. This process, depending on the care that is taken, may reduce or increase the bacterial content. Rather than hosing or just immersing in tubs of water, the oysters are often cleaned by blowing air through the oysters and water. The oysters are then placed in tins and iced. If kept properly iced, there is only a minimum danger of spoilage. At the shucking houses there are inspectors both for the state and federal governments whose duty it is to enforce the sanitary regulations. The state inspector has the most authority, while the federal inspector merely supervises the work.

Propagation of Oysters.—In order to propagate oysters, small embryonic oysters or "spats" must be obtained from the feeding beds. The mortality rate of embryonic oysters in natural breeding beds is very high. Usually large numbers of the "spats" never develop into small oysters. Cement floors are constructed and located at a point between high and low tide. The young oysters or breeding stock are allowed to grow in these beds. The "spats" have a natural tendency to attach themselves to rocks, shells, or other objects during their growing period. It is a common practice to dump oyster shells from the mature oysters back into the water and this increases the yield of oysters.

The shell to which the "spat" attaches itself is called the "cultch."

When the oysters reach maturity they free themselves from the "cultch" so the shell may serve the same purpose for another embryonic oyster to attach itself.

Growth requirements.—In many of the northern oyster beds, the unfavorable weather conditions often contribute to the failure of oyster culture. The southern beds rarely experience such failures. Oysters grow much better in a saline environment that is lower than that of sea water. Fifty per cent of the salinity of sea water approximates ideal growing conditions for oysters. A mixture of fresh and sea waters seems to offer an ideal situation, provided a minimum of sewage pollution in the fresh water can be maintained thereby reducing the public health hazard.

Public Health Aspects of Oyster Production.—The danger of polluted oysters becomes even more acute when it is realized that a large per cent of the oysters are eaten raw or in oyster soup. In studies made on the effect of cooking on the microbial content after inoculation, it has been found that in general the usual methods of cooking oysters do not necessarily sterilize them. Probably the reason for this is that to retain their fine taste and texture, they must not be cooked too long nor at too high a temperature.

Obviously, oyster cultures should be located in water free of pollution if public health standards are to be observed. A sanitary survey, made by the state and often by the United States Public Health Service, should include all good and acceptable sanitary standards that will insure the public a wholesome food product.

Purification of Oysters.—There are at least two ways in which oysters may be handled in order to eliminate harmful organisms to man. Self purification in which the oyster tends to eliminate the micro-organisms is one method.

One good way to accomplish this is to transplant the oysters to a sewage-free bed and in one or two days they will be relatively free of coliform organisms. The rapidity of this cleansing, of course, depends largely on the conditions under which the oysters are placed. The best results are attained when the oysters are placed under optimum feeding conditions, because the rapidity with which they pass water through their shells determines the necessary time of cleansing. Temperature, salinity, and seasons of the year all play an important role. It has been estimated that an oyster can imbibe and expel water two times its own weight every minute. The second method is artificial purification. Due to the lack of clear, natural water in which to purify oysters by natural or self purification, the use of chlorination has been practiced. When *6 p.p.m.* of chlorine was added to water, the surface or shell of the oyster was partially sterilized. When oysters were exposed to this concentration of chlorine, they resorted to the natural phenomenon of hibernation. In this condition the oyster did not imbibe or expel water from its body due to the irritation caused by the chlorine. Later the use of calcium hypochlorite in the water greatly reduced the irritation to the oyster caused by free chlorine; therefore, they carried on normal activity and at the same time the hypochlorite destroyed many of the harmful organisms in the water. The oysters were allowed to remain in this chlorine bath for approximately 24 hours. This period of exposure to a low chlorine concentration permitted the oyster to practically wash and sterilize itself. Perhaps a more appropriate designation would be "self purification in its natural environment."

Regardless of the efficiency of this procedure, the method is not used extensively because the present state and federal laws do not permit the removal of oysters from polluted beds, except for seed. The tendency at the present time is to prohibit the dumping of raw sewage into a surface water supply. Such a procedure greatly reduces the public health hazards associated with polluted water used for oyster culture. Perhaps the use of a low concentration of chlorine in the final wash water may be a step forward in producing oysters free from harmful organisms.

Bacterial flora of oysters.—An oyster can be bacteriologically clean if it is permitted to grow in unpolluted water. As already stated, a viable oyster can imbibe and expel water from its body at a rapid rate. This mechanism is necessary for the survival of the oyster because it is the only way it can obtain its food supply.

Studies that have been made on oysters indicate that a variety of bacteria are present such as micrococci, gram-negative bacilli and gram-positive aerobes and anaerobes. Since *Escherichia coli* is a common inhabitant of the intestinal tract of man and animals, its presence in large numbers in the water and even in the oyster itself indicates fecal pollution. Therefore, *E. coli* has been used as an indicator to detect polluted water as used in the presumptive test for detecting contaminated drinking water supplies. Preliminary studies have shown that *Escherichia coli* survived in raw river water from 100 to 180 days and that *Salmonella typhi* survived approximately the same length of time.

In general the bacteriology of oysters can be applicable to other marine foods used for human consumption. Again the sanitary aspects of any food are no better than the raw product. The sanitary production, handling, processing, and distribution does not insure the public that all food is perfectly safe from the public health standpoint.

Survival of Enteric Organisms in Shellfish

The microbiology of shellfish depends largely on the potability of the water in which they grow. Public Health recommendations emphasize the importance of coliform organisms in the waters for the growing area. The value of any indicator organism depends on its survival as compared to the pathogens on the shellfish and in the shellfish after they have been removed from the water.

There is sufficient experimental evidence to indicate the transmission of enteric diseases by shellfish. It has been shown that *Salmonella typhi* will survive for several months in both shell and shucked oysters.

The workers at the Public Health Service Shellfish Sanitation Laboratory at Woods Hole, Mass., indicate that *S. schottmuelleri* remains viable as long as *Escherichia coli*. Both of these organisms survived in shell oysters and soft clams when stored for periods comparable to those which might be used in transit from the point of harvesting to consumption.

The Biology of Oysters

The life of an oyster is still mysterious. It defies many elementary rules of animal biology. An oyster is non-motile; it spends its lifetime in the same place where it was born. It can live with and without oxygen during certain stages of its life. The oyster possesses neither head nor tail. In this respect it differs from snails and cuttlefishes. It appears to have no brain, although its senses (chemical and tactile) are extremely acute.

The bivalve mechanism of the oyster pumps sea water through its system. The water brings in food and oxygen and carries out its waste products. In fact, the pumping system is very efficient, pumping as much as 35 to 40 quarts of water per hour through its body.

The oyster's feeding mechanism can detect whether the quality of the water is suitable and contains sufficient soluble food materials. Its chemical receptors also warn it not to feed when poisonous organic substances are present in the water. It also possesses a filter mechanism that can reject undesirable food materials.

The principal enemy of the oyster is the starfish. Realizing that the resistant armor shell is the protecting device of the oyster, the starfish waits until the oyster opens its shell, then cleverly injects a poison into the oyster thus preventing the shell from closing. The oyster shell is largely calcium carbonate, yet it does not utilize calcium carbonate, which is sparse in sea water. Just how the oyster catches these calcium ions and deposits them in the shell is unknown. It is still a mystery how and why the oyster accumulates other ions, such as copper, zinc, iron, and manganese in concentrations many thousands of times higher than in the sea water. These elements are in a digestible form thus making the oyster a nutritious food.

Public Health Significance of Paralytic Shellfish Poison

The ingestion of toxic shellfish has been a public health problem for many years because of their extreme toxicity and no known antidote has been found. The lethal properties to man are almost comparable to botulism. There are two general types of poisons which resemble shellfish poison. One of the types is the so-called "waterbloom poisoning" which may be elaborated by the profuse growth of fresh water algae or by their subsequent decay. Farm animals, deer, duck, and other wild birds have been killed by this poison. There are no reported cases of poisoning human beings by drinking water containing large quantities of algae.

The other related group of poisons are found in the flesh and organs of fish. Three different types of fish poisoning have been investigated, but little is known concerning the origin or nature of these poisons. One of the types, *Ciguatear*, is common in the Carribean and in several instances has been reported as causing intoxications in Florida. The great barracuda is one of the several fish species involved and is the most frequently associated with poisoning in Florida. A second type of fish poisoning is found throughout the South Pacific areas and is generally associated with the coral belt. The third type of poison, Tetrodon, is found primarily in the Japanese areas. Of the three types, the Tetrodon is the most deadly and causes symptoms most similar to those of shellfish poisoning in man and animals.

Source of the Poison.—The original source of the poison in shellfish is found in certain species of unicellular microscopic marine organisms of which the dinoflagellate, *Gonyaulax catenella* is perhaps the best known. It is a free-swimming organism, multiplying by formation of chains of two, four, or even eight individuals of dark orange or greenish brown color, and lives like a true plant cell by photosynthesis. Like all plankton organisms, it is most abundant in the summer. At times it may multiply to 40 million per liter. At such times the water presents a deep rust color—the so-called "red water"—in the day time and a beautiful luminescent spectacle at night.

Scallops may become highly toxic, but they are of limited public health significance because ordinarily only the non-toxic adductor muscle is eaten. The principal types of shellfish which reach dangerous levels of toxicity and may be consumed by man are mussels and clams. The poison evidently does not harm the shellfish. If a large number of Gonyaulax is present in the water, the toxicity of the bivalves may rise to dangerous levels within a few days. In the absence of the organisms, the stored poison is slowly eliminated.

Physiology and Toxicology.—The symptoms of poisoning in human beings are primarily peripheral paralysis which may vary from a slight tingling and numbness about the lips to a complete loss of strength in the muscles of the extremities and neck, and to ultimate death by respiratory failure. In a severe case of poisoning the tingling, stinging sensation around the lips, gums, and tongue develops about five to thirty minutes after the consumption of the mussels. This is regularly followed by a numbness or a prickly feeling in the finger tips and toes, and within four to six hours, the same sensation may progress to the arms, legs and neck, so that voluntary movements, as for example raising of the head, can be made only with great difficulty. In all cases of moderate severity this toxic weakness and stiffness of locomotion is accompanied by a peculiar feeling of lightness. Vomiting is an inconstant symptom and diarrhea and abdominal pain have not been recorded in untreated cases. In fact, there is a tendency to constipation which persists for several days. Records of carefully observed cases show the average temperature to be slightly subnormal (mean 98°F). The pulse is firm and slightly accelerated (80–100 per minute). During recovery some patients have chilly sensations in their limbs and may feel stupefied or become easily fatigued for a number of days. The longest recorded interval between eating poisonous shellfish and death is ten hours and the shortest interval is three hours. Intoxications may be mild or fail to develop in those who have consumed the shellfish in conjunction with a heavy meal or who have boiled the mollusks with rice and garlic, or fried them in oil. When the shellfish are taken into an empty stomach, the intoxication rate seems to be higher. As soon as intoxication is recognized, emptying of the stomach by an emetic and purging by brisk laxatives has been the usual practice, but in severe cases, these measures cannot be relied upon to prevent the absorption of a fatal dose of poison. As soon as difficult breathing develops artificial respiration should be applied. Clinical observations indicate that, even in severe cases, this procedure may prevent a fatal issue if extended over several hours.

A number of physiological and pharmacological studies have been made on shellfish poison in order to investigate its mode of action. In autopsies on humans no significant findings were recorded in the abdominal or chest cavities except a slight pulmonary congestion. In every case the folds of the stomach were studded with small hemorrhages.

From a group of experiments on frog muscle and nerves, Kelloway, as reported by McFarren, *et al.* (1956), concludes that the shellfish poison is a neurotoxin with a central effect upon the cardiovascular and respiration centers and a peripheral effect upon the nerve endings, both motor and sensory.

Characteristics of the Poison.—Medcof *et al.*, as reported by McFarren *et al.* (1956), reported the effects of domestic cooking on toxicity. Their results show that ordinary cooking of shellfish in a little water, even for brief periods, provides the consumer with some degree of protection. On the average, 100 gm. of steamed, boiled, or pan-fried meat contained only about 30 per cent of the poison present in 100 gm. of raw meat. Cooking may actually reduce the toxicity of the meat by considerably more than 70 per cent because a part of the poison is expressed in the juices. However, when clams are steamed or boiled, varying amounts of the juices may be ingested with the meats, either in the form of bouillon or broth. The temperatures involved in pan frying are considerably higher than in steaming or boiling and seem to be somewhat more effective in destroying the poison even though none of the extractives are discarded.

Commercial harvesting of mussels of any species from the Bay of Fundy, either for canning or for sale as raw food, has been prohibited at all seasons since the autumn of 1943, when their toxicities were found to be several times higher than those for clams. Likewise the marking of beaches or quarantine of an area to prevent local residents and tourists from digging clams or mussels has been generally indicated when the toxicity of the shellfish has been shown by laboratory tests to exceed 400 mouse units per 100 gm. of meat.

BIBLIOGRAPHY

Augustine, D. L. 1933. Effects of low temperature upon encysted *Trichinella spiralis*. Am. J. Hyg. *17*, 697–710.

Arnold, L. 1928. The passage of living bacteria through the wall of the intestine and the influence of diet and climate upon intestinal auto-infection. Am. J. Hyg. *8*, 604–632.

Ayres, J. C. 1955. Microbiological implications in the handling, slaughtering, and dressing of meat animals. Advan. Food Res. *6*, 109–161, Academic Press, New York.

Burns, C. G. 1934. Experimental studies of post mortem bacterial invasion in animals. J. Infect. Diseases *54*, 388–394.

Chadat, A. 1897. Bull. De l'Hrbier Boussier, *890*.

Dubois, C. W., and Tressler, D. K. 1943. Seasonings, their effects on maintenance of quality in storage of frozen ground pork and beef. Proc. Inst. Food Technol. *4*, 202–207.

Elliott, R. P., and Michener, H. D. 1965. Factors affecting the growth of psychrophilic micro-organisms in foods. U. S. Dept. Agr. Tech. Bull. *1320*.

Evans, J. B., and Niven, C. F. 1960. Microbiology of meat. *In* The Science of Meat and Meat Products. W. H. Freeman and Co., San Francisco.

Frazier, W. C. 1967. Food Microbiology, 2nd ed. McGraw-Hill Book Co., New York.

Jensen, L. B. 1954. Microbiology of Meats, 3rd ed. Garrard Press, Champaign, Ill.

Kelley, F., and Arcizz, C. S. 1954. Survival of enteric organisms in shell-fish. Public Health Reports *69*, No. 12.

Lang, O. W. 1935. Studies on the presence of *Clostridium botulinum* in canned fish. Univ. of Cal. Public Health Reports *2*, 26.

McFarren, E. F., Schafer, M. L., Campbell, J. E., Lewis, K. H., Taft, R. E., Jensen, E. T., and Schantz, E. J. 1956. Public Health Significance of Paralytic Shellfish Poison. A Review of the Literature. Robert A. Taft Sanitary Engineering Center, Cincinnati, Ohio. Special Communication.

Mountney, G. J. 1966. Poultry Products Technology. Avi Publishing Co., Westport, Conn.

Niven, C. F. 1956. Vinegar pickled meats. Curing problems in processing. Am. Meat Inst. Foundation Bull. *27*.

Pulley, A., and Von Loesecke, H. W. 1941. Tenderizing meat with papain. Fruit Products J. *21*, 37–39.

Price, J. F. 1965. Materials and Methods for Extension Education Programs in Meat and Poultry Processing. Mich. State Univ. Mimeo. E. Lansing, Mich.

Prudent, Inez. 1947. Collagen and Elastin Content of Fore Muscles Aged Varying Periods of Time. Unpublished, Ph.D. Thesis, Iowa State College Library, Ames, Iowa.

Tanner, F. W. 1944. Microbiology of Foods, 2nd ed. Garrard Press,Champaign, Ill.

Topley, W. W. C., and Wilson, G. S. 1938. The Principles of Bacteriology and Immunology, 2nd ed. Williams and Wood Co., New York.

Walker, H. W., and Ayres, J. C. 1956. Incidence and kinds of organisms associated with commercially dressed poultry. Appl. Microbiol. *4*, 345–349.

Watson, C. 1934. Keeping qualities of fish. Canadian Fisherman *21*, 21–28.

Winegarden, M. W., Lowe, B., Kastelic, J., Kline, E. A., Plagge, A. R., and Shearer, P. S. 1952. Physical changes of connective tissues of beef during heating. Food Research *17*, 172–184.

CHAPTER 11

Microbiology of Fruits and Vegetables

Fruits are grown over a wide area and in many parts of the world. The climatic conditions, type of soil and kind of fruit are just a few factors that may influence the kind of micro-organisms present. The numbers and kinds of organisms will also depend on the stage of maturity and composition.

Natural Protection of Fruit

The skins of nearly all fruits are protective. Some fruits have a hard impervious shell as found on various kinds of nuts. The outer covering serves to protect the fruit or nut meats from microbial invasion, to stabilize enzymatic changes in the product and to minimize a loss of moisture from the fruit. Unfortunately, bacteria, viruses, and certain pests may invade the fruit while it is in the process of forming on the tree or vine. These may remain inactive and then as the product reaches maturity or shortly thereafter bring about profound changes in the fruit, usually resulting in spoilage. This is one reason why a series of sprays are recommended during the growth of the fruit.

Presence of Bactericidal Substances on Fruits.—Nature has provided the fruit with means of protection from micro-organisms that may cause decay. The skin of the fruit tends to be bactericidal. Also the outer covering contains a waxy substance that offers very little opportunity for organisms to enter the interior of the fruit. When the covering is broken by bruises or other mechanical injury or attacked by insect stings, micro-organisms may enter readily.

Immature fruits as a rule have a higher germicidal power as compared with the mature or ripe fruits. Lemons have very definite bactericidal properties, while oranges have very little effect upon micro-organisms.

External Contamination of Fresh Fruits.—Fresh fruits and vegetables may be sold on fruit stands where sanitary conditions may not be satisfactory. The constant handling of the products by prospective customers is not conducive to good sanitary practices. Continued exposure of the product greatly enhances the possibility of unusual microflora on the fruit. Grading and merchandising the fruit in cellophane see-through containers has been helpful in preserving the crispness, freshness, and water content, and it has a tendency to reduce microflora.

The kinds and numbers of micro-organisms on the fruit will depend largely upon a variety of conditions. Dirty fruit resulting from lying on the ground as compared to the product on the tree or upright plant will certainly influence the presence of a heterogenous microflora. Storage, packaging, dust in the air, insect contamination, and climatic conditions are all significant factors that must be considered for maximum retention of product quality.

True bacteria do not play an important role in fruit spoilage due to the inherent acidity associated with most fruits. Also, the presence of bactericidal substances in these products has a tendency to destroy many kinds of bacteria. The author has found that bacteria, molds, and yeasts present on strawberries were viable after 3 years' storage at $15°F$ ($-9.44°C$). Moreover, bacteria were found repeatedly and in appreciable numbers on dates. There is no doubt that the human factor plays a major role in the contamination of fruits by bacteria. Grapes sold on sidewalk stands often contain pathogenic organisms and should be considered potentially dangerous.

Many varieties of fruits contain appreciable amounts of inherent sugars and acids, hence the juices are easily attacked by molds and yeasts. Mold spoilage of fruits during storage may be significant. They are common on citrus fruits. Moreover, mold induces spoilage very quickly when the fruit is injured. There are many kinds of spoilage associated with fruits, but the most characteristic one is the softening of the flesh which is followed by rotting, making the product inedible. In certain kinds of rot in fruits the organism actually invades the fruit while it is attached to the plant.

Yeasts, like the molds, occupy about the same importance in fruits. The former are well known for their part in alcohol and vinegar fermentation. These products have a high commercial value. On the other hand, yeasts may be undesirable by producing a yeasty flavor in certain fruits, especially dried figs and dates. Yeasts like bacteria and molds are widely distributed in nature. Yeasts have been reported in large numbers in vineyard soil and are spread to grapes by dust and insects as reported by Smeall (1932).

Mechanism of Contamination.—Any mechanical injury to the fruit, or an insect sting, either in harvesting or storage, that will rupture the outer pericarp, creates conditions favorable for organisms to enter the product and induce undesirable biochemical changes. Rowalter and Kiraly (1939) have reported the presence of micro-organisms in the inner structure of the fruit, seeds, and in the sap.

Preservation and Public Health Aspect of Fruits

Since many fruits are eaten raw, certain public health problems are involved, and, as already shown, fruits are not entirely free of pathogenic organisms. The preservation of many fruits by freezing simplifies this problem. Very little, if any, pretreatment is given to the product prior to freezing to eliminate the initial microflora present.

Methods for Reducing the Microflora on Fruits.—Mechanical washing is perhaps the oldest method used. However, the idea was to remove excess extraneous matter so as to gain an attractive appearance, not to reduce microbial contamination, but to win consumers preference. There is no doubt that large numbers of organisms are removed by mechanical washing. However, the method should not be accepted as an effective means of rendering the product sterile.

Rubbing the fruit, particularly apples, to bring out the bright color of the product is not acceptable. Rubbing tends to remove the natural wax coating on the skin of the fruit. This coating is a natural protection to the product from the invasion of organisms and perhaps insects. Moreover, this wax contains some bactericidal substances which is nature's way of protecting fruit, consequently it should not be removed.

Washing and Disinfecting Fruits.—Champion and Vande Velde (1921) studied the survival of *Escherichia coli* on strawberries, lettuce, and carrots when exposed to 0.2 per cent solution of chloride of lime for 30 minutes. The test organism was destroyed.

The use of chlorinated lime (20 per cent available chlorine) has been practiced, followed by a washing of the fruit in dilute sodium thiosulfate to remove the chlorine. A wash with approximately 5 per cent formalin followed by a liberal washing in water was fairly satisfactory.

With the development and use of many new detergents and detergent sanitizers more effective means of controlling surface contamination should be forthcoming.

Pasteurization of Fruits.—The use of chlorine compounds in destroying pathogenic bacteria has been practiced with a fair degree of success. The use of hot water for disinfecting some fruits has been tried. Ommyoji (1931) exposed grapes to water at 176°F (80°C) with no undesirable effects. However, many bacteria and viruses were not killed. Likewise, bacilli associated with decaying areas on pears were not destroyed. Presumably they were spore forming organisms.

The Preservation of Fruits

Drying Fruits.—Sufficient moisture is necessary for micro-organisms to survive and in all fresh fruits the moisture content is sufficient for organisms to grow. If the moisture content is lowered as in the drying of the fruits, an unfavorable environment for micro-organisms is created. The type of fruit, age of fruit, storage conditions, the residual moisture, kind of organisms, and conditions under which fruits have been grown will determine the microflora present on the dried product. As a rule dried foods are not sterile.

Drying of the fruit reduces the volume of the food from one-half to three-fourths its original size.

Drying of Foods Other Than Fruits.—The following methods of drying have been used.

1. Sun drying—Foods marketed as dried—exposed to the sun.
2. Kiln drying—Foods marketed as evaporated—kiln dried.
3. Sprayer process—powdered or liquid products—requires control of air temperature, humidity, air flow, and particle size of product.
4. Some commercially dried foods are treated with sulfur dioxide which shows a marked inhibitory action toward micro-organisms. Example: apricots, peaches.

Factors Associated with the Drying of Fruits.—Fruits are easier to dry than are vegetables as they do not need to be blanched. However, certain chemical changes due to enzymes and air tend to discolor fruit during drying.

Sulfuring will stop the discoloration and help to preserve vitamin C content. The fruit is exposed to fumes of burning sulphur. Sulfur burned in the air forms SO_2 which is a gas. This gas penetrates the moist fruit, forming sulfurous acid (H_2SO_3) with the water of the fruit. This acid inactivates the enzymes, stops discoloration, taste and odor changes, and prevents spoilage by micro-organisms and insects.

Potassium metabisulfite or sodium bisulfite solutions may be used instead of sulfur dioxide but the results are not very satisfactory because:

1. Penetration into fruit is very slow, thus allowing the sugar to diffuse out of the fruit.
2. The long soaking process allows fruit to absorb much water, which is then evaporated, thereby increasing the drying time.

Number of Micro-organisms on Dried Fruits.—The microbial content of dried foods according to Clague (1936) may vary from several hundred per gram on dried fruits as contrasted to many million per gram on dried vegetables. Molds were found in all samples studied while yeasts and bacteria were less numerous.

Types of Spoilage Associated with Dried Fruits.—If favorable moisture and temperature are available, several types of spoilage may take place. Esau and Cruess (1933) found yeasts to be responsible for souring in prunes and dates. These authors also observed a sugar-like substance on dried fruit due to yeasts which gave the product a yeasty flavor. Sometimes a bitter or acid flavor may be produced. Bacteria present are usually the result of contamination, especially under unsanitary conditions.

Spoilage of Fresh Fruits

The microbiology of fresh fruits is interesting because the normal flora present on the fruit may be involved in spoilage of the product later. Moreover, the possibility of the presence of pathogenic organisms may be significant for public health if the fruits are eaten raw without washing or sterilizing. Lastly, many of the organisms present may be desirable if the juices of the fruits are to be fermented. As a rule molds and yeasts rather than bacteria are largely responsible for much of the spoilage in fruits.

A consideration of mold spoilage of stored fruits and vegetables leads one into the domain of plant pathology, for certain rots of such products are due to these organisms invading the fruit while it is on the living plant. Some species of fungi occur characteristically on each kind of fruit or vegetable.

Thus with cherries, peaches, and plums, spoilage is due primarily to *Penicillium expansum* which causes green to blue mold rot. *Physalospora malorum* causes black rot, while a variety of other molds may be involved. This type of spoilage of fruits is characterized by softness of the tissue and eventually the product becomes rotten.

Plant pathogens also cause spoilage as well as infecting the tree. The common brown soft spots in stored apples are most frequently caused by *Penicillium expansum*.

Yeasts are usually responsible for the characteristic alcoholic fermentations of various fruit juices. It has been observed that a variety of yeast known as *Saccharomyces ellipsoideus* has been isolated from grapes during the vintage season.

Microbiology of Frozen Orange Concentrate

Hahn and Appleman (1952) inoculated stock cultures of *Escherichia coli, Salmonella typhi* and *Shigella paradysenteriae* into pasteurized orange concentrate which was then frozen at 1°F (-17°C). After 24 hours aliquot samples were examined for the survival of the test organisms on differential and enrichment culture media. After 48 hours no enteric pathogens could be detected. However a freshly isolated culture of *Streptococcus faecalis* was studied and the organism remained viable much longer than the original test organisms, but eventually died.

The processing of fruit and vegetable juices changes the composition of the product. The pH, moisture, and solids will determine the type of spoilage organisms present. A high moisture content favors bacteria and yeasts. The reduction of solids by processing may change the oxidation-reduction potential in favor of yeasts, by the presence of residual acids and sugar. Thus at room temperature an alcoholic fermentation may take place.

However, a temperature around 50°F (10°C) may be more favorable for bacteria and molds. *Leuconostoc mesenteroides*, a lactic acid producing organism, may enter the picture and create environmental conditions favorable for mold growth. Molds can tolerate acids and some may utilize the acid as a source of energy.

Viability of Micro-organisms from Frozen Fruits and Vegetables.—The effect of low temperatures on micro-organisms as they normally occur in fruits and vegetables has been studied by many research workers. They have concluded that freezing brings about many physical changes in the food as well as reducing the initial microbial content. Eventually some biochemical changes may take place which alter the flavor and texture of the food.

There are many kinds of micro-organisms associated with fruits and vegetables during the growth of these products. Many of the organisms are soil types and have little, if any, public health significance. However, if these food products are held under a favorable environment, then and only then will undesirable changes take place in the food. The rate of spoilage will depend very largely on the type of organisms present.

Obviously, thorough washing and blanching of the product will materially reduce the microflora present on the raw product, before it enters the freezer. The blanching process alone may reduce the microbial load more than 99 per cent, provided the product is not recontaminated.

There are many variable factors to be considered which influence the rate of survival of micro-organisms during freezing and subsequent frozen storage. Studies were made by Jones and Fabian (1952) in which they isolated more than 100 different species of bacteria from fruits and vegetable products. Some species were markedly reduced in numbers when stored at 0°F (−17.8°C) for 6 weeks while other organisms showed a high degree of resistance to freezing under similar conditions. A few species of *Escherichia coli* were not able to survive during the first 4 hours of freezing. However these investigators concluded that all organisms studied showed reduction in numbers after 6 weeks of freezing storage.

Naturally the substrate in which the organism is suspended for freezing will influence the survival time. For instance, organisms suspended in vegetable extract and 40 per cent sucrose showed that some organisms were not appreciably protected by these substrates.

Jones and Fabian (1952) have demonstrated in their work that the temperature of freezing may not be such an important factor, although certain cultures show some difference in the rate of survival at the different temperatures used. In these instances $-20\,°F$ ($-28.9\,°C$) offers the greatest protection. It has been observed that intermittent freezing is more destructive to micro-organisms than continuous freezing. This is an unfortunate observation since a product may show a deterioration in quality due to defrosting and refreezing and at the same time show a low microbial content. One should not interpret the microbiological results alone as being the final basis for judging the quality of frozen fruits and vegetables.

Fruits that have not been blanched present a problem in controlling the numbers of micro-organisms present when these products are frozen. However, the natural pH of many fruits will limit the growth of certain types of micro-organisms. This is an assurance the product will maintain a high quality throughout the freezing storage period.

Luyet and Gehenio (1940) have proposed different theories in regard to the fate of the bacterial cell during the freezing process. These are as follows: (a) a withdrawal of energy, (b) the attainment of minimum temperature, (c) mechanical injury, (d) too rapid thawing, (e) dehydration, (f) various physiological, physical, and chemical changes. However, Jones and Fabian (1952) do not subscribe to these theories as being adequate to explain the mechanism of death of the cell. These theories do not account for those cells in an actively growing culture that are killed during the process of freezing while other cells suffer no apparent change. These authors believe that "weak cells" in a bacterial suspension are easily destroyed while the more resistant cells survive. Why some cells are weaker than others in the same suspension is not easy to explain.

The preservation of foods in concentrated solutions of salt (brine) or sugar (syrup) has been used for a long time in the food industry. Sometimes a mixture of salt and sugar solutions are used as a preservative and as a sweetening agent. The mechanism of preservation is largely due to the plasmolyzing effect on the bacterial cell.

Micro-organisms on Vegetables and Vegetable Products

Many vegetables are grown near the surface of the soil. Others such as potatoes and carrots, grow beneath the surface of the soil. These conditions are responsible for a heterogenous microflora on the vegetables. The microflora of vegetables and vegetable products may be significant from the standpoint of spoilage of the product or the public health hazards involved.

Wurz and Bouges (1901) inspected vegetables grown in infected soil and polluted water and they concluded that the vegetables could be a factor in transmitting disease producing bacteria. *Clostridium tetani* was isolated on the surface of the vegetables. While several species of intestinal organisms were secured, the interior of the vegetables examined were free of micro-organisms.

However, surface contamination by handling in market stands and unfavorable conditions for proper storage of the product play an important role in the numbers and kinds of organisms on the vegetable. The author has isolated *Escherichia coli* on more than 40 per cent of the vegetables purchased at the curb stand market. A marked reduction of the microflora is evident where such vegetables are trimmed. The removal of the outer leaves from lettuce and cabbage reduces the chances of enteric organisms, especially *Salmonella typhi* being present.

There is ample evidence at the present time that fresh vegetables grown on polluted soil can be responsible for certain communicable diseases. Water cress, by nature of its growth and cultivation, is a good example of this contamination. Moreover, *Salmonella typhi* has been known to live in the soil from 30 to 36 days and in sterile sand for more than 60 days.

The survival of any pathogenic bacteria in the soil is influenced by several factors. Obviously any material containing pathogenic organisms added to the soil certainly has some sanitary significance and sewage sludge is an excellent example. The character of the strain of bacteria, its ability to compete with other organisms present in the soil, hydrogen ion concentration, kind of soil, moisture content and penetration of air and light are important factors that must be considered.

The spoilage of potatoes is usually associated with "rots" caused by molds. The rot of tubers may give them the appearance of being shriveled or shrunken and covered with mold mycelium ranging from dark brown to white in color. *Fusarium* species is usually the organism involved.

Bacterial soft rot causes a soft mushy condition in the tuber. *Pythium debaryanum* is largely responsible for this condition.

Erwinia carotovora is a typical bacterium that causes a soft rot, mushy consistency and bad odors in carrots, radishes and potatoes.

This organism has a unique enzyme system that enables it to attack pectins in these products thus rendering them inedible.

Distribution of Enzymes in Vegetables

Mergentime (1939) states that the distribution of the enzyme systems varies with different vegetables. Peroxidase activity is much greater in the tissue than in other parts of the plant structure. He also noted that this enzyme was more active in the skin of young lima beans and very weak in the cotyledon. According to Bullis and Wiegand, (1945), the corn cob tissue contains more peroxidase than the kernel tissue. Likewise vegetable tissue damaged by mechanical injury or improper storage gives a marked peroxidase reaction as reported by Phaff and Joslyn (1943).

The information is very meager on the biological factors with reference to the distribution of an enzyme system in the plant tissue and the heat-stable catalytic systems.

Sterilization of Vegetables

Sterilization implies a chemical treatment in order to destroy many kinds of undesirable micro-organisms. Chloride of lime in 0.2 per cent solution is effective in reducing the total microflora of lettuce and carrots. Specific studies indicate that *Escherichia coli* is completely destroyed. Apples and radishes are effectively sterilized in 30 minutes in a solution containing 50 p.p.m. of available chlorine. However, one must recognize that much of the chlorine is dissipated by the vegetable tissue.

However, it is generally agreed that green vegetables cannot be satisfactorily sterilized with chlorine compounds, regardless of its concentration or length of exposure.

Public Health Aspect of Sewage Sludge Used as Fertilizer

The epidemiological factor and the longevity of pathogenic bacteria in nature and soil, the intimate relationship of vegetables grown in polluted soil, and the fact that many vegetables are eaten raw constitute an important public health problem.

Frozen Vegetables

Freezing is another form of food preservation but as such is not an effective means of destroying organisms. It merely slows up their metabolic activity without killing them.

Obviously the greater the microflora on fresh raw vegetables the more important sanitary aspects become when the product is frozen. The blanching of the product prior to freezing removes large numbers of surface organisms and at the same time inactivates many of the inherent enzymes in the vegetables. There are many advantages of blanching vegetables as reported elsewhere and it is now considered a standard practice in freezing certain kinds of foods.

Tressler (1938) thought that a bacterial count under 80,000 per gram indicated a good blanching job. The product should be quickly cooled in clean water and properly handled before and after freezing.

Organisms on Tomatoes Grown in Polluted Soil

The possibility of the transmission of certain pathogens by eating raw vegetables grown in soil fertilized by nightsoil or the use of polluted water for irrigation of crops is a timely problem from the public health standpoint. Moreover the use of sewage sludge for fertilizer may also have certain health aspects.

The literature has revealed very little direct evidence of extensive transmission of bacterial enteric diseases by consumption of night-soil fertilized vegetables. It is difficult to separate contaminated vegetables from the influences of polluted drinking water or insect vectors. The entire problem of vegetable contamination may be appreciably altered in the case of environments containing cysts and eggs as well as bacterial organisms.

The work of several investigators clearly summarized the whole problem of bacterial contamination of tomatoes grown in polluted soil. They conclude that the residual coliform organisms on the surface of sound uncracked stems of tomatoes is no greater than on tomatoes grown on unpolluted soil. Also it made no appreciable difference in the coliform count whether the pollution was added to the soil prior to or concurrent with the growth of the plants.

When the stem ends of the tomatoes were split, the coliform organisms gave a high count regardless of the soil contamination. However, the bacterial microflora was three times higher on the tomatoes when the soil received sewage irrigation during growth.

Sunlight appeared to reduce the contamination when the tomatoes were exposed, but cracks and crevices on the product reduced the effect of the sunlight.

Dust, wind current, cultivation, and insect movements are important factors in the contamination of tomatoes.

The spraying of tomatoes with suspensions of *Escherichia coli* resulted in a lower coliform count after 30 days as compared to the unsprayed controls. When *Salmonella* suspensions were sprayed on tomatoes in the field, the organisms could not be recovered after 7 days.

Microbiology of Tomato Products

Tomatoes, raw and canned, as well as tomato products, are widely used in the American diet. Consequently, micro-organisms play an important role in certain types of spoilage, while others may be a menace to public health.

Canned tomatoes have sufficient acidity so that they are usually sterile when processed and placed in sealed containers. However, the quality of the raw product is important as in any food to be processed, if a high grade food is to be attained.

Spoilage of Canned Tomatoes.—There are several types of spoilage associated with this product, although the loss through spoilage is not great in tomatoes. Perhaps a few types of defects should be mentioned. These are as follows:

1. Hydrogen swell is a physical chemical reaction between the metal of the can and the acids in the fruits, and usually no micro-organisms are involved.

2. Bacterial swell is usually caused by one or more members of the Lactobacillus group of which *Lactobacillus lycopersici* is the principal one. This organism is non-spore forming, but can tolerate the high temperatures used in the processing of the product, or it may gain entrance into the can through a slight defect. Tomatoes and their products are an ideal medium for the growth of these organisms. They produce gas which causes the can to swell.

3. Flat-sour is characterized by an off-flavor and a cloudy appearance of the product. *Bacillus thermoacidurans* is the principal organism involved. Its growth in the tomatoes does not cause the cans to swell thus making it difficult to differentiate between spoiled and unspoiled cans because spoilage is not apparent until the can is opened. Catsup and tomato juice are usually involved in this type of spoilage.

4. Certain fermenting yeasts have caused much trouble in catsup. The yeasts were thermoduric and no doubt survived the heating process used in the preparation of this product. A yeasty flavor and odor along with gas formation are the characteristics of this defect.

Tomato Juice.—This is one of the more popular tomato products. Fresh juice is extracted from the fruit. Temperatures used for extraction vary with the manufacturer. The juice is usually flash pasteurized at 252°F (122°C) for 42 seconds. Salt is added as the product is being filled in the can.

Color and flavor are the principal quality characteristics of this product. If the juice is from green tomatoes, the color and flavor are poor; if the tomatoes are overripe, the flavor may also be inferior. Although a variety of manufacturing procedures are used, the main objective is to obtain a sterile product without affecting the fine delicate flavor of the juice during heating.

Bacterial spoilage of tomato juice.—Perhaps the most troublesome spoilage in tomato juice is an off-flavor. Over-heating can bring about cooked flavors in the juice. *Bacillus thermoacidurans* may cause a high incidence of spoilage. This organism is very heat resistant and can withstand a processing temperature of 212°F (100°C) for 20 minutes. It not only produces an off-flavor in the tomato juice, but may eventually produce a "flat-sour" type of spoilage. It appears that the organism is widely distributed in the soil so its entrance into tomato products is not unusual.

Catsup.—This is a common type of a tomato product. Like tomato juice, it is subject to spoilage. Molds and yeasts find a favorable environment in catsup and reflect the general sanitary practices used in the processing of this product. In fact mold counts are a routine laboratory procedure followed during the processing. The presence of yeasts give a yeasty flavor along with gas formation, certainly an undesirable defect in the catsup. *Lactobacillus lycopersici* has been reported as a troublesome bacterium in catsup by causing a gaseous spoilage and off-flavor. The organism can be destroyed in 2 minutes at 167°F (75°C). Here again, the presence of these organisms in the product indicates that unsanitary methods were employed. Where strict sanitary practices are used, very little trouble is encountered in the finished product.

Preservation of catsup.—Salt is usually added to catsup to improve the flavor and not for its germicidal action. However the salt content added may vary from 1.5 to 3.8 per cent, and some germicidal action may be effective against certain types of micro-organisms.

Sugar is another flavoring agent like salt. The usual concentration for catsup is not sufficient to inhibit the growth of most micro-organisms. However, when 15 per cent sugar and 4 per cent salt were added together to catsup, microbial growth was reduced to a minimum.

Sodium benzoate.—This compound cannot be used to preserve catsup. It appears that a concentration between 0.2 and 0.5 per cent is necessary in order to stop the growth of most varieties of bacteria. However, yeasts and molds are known to be very resistant to sodium benzoate. These observations seem to limit the effectiveness of sodium benzoate as a preservative in tomato products.

BIBLIOGRAPHY

Bilenker, E. N., and Dunn, C. G. 1960. Growth of food spoilage bacteria in banana puree. Food Research 25, 309–320.

Bullis, D. E., and Wiegand, E. H. 1945. Blanching experiments on frozen corn on the cob. Fruit Products J. 24, 361–367, 377.

Champion, M., and Vande Velde, E. V. 1921. Washing and disinfecting fruits. J. Am. Med. Assoc. 76, 1511–1512. As quoted by Tanner (1944).

Clague, J. A. 1936. Microbiological examination of dried foods. Food Research 1, 45–59.

Esau, P., and Cruess, W. V. 1933. Yeasts in dates. Fruit Products J. 12, 144–147.

Frazier, W. C. 1967. Food Microbiology, 2nd ed. McGraw-Hill Book Co., New York.

Fuller, G. W., Elbisi, H. M., and Francis, F. J. 1965. Microbial spoilage of prepeeled potatoes. Food Technol. 19, No. 6, 103–107.

Hahn, S. S., and Appleman, M. D. 1952. Microbiology of frozen orange concentrate. Food Technol. 6, 156–158.

Jones, A. H., and Lochhead, A. G. 1939. A study of micrococci surviving in frozen-pack vegetables and their enterotoxic properties. Food Research 4, 203–216.

Jones, R., and Fabian, F. W. 1952. The Viability of Micro-Organisms Isolated from Fruits and Vegetables when Frozen in Different Menstrua. Tech. Bull. 229, Michigan Agr. Expt. Station, East Lansing, Mich.

Luyet, B. J., and Gehenio, P. M. 1940. Life and Death at Low Temperatures. Biodynamica, Normandy, Missouri.

Mergentime, M. 1939. Control methods for scalding vegetables for freezing. Quick Frozen Foods 1, No 8, 14–15.

Mundt, J. O. 1956. The direct microscopic enumeration of bacteria in the washings of green beans. Food Research 21, 21–26.

Mundt, J. O., McCarty, I. E., and D. B. Williams. 1966. The safety of home-made pickles and relishes. Tenn. Farm Home Res. 57, 6–8.

Ommyoji, A. 1931. Effect of temperature on grapes. J. Oriental Medicine 14, 46–48.

Phaff, H. J., and Joslyn, M. A. 1943. Peroxidase test for blanching requires careful application. Food Industries 15, No. 3, 50–52.

Rowalter, L., and Kiraly, E. R. 1939. Micro-organisms in the inner tissues of fruits. Arch. Mikrobiol. 10, 13–25.

Rushing, N. B., and Senn, V. J. 1962. Effect of preservatives and storage temperatures on shelf life of chilled citrus salads. Food Technol. 16, No. 2, 77–79.

Samish, Z., Etinger-Tulczynska, R., and Bick, M. 1963. The microflora within the tissue of fruits and vegetables. J. Food Sci. 28, 259–266.

Smart, H. F. 1939. Microbiological studies on commercial packs of frozen fruits and vegetables. Food Research 4, 293–298.

Smart, H. F., Etinger-Tulczynska, R. and Bick, M. 1961. Microflora within healthy tomatoes. Appl. Microbiol. 9, 20–25.

Smeall, R. 1932. Yeasts in vineyard soil. Brit. Med. J. 41, 917–919. Quoted by Tanner (1944).

Splittstoesser, D. F., Wettergreen, W. P., and Pederson, C. S. 1961A. Control of microorganisms during preparation of vegetables for freezing. I. Green beans. Food Technol. 15, 329–331.

Splittstoesser, D. F., Wettergreen, W. P., and Pederson, C. S. 1961B. Control of microorganisms during preparation of vegetables for freezing. II. Peas and corn. Food Technol. 15, 332–334.

Splittstoesser, D. F., and Wettergreen, W. P. 1964. The significance of coliforms in frozen vegetables. Food Technol. 18, No. 3, 134–136.

Tanner, F. W. 1944. The Microbiology of Foods. Garrard Press, Champaign, Ill.

Tressler, D. K. 1938. Microbiology of frozen vegetables. Refrig. Eng. 36, 319–321.

Tressler, D. K., and Joslyn, M. A. 1971. Fruit and Vegetable Juice Processing Technology. 2nd Edition. Avi Publ. Co., Westport, Conn.

Wolford, E. R., and King, A. D., Jr. 1965. Variations in bacterial count in commercial corn freezing. J. Milk Food Technol. 28, 183–187.

Wurz, C., and Bouges, E. 1901. The effect of polluted soil and water on vegetables. Arch. Med. Expt. et Anat. Path. 13, 575. Quoted by Tanner (1944).

CHAPTER 12

Microbiology of Flour, Bread, and Cereal

Organisms associated with grains are sometimes referred to as the epiphytic microflora. Morphologically, they are largely rod shaped bacteria. Some of these are spore-formers such as *Bacillus mesentericus*, others are chromogenic and there are numerous gram-negative bacteria of which *Flavobacterium* predominate. In addition members of the *Escherichia-Aerobacter* group may be present. Molds and yeasts also constitute a part of the epiphytic microflora.

Many investigators have assumed that the epiphytic flora of grain are not affected by the microflora of the soil in which the grain grew. However, it is possible for organisms to be transmitted from seed to the new plant. Hence, the practice of treating seed before planting is employed in controlling certain types of grain diseases although they may not necessarily be of bacterial origin.

Microbial Growth on Grain

The survival of organisms on grain depends upon moisture and temperature. Studies have been made to determine the minimum moisture content that will sustain the organisms: oats about 16, barley 14, and corn 13 per cent. Micro-organisms will not grow below these levels. A higher moisture content is favorable for mold growth.

Moisture content of grain is an important problem at the present time due primarily to the modern methods of harvesting grains. The combine has largely replaced the grain binder and threshing machine. The corn picker has taken the place of cutting, shocking, and husking corn. These new developments in harvesting have allowed a maximum amount of moisture to remain in the grain, as compared to the old method which provided for a "drying out" period of the grain in the shock. The weather conditions prior to and during the harvesting season play an important part in the moisture content of stored grain.

All of these factors are important in the milling process and in providing moisture for microbial survival on the grain. Hence, artificial drying of the grain in storage is necessary.

Microbiology of Flour

Studies show that microbial growth occurs more readily in flour than in the whole grain providing the moisture content is the same in both products. Apparently, moisture content will determine the number and kinds of organisms present. The bacterial content of flour may range from 20,000 to 5,000,000 per gram with an extremely heterogenous flora present; this will include many secondary invaders as well as the epiphytic flora of grain. *Serratia marcescens* has been shown to cause discoloration and changes in the starch content of damp cereals. *Flavobacterium* species are usually very numerous in addition to *Aerobacter, Staphylococcus* and members of the *Cellulomonas* group. If the moisture content is favorable the cellulose digesting organisms will break down the outer coating of the grain kernel and this in turn will accelerate starch hydrolysis by certain organisms.

Undesirable Micro-organisms Associated with Flour.—Flour may contain an appreciable number of mold spores and if they are not destroyed in baking they may cause the bread to become moldy very quickly. Various kinds of yeasts may occur in flour but they do not cause any particular harm. Sometimes an epidemic of "ropy bread" is encountered and may be due largely to *Bacillus mesentericus* being present in the flour. Since this organism is very resistant to heat it may survive the baking temperature of the bread. *Serratia marcescens*, a chromogenic organism, may cause a defect in bread known as "bloody bread." Moldy bread is, of course, due to various molds which may be present either in the flour with the spores surviving the baking process or may arise from external contamination of wrapping paper or unsanitary equipment, or from general unsanitary conditions in the bakery.

Certain anaerobic bacteria such as *Clostridium butyricum* may cause off-flavors in flour. This defect reflects upon the quality of the product.

Control of Mold in Bread.—The following practices have been helpful in controlling molds:

a. Strict sanitary practices in the bakery and on the part of personnel

b. Use of ultraviolet lights

c. Air conditioning of the building

In addition certain mold inhibitors have been used in the industry. They are discussed below.

Microbiology of Bread

The use of bread by man goes back to earliest times. Bread is a clean product because it is wrapped. National Bakers Association objected to wrapping at first because it held moisture on the surface of the bread. Now porous paper is used and no objections are offered. Bread baked and wrapped by machinery yields a good clean sanitary product.

Breads are generally classified into two groups, leavened and unleavened. Leavened or "raised" bread is the result of gas formation. It can be subdivided further according to the mechanism responsible for the formation of gas.

Classification of Breads

A. Leavened Breads
1. Gas—chemical—baking powder—biscuits.
2. Gas—yeast—regular dough—bread generally used in this country
3. Gas—bacteria—*Escherichia coli* and other bacteria—Sauerteig
B. Unleavened Breads
1. No gas—No organisms—crackers, tortillas and matzoth.

While some micro-organisms are responsible for gas formation, others impart desirable characteristic flavors and odors to particular types of bread. For example, *Sauerteig* dough is inoculated with desirable acid forming organisms such as *Aerobacter levans* and *Escherichia coli* which help to give this bread its characteristic flavor.

Black bread is a coarse wheat or rye bread similar to sauerteig bread. In the process of making black bread, *Streptococcus mesentericus*, an active peptonizing bacterium, changes the dough from a thick to a more plastic state.

Jamin-bang is a coarse bread prepared by the Indians of Brazil. The leavening action is brought about by a mixture of yeasts and bacteria. The resulting fermentation is an acid-alcoholic type.

Salt Rising bread is the result of a fermentation process in which *Escherichia coli, Aerobacter levans*, and *Lactobacillus bulgaricus* take part and give this bread its peculiar flavor. *Clostridium perfringens*, an anaerobic pathogen, has also been used as the starter organism. The source of this culture is its natural presence in the meal used.

Success or failure in breadmaking depends very largely upon the leavening agent used. In general, the yeast, *Saccharomyces cerevisiae* is the principal leavening agent used.

Microbiology of Cereals.—Most of the cereals are processed and packaged under good sanitary conditions and many of the products are practically free of organisms. However, cereals containing raisins or figs may contain a few bacteria and yeasts but in most cases the number of organisms is not large.

Microbiology of Cracked Meal, Coarse Flour, Wheat, Corn, Soybean, and Tapioca Flour

Many investigators have concluded that flat sour producing bacteria are the predominant type of microflora present. Thermophilic bacteria are more numerous in wheat flour than any of the other products. The composition of soybean flour seems to favor the development of flat sour-producing organisms, sulfide spoilage organisms, and thermophilic anaerobes.

General sanitary practices in processing the various grains, no doubt, play a role in microbial activity. The season, stage of maturity, moisture content and storage conditions are important factors in governing the activity of micro-organisms in the products.

Defects of Bread

There is no assurance that bread will not undergo undesirable changes because it is baked at a high temperature. The flour and other ingredients are not free of organisms and they can, under certain conditions, survive the baking process. Sanitary practices in the bakery may influence the microbial content of the finished product.

Ropy Bread.—This condition results in a discoloration of the bread ranging from brown to black. An unpleasant odor is usually present. The center of the loaf is soft and discolored, and from this portion long threads can be drawn out when touched with a glass rod.

Bacillus mesentericus is one of the principal organisms responsible for ropy bread. It is strictly an aerobe and is proteolytic, as well as being a spore forming organism.

The Source or Causes for Ropy Bread.—The spores present in flour, yeast, malt, and powdered milk may contribute their share of micro-organisms.

Prevention of Ropy Bread.—Chlorine, 1000 p.p.m. in the form of hypochlorite solution has been used as an equipment sanitizer but regardless of the method used a strict sanitary program must be followed in order to destroy spores and control this defect. Mycoban is also used to prevent ropiness in bread.

Sour Bread.—This defect is usually due to an overtime fermentation resulting in the production of acids in the dough. Lactic acid bacteria are responsible for this condition and no doubt are introduced either in the flour, or yeast, or by dirty equipment. Again, sanitation is the best method for controlling this defect.

Red Bread.—The growth of *Serratia marcescens* or *Torula glutinis* on or near the surface of the bread gives the product distinct red patchy areas which are very undesirable. These organisms are not heat-resistant nor are they spore formers. Obviously, their presence in bread comes after the bread is baked. No specific recommendation can be made except to follow a strict sanitary program throughout the bakery.

Moldy Bread.—This is another defect that is evident, especially in warm humid weather. The universal wrapping of the bread helps to favor mold growth by retaining the moisture content in the loaf. Then the process of slicing the bread helps to spread mold spores from the surface of the loaf to the interior. This may be one reason why sliced bread tends to mold more readily then unsliced bread in the loaf.

Control of mold in bread may be difficult since many varying conditions are present. Various physical and chemical methods have been used with some success. Air conditioning the bakery and washing the air along with filtering it certainly has been helpful. The use of ultraviolet rays has been disappointing not only in destroying the mold spores but also in producing undesirable changes in the bread. The toxicity of certain fatty acids along with organic acids such as citric, lactic, malic, and tartaric have been used. The use of acetic and other fatty acids of this series has proved helpful in retarding mold growth. Dilute acetic acid applied to the surface of the loaf of bread is also effective in controlling mold.

Certain mold inhibitors have been suggested. Calcium or sodium salts of propionic acid have been used to treat the parchment paper used in wrapping butter with surprisingly good results. Likewise, the control of mold on cheese was very successful. These propionates have had wide use under the name "Mycoban" and more recently "Badex" or sodium diacetate has been used.

Mold inhibitors for bread have not been widely accepted. A good inhibitor must be potent in low concentrations, must not be poisonous, and must not cause any undesirable changes in the product. The propionates seem to meet these requirements except that they do not completely inhibit mold growth in bread.

Again, the adherence to a strict sanitary program in the bakery will offer the best assurance against molds in bread.

BIBLIOGRAPHY

Cathcart, W. H., and Jacobs, M. 1951. Baking and Bakery Products. The Chemistry and Technology of Food and Food Products. Interscience Publishers, New York.
Frazier, W. C. 1967. Food Microbiology, 2nd ed. McGraw-Hill Book Co., New York.
Matz, S. A. 1960. Bakery Technology and Engineering. Avi Publ. Co., Westport, Conn.
Matz, S. A. (Editor). 1969. Cereal Science. Avi Publ. Co., Westport, Conn.

CHAPTER 13

Microbiology of Spices

INTRODUCTION

Spices, according to the American Spice Trade Association are tropical plants whose parts are used to season foods. Botanically, spices are the roots, bark, buds, seeds, or fruits of aromatic plants which usually grow in the tropics. The "true spices," numbering about 13, include allspice, clove, and black pepper. Herbs are leafy parts of temperate zone plants. Condiments are mixtures of spices and other ingredients usually made into a saucelike consistency. Examples are catsup and mustard.

Some ingredients, while used in spice blends, are not classed as spices. Sugar and salt, for example, are used only as flavoring or preservatives, while both green and pimento peppers are classed as embellishments.

Spices have an illustrious past, for down through the centuries they have shaped world history. Trade routes were established, ships plundered, battles fought, empires won and lost, and America discovered—all because of man's unquenchable desire for these tangy, aromatic flavorings. Even savages, unused to condiments in their simple cookery, quickly respond to the agreeable effect that spices have upon the organs of taste and smell.

The early scientists thought that spices had germicidal properties and that is one reason they were used in food preservation. In fact, very few, if any, of the spices are germicidal, though some may induce a bacteriostatic action if used in large enough quantity. The commercial spices harbor large numbers of micro-organisms, including molds.

The Role of Spices in the Livestock Industry

More than a score of the spices of commerce are very necessary accessories in marketing one-sixth of the nation's meat. Small pieces trimmed from primal cuts of beef, pork, lamb, and veal must be made into sausage and canned meats before they can be marketed. Also a very large proportion of the meat from older, lean cattle and heavy hogs is more acceptable in the form of sausage than as fresh or cured meat.

The annual bill of the meat packing industry for spices probably runs from $12,000,000 to $15,000,000. World shortages sometimes send the prices of certain spices skyrocketing, but the sausage makers and meat canners still have to maintain a full assortment.

Also of interest from an agricultural standpoint is the fact that few spices are produced in the United States. We have to go all over the world to get them.

In medieval, ancient and even prehistoric times spices were used because it was believed that they preserved meats and other foods. Actually they served only to mask the bad flavors which resulted from varying degrees of decomposition.

Modern meat processors are equally dependent on spices, but their reasons are quite different. Today's refrigeration and curing practices have largely displaced spices in meat preservation, and they have removed the need for covering up off-flavors. Spice blends now are developed to produce hundreds of variations and scores of new products. Many sausages have almost exactly the same meat ingredients but differ markedly in taste because of the kinds and proportions of spices.

The meat processing industry now takes around 20 per cent of the 150,000,000 lbs. of spices consumed annually in the United States. The top five on this list are white pepper, sage, coriander, black pepper, and nutmeg.

Basic Spice Facts

Spices themselves have little or no nutritional value, but as seasonings they add zest to diets which would be insipid indeed as mere collections of carbohydrates, fats, and proteins. Of potential interest to many is the fact that spices contain no calories.

Most spices owe much of their flavoring properties to volatile oils, but in some cases the flavor is due to a fixed oil. In several instances no single ingredient can be named, and the flavor is credited to a natural blending of flavors from many different components. These include the alcohols, esters, terpenes, phenols and their derivatives, organic acids, alkaloids, resins, and sulfur-containing compounds. Some as yet have not been identified.

The use of spices goes back many centuries when they were used to cover up the taints in foods and give the food an appetizing flavor. Consequently, putrefactive products which could be very offensive were masked by liberal use of spices. Since spices harbor many kinds of organisms, including those associated with food spoilage, the question of spices became a problem as a source of undesirable organisms in foods. Yesair and Williams (1942) studied the microbial content of untreated spices. The results are shown in Table 21.

Romance of Spices

The Arabs have for centuries monopolized the oriental spice trade. They actually bought their spices from China, India, and Japan by

TABLE 21

MICROBIAL CONTENT OF UNTREATED SPICES

Kind of Spice or Herb	Untreated Spice Suspensions Incubated at: 37°C (98.6°F) Total Micro-organisms per Gram Bacteria	Room Temp Molds
Whole allspice	1,000,000	70,000
Ground allspice	64,000	50,000
Sweet basil	525,000	50
Whole cloves	4,400	100
Whole Zanzibar cloves	190	0
Ground China cinnamon	36,000	60,000
Crushed cinnamon	8,000	600
Ground ginger	60,000	2,000
Bay leaves	15,000	350
Ground Bandamace	2,800	400
Ground mustard	1,800	0
Ground East Indian nutmeg	1,200	700
Ground paprika	680,000	5,000
Ground red pepper	2,190,000	1,220,000
Ground white pepper	42,000	9,000
Decorticated pepper	1,780,000	70,000
Ground black pepper	10,400,000	1,300,000
Savory	4,000	450
Ground sage	270,000	20,000
Whole thyme	2,700,000	12,000
Ground thyme	35,000	30,000
Miscellaneous:		
Celery seed	1,150,000	10,000
Onion powder	6,000	0
Garlic cloves	200	20,000
Onion juice	30,000,000	100
Ground garlic powder	90,000	200
Liquid garlic	10,000	10,000
Emulsified spice oil	10	10

frightening the oriental merchants into some fantastic bargaining schemes, to gain a business advantage over these merchants. For instance, the Arabs invented a tale in which they told the oriental merchants that cinnamon could be procured only on a mysterious isle in the center of a huge lake. The cinnamon trees were guarded by large flesh-eating birds, which could be lured away from their posts with chunks of donkey meat. The Arabs would rush to the trees and snatch their boughs and run to their boats.

The Romans would hang an anise plant near their pillow to prevent bad dreams. The natives of the Molucca Islands always planted a clove tree whenever a child was born and destruction of the tree was thought to spell doom for the one for whom it was planted.

Classification of Spices and Flavorings

Spices may be classified into 3 groups as follows:

1. Hot or "Pungent" Spices

Pepper is a good example of this class of spices. Cayenne and red pepper come from the *Capsicum frutescens*. Black and white pepper come from the plant botanically classified as *Piper nigrum*. Black pepper is made from immature berries while white pepper comes from the mature berries which have the hull removed by fermentation.

The condimental properties are caused chiefly by a volatile oil which is a hydrocarbon ($C_{10}H_{16}$ and the nitrogenous bases piperidine and piperine).

2. Aromatic Spices

All spice or pimento is obtained from an evergreen tree.

All spice, like the clove, contains a volatile oil eugenol ($C_{10}H_{12}O_2$).

Cinnamon is obtained from the dried inner bark of the cinnamomum tree.

Cloves are prepared from dried flower buds of the clove plant, an evergreen-like plant which grows 20 to 40 feet in height. The condimental property is due primarily to the volatile oil.

Ginger is prepared from root stock of an annual plant growing 3 to 4 feet high. The root is washed, peeled, and then dried. Sometimes carbonate of lime is added. Preserved ginger is prepared by boiling the root and then adding sugar or honey.

3. Flavoring Extracts

Vanilla extract is obtained from the vanilla bean, the fruit of a climbing vine. The odor is due to vanillin ($C_8H_8O_3$).

Imitation vanilla is made from coumarin extracted from the tonka bean together with dextrose and glycerin.

Lemon extract is prepared by soaking lemon peel in strong alcohol. Citral ($C_{10}H_{16}O$) is the volatile oil flavoring compound.

Germicidal Action of Spices

Blum and Fabian (1943) studied the efficacy of the spice oils and their components on different test organisms with respect to alcohol production by a true yeast; inhibition and germicidal action in cider for all the test organisms; and their inhibiting action on yeasts by the agar cup method.

Emulsions of the oils were more effective than the unemulsified oils in all cases except mustard, in retarding the growth of *Saccharomyces ellipsoideus* as measured by alcohol production. The emulsion oils of black pepper, angelica, calamus, celery seed, ginger, sweet marjoram, and lime had very little effect upon *S. ellipsoideus*. However, oils of allspice, mace, and sweet orange showed a weak effect as free oil but in the emulsified form they had a strong inhibiting action. By comparison, it was observed that an emulsion of the oil was more efficient in germicidal action than its respective components.

The authors compared the relative penetrating and inhibiting properties of various emulsions of the oils. They concluded that mustard was the most effective while cassia and cinnamon were almost as good. Black pepper, calamus, ginger, and lime were not effective in their germicidal properties.

There was no correlation between surface tension and germicidal efficiency in the spice oils. This observation may suggest that their germicidal value was chemical rather than physical in nature.

Cinnamon and cloves possess greater bactericidal activity than other spices. The active ingredient in cinnamon is cinnamic aldehyde and in cloves eugenol.

Extracts of various spices do not effectively inhibit the growth of micro-organisms. However, oils obtained from ground mustard, cloves, and cinnamon, respectively, display a fair degree of bactericidal activity. In fact, some spices may accelerate the growth of organisms. The volatile oil of mustard has a stronger preserving power as compared to cinnamon oil, oil of cloves, thyme, and bay leaves named in that order. Fabian et al. (1939), observed a great difference in the resistance of different bacteria to the same spice and of the same organism to different spices. Many spices tend to inhibit the growth of Staphylococcus aureus. The spice oils appear to be more inhibitory than ground spices.

The bactericidal properties of horseradish were studied by Foter and Gorlick (1938). They reported that the vapors were most effective at 99.5°F (37.5°C) and their activity decreased rapidly at lower temperatures. By comparison horseradish vapors were more active than those of garlic and onion. These authors state that the active ingredient in crushed horseradish is allyl isothiocyanate, a pungent volatile oil which irritates the eyes and burns the skin. It is very effective against several varieties of micro-organisms when tested by different methods.

The bactericidal strength of spice oils can be measured more accurately in liquid form than as vapors.

Selective Action of Spices and Oils on Micro-organisms.— Molds are most sensitive, yeasts are intermediate, and bacteria, especially those in spore form, are least sensitive to the germicidal effects of spices and their oils.

Storage Problems with Spices.—The storage and processing of spices are important factors in quality retention. The highest quality meats can be spoiled by spices that have been improperly stored. The basic principles of storage are keeping the spice covered and stored in a cool, dry place and away from sunlight. Armour Research Laboratories (1955) recommend 60 days as the time limit on natural spices without refrigeration. However, at 25°F (-3.89°C) spices can be kept in excellent condition for an indefinite period without any appreciable volatilization of oil.

Treatment to Reduce Microbial Content of Spices.—Untreated spices may contain appreciable numbers of organisms. McBride (1938) described an ethylene oxide treatment of the spices as an effective means of reducing the micro-organisms. Studies on the use of treated and untreated spices used in fresh pork sausage showed a marked delay in spoilage when treated spices were used.

In general many of the oils are valued for their antiseptic properties rather than their germicidal action. The germicidal power of any spice or oil is limited because they are not present in sufficient quantities to be actively germicidal. However, animal oils, such as seal oil and tuna oil, emit vapors which are germicidal and more active than the oils of spices. If cod-liver oil and sardine oil are exposed to sunlight or ultraviolet light they become extremely germicidal.

Research in Spices

Research is necessary for technical progress with spices, just as with phases of meat processing. In these research efforts, chemists give their attention to the strength of ingredients, while the food technologists concentrate on blending problems. In recent years, a great deal of time and attention have been devoted to converting formulas involving natural spices to others in which oleoresins and essential oils are used.

Many research problems still lie ahead. One is standardization. For example, piperine, the fraction of pepper that produces the burning sensation, does not register the same degree of "bite" when submitted to a taste test panel that it does when analyzed chemically. For another, an exact scale of equivalents for natural spices and spice extracts still remains to be worked out.

BIBLIOGRAPHY

Armour Research Laboratories. 1955. Armour's Livestock Bureau 4, No. 2.
Blum, H. B., and Fabian, F. W. 1943. Spice oils and their components for controlling microbial surface growth. Fruit Prod. J. 22, No. 11, 326–329, 347.

Cartwright, L. C., and Nanz, R. A. 1948. Comparative evaluation of spices. Food Technol. *2*, 330–336.

Chipault, J. R., Mizuno, G. R., Hawkins, J. M., and Lundberg, W. O. 1952. The antioxidant properties of natural spices. Food Research *17*, 46–55.

Chipault, J. R., Mizuno, G. R., and Lundberg, W. O. 1956. The antioxidant properties of spices in foods. Food Technol. *10*, 209–211.

Datta, P. R., Susi, H., Higman, H. C., and Fillpic, V. J. 1962. Use of gas chromatography to identify geographical origin of some spices. Food Technol. *16*, No. 10, 116–119.

Fabian, F. W., Krehl, C. F., and Little, N. W. 1939. The role of spices in pickled food spoilage. Food Research *4*, 269–286.

Foter, M. J., and Gorlick, A. M. 1938. Inhibitory properties of horseradish vapors. Food Research *3*, 609–613.

Jones, S. E. 1949. Spices, the essence of geography. Natl. Geographic Mag. *96*, 401–420.

Nanz, R. A., Tyler, C. A., and Cartwright, L. C. 1950. Comparative evaluation of spices: II. Flavor evaluation of natural spices and spice substitutes in representative test foods. Food Technol. *4*, 252–258.

Nanz, R. A., and Cartwright, L. C. 1951. Comparative evaluation of spices: III. Flavor retention of natural spices and of spice oils and spice extractives after boiling and baking. Food Technol. *5*, 246–250.

Proctor, B. E., Goldblith, S., and Fram, H. 1950. Effect of supervoltage cathode rays on bacterial flora of spices and other dry food materials. Food Research *15*, 490–493.

Todd, P. H., Jr. 1958. Detection of foreign pungent compounds: Oleoresin capsicum, ground capsicum and chili spices. Food Technol. *12*, 468–469.

Tousig, F., Suzuki, J. I., and Morse, R. E. 1956. Observations on black pepper: I. Analysis of bite principles. Food Technol. *10*, 151–154.

Yesair, J., and Williams, M. H. 1942. Spice contamination and its control. Food Research *7*, 118–126.

CHAPTER 14

Food Spoilage

Food spoilage may be attributed to two principal causes, chemical and biological.

The most significant changes in food are due to biological factors. Inherent enzymes that are naturally present in the food under certain conditions may alter the texture, flavor, and odor. These enzymes are not so important in food spoilage, when food is canned commercially since the cooking or canning process, if continued long enough, will completely inactivate the enzymes present. Many enzymes present in food are highly desirable. The ripening of immature fruit, such as bananas and tomatoes which are harvested in many cases while green, occurs when the fruit is separated from the plant. The tenderization of meat also occurs when held for an extended period in cold storage.

On the other hand, if the action of the enzymes is not checked, they eventually bring about marked deteriorative biochemical changes in the food, a condition we usually associate with food spoilage. For example, the enzyme lipase in raw, fresh milk will, under certain conditions, cause a series of undesirable changes in the milk fat, particularly rancidity. In commercial practice the action of enzymes can be minimized by canning the food shortly after it is harvested. If the food must be stored for a period of time prior to processing, it should be kept at a low enough temperature to retard enzyme action.

The presence and growth of bacteria, molds, and yeasts in foods is far more serious in canning spoilage than the action of inherent enzymes present in the food. Micro-organisms are present in the air, water, on most foods, on our hands and, in fact, they are ubiquitous.

Usually there are many kinds of micro-organisms present in the raw food before it is preserved and under certain conditions the method of food preservation may actually create a favorable environment for their growth. A good example is anaerobic bacteria, which grow in the absence of atmospheric oxygen. Since these organisms are spore formers and the spores are very difficult to destroy by heat, they may create a serious problem in the spoilage of certain kinds of canned foods. Molds and yeasts are usually associated with canned products in which the air seal is not secure, because they usually require atmospheric oxygen for growth. A summary of food preservation methods is given in Table 22.

TABLE 22

FOOD PRESERVATION METHODS

   I. Asepsis
  II. Additives
      A. Salt or sugar, or both
      B. Spices
      C. Acids (vinegar, sour milk, etc.)
      D. Smoking
      E. Inhibitors
 III. Refrigeration
      A. Chilling
      B. Freezing
  IV. Heat Processing
      A. Pasteurization
      B. Boiling
      C. Canning
      D. Pressure processing
   V. Fermentation
      A. Acid
      B. Alcohol
  VI. Removal of moisture, or osmotic pressure (dehydration)
      A. Meats
      B. Vegetables
      C. Fruits
 VII. Filtration
VIII. Pressure
  IX. Gases: controlled atmosphere
   X. Radiation
      A. Ultraviolet
      B. Ionizing radiations
  XI. Fungicides (yeasts and mold inhibitors)
      A. Sorbic acid
      B. Sodium benzoate

Some Differences Between Aerobic and Anaerobic Bacteria Found in Protein Material

Usually aerobic bacteria break down the protein molecule to simple protein substances by a series of oxidation reactions. The end-products remaining are completely oxidized and no odoriferous compounds are noticeable. Where hydrogen sulfide is present it may appear as sulfate, or the ammonia may be oxidized to nitrate, but the end products are odorless.

Proteins as a rule may contain numerous amino acid radicals in a typical peptide linkage. The general breakdown of a complex protein molecule proceeds as follows: protein—proteose—peptone—polypeptide—dipeptide—peptide—amino acid—ammonia—elemental nitrogen. The building up of protein in animal and vegetable tissues may involve a complex peptide linkage of some of the simple protein products such as a dipeptide linkage of two amino acids (glycine as shown below).

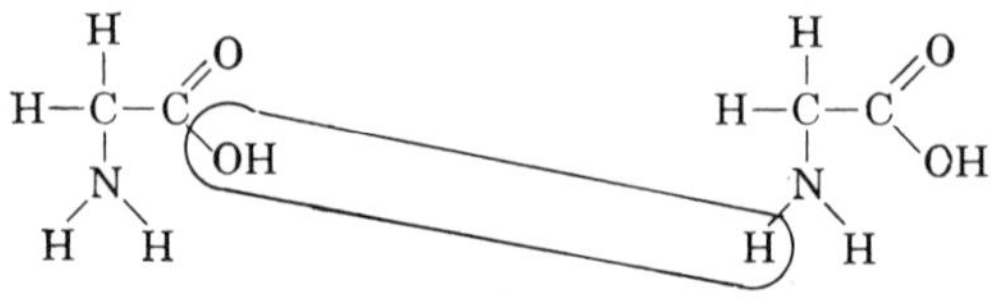

The splitting out of water as shown in the chemical formula for glycine forms the first dipeptide linkage in the formation of an animal or vegetable protein.

Obviously the process is much more complicated than the diagram shows but it serves to illustrate how proteins are broken down and then under certain conditions how protein synthesis takes place.

When putrefaction of protein takes place by anaerobes the end-products are not completely oxidized to stable compounds as in the case of aerobic decomposition. Usually offensive odors are present in anaerobic metabolism; some of these products are indole, mercaptans, hydrogen sulfide and ammonia, especially in canned meats and vegetables with low acidity.

Bacteria.—Bacteria are found everywhere and may be either in an active or resting form. The resting form is known as the spore stage, a form in which they are very difficult to kill. In the active or vegetative stage, bacteria are destroyed at boiling temperature, but in the resting period or spore form they have been known to live after being subjected to boiling water for several hours. The presence of biological and inherent acidity in the food will materially shorten the time required to render the product sterile.

In foods with high acid content (all fruits, tomatoes, and pickles), all forms of bacteria are killed after a period of time at the temperature of boiling water. With low-acid foods such as meats, corn, peas, beans, and practically all vegetables except tomatoes, bacteria will be killed faster by processing in a steam pressure canner. Six hours heating at boiling temperature 212°F (100°C) may be required to destroy spores, but they may also be killed in 30 minutes at 240°F (115.6°C), the temperature obtained by steam under 10 lbs. pressure.

The temperature maintained and the length of time the food is held will vary with each kind of food. In order to be safe, one should follow a dependable processing table.

Types of bacteria vary with different foods, with the time of year, the locality, and the conditions under which the food is produced. Some of the most heat-resistant bacteria are in the soil—hence, the need for special care in preparation and processing such foods as spinach, snap beans, and many other foods.

Yeasts.—Yeasts are responsible for much of the fermentation of fruits and fruit products. They eventually cause the food material to become sour. They may easily be killed by heat during pre-heating or processing. There are a few heat resistant varieties of yeasts that have been found in canned orange juice, tomato products, and catsup.

The acid tolerance of certain varieties of yeast make them important in "foamy cream," a term that is used to describe the gassy condition in sour cream due primarily to the growth of *Candida pseudotrophicalis* (*Torula cremoris*). Foaminess in cream is due to associated action, the yeasts producing the gas and some other species, perhaps bacteria, causing the coagulation by acid production.

Molds.—Molds will grow on many kinds of food, especially where temperature, air, and humidity are favorable for their growth.

The mold can be seen only on the surface of the food, but it often changes the flavor and quality of the contents of the entire jar. Molds are easily killed by moist heat. A temperature of 160° to 180°F (71° to 82°C) for 60 minutes will usually be sufficient to kill most mold spores.

Experimental results show that a temperature of 212°F (100°C) for several minutes will destroy a large percentage of mold spores. As a rule, molds are not involved in canned food spoilage because of the unfavorable conditions for their growth in an airtight container. Moreover, mold spores are unable to survive the temperature used in the processing of most foods.

A valuable pamphlet on "Mold Counting of Tomato Products" which gives much detailed information on methods, equipment, significance of molds, mold species involved, and methods of handling tomatoes is published by the Continental Can Company, New York (1960).

According to Kaufman (1947) spoilage of all edible foods would eventually take place if man did not do something to stop or at least partially slow up biological processes that normally take place in foods. Various methods of food preservation have been used by man for many centuries to preserve his food supply. However, there are other advantages in preserving a food supply such as keeping surplus food for future use. At the present time it is possible to have a great variety of foods available for consumption in every month of the year. The economical advantage of having food preserved and processed in convenient packages for immediate use is now accepted whole-heartedly by the average American family.

The chemical composition of foods plays a role in food spoilage under certain conditions. Since all foods are essentially made up of chemical elements and compounds, as emphasized previously, they undergo chemical changes that are independent of any biological factors. Atmospheric oxygen and even sunlight will cause certain foods to undergo various undesirable changes. For example, foods high in fat content will become rancid when exposed to atmospheric oxygen. Apparently, the oxygen acts as a catalyst in starting a series of chemical changes. In other foods, the formation of hydrogen gas results from a chemical reaction of the food constituents. In canned foods where the oxygen has not been completely exhausted from tin lined cans after sealing, it will initiate a chemical reaction, thus causing a "detinning" of the can.

SPOILAGE IN CANNED FOODS

Underprocessing of canned food may result in microbial spoilage, especially if high heat resistant spores are present. Aciduric bacteria and yeasts may be present in acid foods where the product receives a short heat treatment thus enabling these organisms to survive. Fabian (1951) claims that heat resistant spores are associated with foods having a pH range above 4.5. He classifies the organisms in the following manner, thermophilic types such as *Bacillus stearothermophilus*, an aerobic flat sour organism, an aerogenic anaerobe, *Clostridium thermosaccharolyticum*, and the non-aerogenic hydrogen sulfide producing anaerobe, *Clostridium nigrificans*. Mesophilic organisms include the putrefactive anaerobes and possibly a few aerobic spore formers.

Types of Canned Food Spoilage

Flat sour spoilage is characterized by the production of acid and no gas. The causative bacteria are usually facultatively anaerobic, although obligate thermophiles may be involved. The spores of these organisms have a very high resistance to heat. The National Canners Association have a test organism, No. 1518, which requires a temperature of 250°F (121°C) for 30 minutes to destroy the organism when 10,000 spores per ml. are suspended in neutral phosphate. These bacteria can cause flat sours in low acid foods such as corn and peas. Their identification is not difficult since gas is not formed and the product remains flat. A slight disagreeable odor may be present but no perceptible change in appearance of the food is evident. A microscopic examination of the food reveals rod-shaped bacteria which is truly characteristic of this defect. Spores are usually present but they are not formed in the presence of acid. Therefore flat sours may be suspected in the food if the organisms produce acid without gas in glucose broth incubated at 130°F (54.4°C) and confirmed by spore production on neutral culture medium.

A flat sour condition in tomato juice and black beets is caused by a small group of mesophilic bacteria. This defect is a nongaseous spoilage and imparts a distinct medicinal flavor to the product. Black beets occur when small amounts of dissolved iron are present in the food. A combination of the causal organism, beet pigment, and iron in solution cause a black color which may extend throughout the beet.

Food spoilage caused by a gas forming thermophilic aerogenic anaerobe is characterized by swelling of the can. Hydrogen gas is formed with other gases. A strong butyric acid odor is evident in the food. *Bacillus stearothermophilus* grows in spinach and asparagus, semi-acid foods, as well as in low acid foods.

Microscopic examination shows long vegetative rods. When cultured in a liver agar shake tube, gas is formed. The organisms will form spores when cultured in a neutral liver agar culture medium.

Sulfide spoilage is characterized by the formation of H_2S and blackening of the food. There is no particular difficulty in recognizing this defect. The odor of H_2S and black appearance of the food is sufficient to recognize this type of spoilage.

Putrefactive spoilage is usually associated with low-acid foods, especially asparagus. The contents of the can become putrid and a marked swelling can eventually burst the container. This is commonly referred to as a "swell" or "bulge."

Bacillus coagulans, sometimes referred to as *Bacillus thermoacidurans*, is responsible for flat sour spoilage in tomato juice. This is an exception because spoilage of this kind is not common in acid foods. As the organism grows in the tomato juice a phenolic-like flavor is evident. The pH of the juice drops from 4.5 to 3.5. A microscopic examination shows large vegetative rods, although the acid environment will destroy the organism very rapidly. As a rule no spores are formed in the product. The causative organism responsible for this type of spoilage may be identified by microscopic examination, a change in pH of the product and a characteristic off-flavor.

An unusual type of biological preservation may be due to "autosterilization" where the high acidity of the food exerts a sterilizing action on the spoilage organisms.

The bacteria causing flat sour spoilage grow best at temperatures of about 130°–140°F (54.4°–60°C). This type of spoilage frequently occurs when foods are not cooled quickly after canning or are held at too high storage temperatures before and after canning. Low-acid foods such as peas, corn, snap beans, and greens are more likely to have flat-sour spoilage than other vegetables.

Putrefaction is most likely to occur in meats and low-acid vegetables. This spoilage is easily recognized by a very bad odor, presence of gas (bulged lid), and the softening and darkening of the canned food.

A few characteristics of anaerobic activity in canned food products are:

a. Development of offensive odors.
b. Formation of black sediment or residue.
c. Reduction in amount of dissolved or free O_2.
d. Reduction in amount of available O_2.
e. Increase in carbonaceous (or oxidizable) matter.

From a public health standpoint *Clostridium botulinum* is a significant member of the putrefactive anaerobe family. The organism is a typical spore former and occurs in nearly all types of soil. The bacteria themselves are not poisonous, but when they grow in food, they produce a powerful exotoxin, which can be absorbed in the digestive tract. The organism has about the same growth requirement as other anaerobic bacteria in food products. During its metabolism an exotoxin is formed called "botulism." This toxin is extremely poisonous to man and gives rise to certain kinds of food poisoning. This subject will be treated in detail under food poisoning. Botulism is technically a toxic amine. Although not all amines produced by different organisms are poisonous, the toxic amines are sometimes called "amines."

Although the spores of *Cl. botulinum* are very resistant to heat, fortunately the toxin can be destroyed by heat much more readily than the spores of the organism. The presence of toxin is not always indicated by spoilage. This makes diagnosis of the disease difficult until an onset of botulism occurs in the victim. Obviously, to render any suspicious foods safe, sanitarians have recommended heating meats and vegetables 10 to 20 minutes and stirring frequently during the boiling period.

Botulinum organisms usually do not grow in foods having a pH value as low as 4.5, such as tomatoes, fruits, pickles, and sauerkraut. The spores that may be present remain viable for long periods or until such organisms as molds or acid tolerant bacteria lower the initial acidity by utilizing the acid as a source of energy. Then, the spores may reproduce and the organism may liberate the toxin. Obviously, any spoiled food, or food that is suspicious, should not be tasted without boiling. Warming the food is not sufficient to inactivate the toxin.

Home canned meats and low-acid vegetables should be removed from the can, brought to the boiling point, and boiled actively for at least 10 minutes before they are tasted or used. One should be sure that all parts of the mass of food in the vessel have been thoroughly cooked. Such treatment destroys the toxin if it is present.

This type of heating does not, however, destroy the bacteria so any food left over should be reboiled for another 10 minute period before using. This type of spoilage is rare, when the amount of canned food used is considered, but because it is so serious all safety measures should be taken.

Clostridium sporogenes and *Cl. putrefaciens* are common types of anaerobic bacteria found widely distributed in the soil. Their presence in canned vegetables and meat products in large numbers usually is evidenced by the production of gas and acid formation in some instances as well as offensive odors and undesirable biochemical changes in the product.

Spoilage in Canned Food Products.—There are two general types of food spoilage and they may be classified as follows:

Chemical and Physical Swells.—Usually a chemical reaction takes place between the constituents in the food and the metal in the container, resulting in the formation of hydrogen gas.

The following causes may contribute to chemical swells:

a. Formation of hydrogen gas resulting from a chemical reaction between the metal of the container and the biological acidity present in the food. A pH of 4.0 is favorable to initiate a chemical reaction.

b. Overfilling the can at too low a temperature causing the container to bulge when room temperature is reached.

c. Filling the can under a reduced pressure such as at high altitude. This would tend to cause collapse rather than swelling.

d. Freezing the liquid portion of the food and thus causing an expansion of the can.

e. Insufficient head space in the can, hence the accumulation of the hydrogen produced tends to cause the can to swell.

f. Oxygen not completely exhausted in the can after sealing, thus bringing about an oxidation reaction which eventually detins the can.

g. Sulfides in the foods with a high acidity may be responsible for marked corrosion on the interior of the container.

Biological Swells of Canned Foods.—The container tends to swell at the ends or in the middle especially along the seams where liquor from the food is forced out due to internal pressure.

Aerobic organisms and thermophilic bacteria are often involved in biological swells. A slight defect or weak point in the seam of the can is often an ideal focal point for these organisms to enter. Members of the coliform bacteria may be involved provided atmospheric oxygen is available for their growth. When conditions are favorable for multiplication such as the presence of carbohydrates or proteins or both, then acid and gas formation is possible in sufficient amounts to bulge the container.

Leakage in the can may cause certain types of spoilage in canned foods. Food spoiled by leakage should never be tasted or eaten.

This defect may be due to non-sporeforming bacteria, molds, or yeasts. The organisms enter the container in air or water sucked in during cooling.

The seals on the jars or tin cans should be carefully checked. It is recommended that sample cans be taken right off the line after sealing for examination which should include "tear down" of the can.

Mechanical damage to cans also contributes to different types of food spoilage and may not necessarily be the characteristic "swells." A slight break in the seam of the container is usually sufficient to admit aerobic organisms, molds, and yeasts into the food.

The type of changes in the food may be varied. The food may have a mold mat on the surface. It may be slimy or it may be frothy. Sometimes a pungent, sour odor is evident. A swelling of the cans due to gas formation is very common; usually the food contents will leak out through the defective seam. In glass jars bubbles of gas are evident, and the contents may leak out around the lid and rubber gasket.

Underprocessing usually results in spoilage by not entirely destroying the organisms present. Ordinarily, the micro-organisms are spore formers. In acid foods, such as some fruits which are processed in a water bath, the spoilage may be due to the survival of non-sporeforming bacteria or yeasts. If the character of the food is of a type having slow heat penetration, the boiling water process may not raise the temperature of the food in the center of the container sufficiently to destroy the organisms.

Again, underprocessed food spoilage may be due to heat resistant organisms which are usually spore forming bacteria. Since these organisms prefer a high temperature for growth, spoilage of non-sterile containers can be reduced by prompt cooling after processing and immediate storage at a low temperature. In this way, thermophilic bacteria will not multiply.

Thermophilic spoilage may be divided into three groups depending upon the changes which occur in the food. They are sulfide spoilage, flat sour spoilage, and "swell" spoilage.

Sulfide spoilage is not common in food preservation. When it occurs it is commonly found in low acid foods, such as corn and peas. The causative organisms produce hydrogen sulfide from the decomposition of proteins containing sulfur and thus impart a "rotten egg" odor to the food. This defect can be easily detected.

Flat sour spoilage is caused by thermophilic bacteria which produce acid without gas in the food. Corn and peas are most susceptible to this defect. The food has a sour taste and this may be the only indication that any microbiological change has taken place. As a rule there is no apparent change in the physical appearance of the food. The organisms causing this type of spoilage are fairly widely distributed in nature so their introduction into the food product may not be unusual. The organisms may be carried into the corn, peas, or meat when infected sugar is added. Other ingredients such as flour, syrups, and spices may be involved.

Spoilage causing "swells" is due to thermophilic anaerobic bacteria. They produce acid and gas which is largely hydrogen. The can swells until the seam is ruptured. The food is sour, and many times it is frothy and has a distinct rancid odor.

Examining Canned Food Before Use

All foods should be examined before using to be sure they are wholesome. Canned food is no exception to this rule. If canned foods can pass the following tests, they can be used with safety.

1. Inspect the can or jar before opening.
   a. Tin cans—both ends should be flat or curved slightly inward. All seams should be tight with no trace of leakage.
   b. Glass jars—metal lids should be firm and flat or curved slightly inward. There should be no signs of leakage around the rubber ring or elsewhere.
2. As the can is opened, notice whether there is an inrush or an outrush of air. Spoilage is indicated when air rushes out or the liquid spurts.
3. Smell the contents at once. *The odor should be characteristic of the food.* An "off" odor probably means spoilage.
4. Examine the food carefully to see that it appears sound and natural in texture and color. The broth over canned meat and chicken may or may not be jellied. *Liquids in all foods*

should be clean. Any change from the natural texture and color indicates spoilage.

5. If the can is tin, notice the appearance of the inside. It should be smooth and clean or well lacquered and not corroded. Foods may be left in a tin can after the can is opened provided the food is kept covered and cool. The same care should be given food stored in an opened can as is given any other cooked food.

6. If foods have passed the above tests, BOIL ALL LOW-ACID VEGETABLES AND MEATS FOR 10 MINUTES BEFORE USING OR TASTING. Boiling for at least 10 minutes removes the danger of botulism.

7. Discard or destroy all food showing signs of spoilage. Spoiled low-acid foods should be burned.

Physical Appearance of Food May Suggest Spoilage

The Ohio Department of Health Circular (1953) entitled "When in doubt throw it out" lists some practical tests for food spoilage.

1. Canned foods.
   a. Swelled top and bottom
   b. Dents along side of the seam
   c. Off-odor
   d. Foam on top of can when opened
   e. Milkiness of juice

These observations may be applied to all canned vegetables, meats, fish, and poultry. Home canned foods should be cooked thoroughly.

2. Fruits and vegetables.
   The appearance of white or grayish powder around stems of fruit and at the junction of leaves and stems of cabbage, cauliflower, celery, and lettuce. The powder indicates spray residues. Most of the chemicals used by growers are not dangerous to public health but some of these compounds may be harmful. All fruits and vegetables must be washed before being eaten or cooked. Cooking will not destroy the toxicity of the spray chemicals.

3. Cereals.
   Insects in cereals or their residues. Spread the cereal on brown paper. If insects are present they can be easily observed. If one insect is seen, the entire batch of cereal

should be destroyed.   Insects are not necessarily dangerous, but neither are they appetizing.

4.   Salads.

Chicken salad, tuna and other fish salads, non-acid potato salad, all types of custard-filled pastries and a few types of cold cuts must be refrigerated at all times.   Refrigeration will keep infection from increasing.   Spoilage is often impossible to detect until foods are completely spoiled.   Salads should be served immediately after they are removed from the refrigerator.

5.   Frozen Foods.

Frozen foods should not be removed from the cold locker until they are ready to be served.   Frozen foods allowed to thaw out will favor the growth of organisms that may induce spoilage in the product.   Frozen vegetables should be thoroughly cooked before serving.

6.   Left-over Foods.

Physical appearance of food.

    1.   Discoloration
    2.   Off-odor
    3.   Mold

All highly perishable food that has not been refrigerated below 45°F may be considered dangerous to eat, especially if the food is discolored.   Abnormal odors of spoiled food are not always apparent.   Do not keep cooked food after 36 hours unless it is cooked again.

7.   Meats.

Fish.

    1.   Off-odor
    2.   Gray or greenish gills
    3.   Sunken eyes
    4.   Flesh easily pulled away from bones
    5.   Much of fingernail indentation remains in flesh
    6.   Not rigid

Raw shrimp.

    1.   Pink color on upper fins and near tail
    2.   Off-odor similar to ammonia

Some types of shrimp are naturally pink.   Cooked shrimp are also pink.   Both are wholesome if the odor is not abnormal.

Beef and Pork.

    1.   Off-odor

2. Slimy to touch

Beef usually spoils first on the surface. Pork spoils first at meeting point of bone and flesh in the inner portions. To test for spoiled pork use a pointed knife to reach the interior of the meat. An off-odor on the knife usually indicates spoilage.

Dressed Poultry.

1. Off-odor under wing, at the point where legs and body join, and on upper surface of the tail
2. Darkening of wing tips
3. Dressed poultry should be washed thoroughly with clean water before cooking. Wash your hands after handling

The Role of Micro-organisms Involved in Meat Spoilage

Bacteria and molds are largely responsible for meat spoilage. Therefore, the creation of an unfavorable environment for the growth of these organisms is desirable. Drying is one of the most primitive methods for preserving food based on the fact that a lack of moisture is not favorable for bacterial growth. The addition of preservatives—such as salt, pepper, and spices—is accepted as a means of preserving meat. Perhaps the most widely used method is canning, in spite of the fact that certain changes in flavor and texture of the food product often take place. Refrigeration is another means of preserving food by retarding the growth of micro-organisms. The organisms are not destroyed, and this may be an important factor relating to public health.

When meat is placed in cold storage, mold growth usually begins at 38°F (3.3°C) when the relative humidity is high. Usually the meat surface becomes musty in odor and later develops a characteristic flavor. Mold growth on meat can be trimmed off, but this represents an economic waste.

Bacteria that may be involved in meat spoilage usually grow at temperatures above 40°F (4.4°C). A slimy film on the surface of the meat is a good indication that bacterial spoilage is present.

Fig. 27 shows the growth of bacteria at various temperatures and relative humidity values.

Terminology of Canned Food Spoilage

Terms often used to indicate the abnormal appearance of the tin container which, in most instances, indicates that microbiological

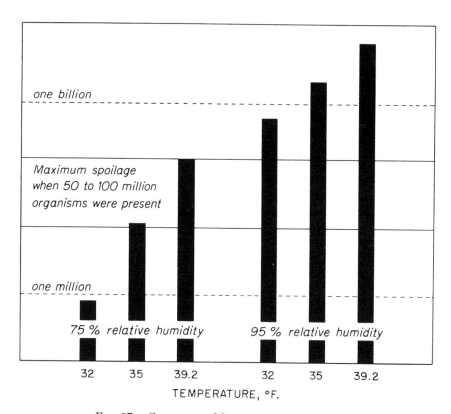

FIG. 27. GROWTH OF MICRO-ORGANISMS IN MEAT

Meat was incubated at different temperatures, and held for 20 days at relative humidities indicated.

or chemical reaction has taken place in the canned food are listed below. However, mechanical injury of the can may cause biological activity in the food. Consequently, all damaged food containers should be considered as potentially dangerous from a food spoilage standpoint.

a. Breather is a term applied to the container that is bacteriologically sealed but not exactly airtight. This condition results in a slow interchange of atmospheric air with the food contents in the can. Naturally, spoilage, if it does occur, takes place after a long period of time.

b. Springers are the result of a marked bulging of the can at one or at both ends. Bacterial or chemical swells or not properly exhausting the air from the can during the filling and sealing process may be responsible for this condition.

c. Flippers usually result from excessive mechanical pressure exerted on the can externally. As a rule, the food in the container does not undergo any spoilage.

d. Buckles may occur, especially in large cans, and are due to the formation of a vacuum set up inside the container. The condition is usually serious when it causes the seam to open and thus favors microbiological spoilage.

Survival of Selected Enteric Bacteria in Various Types of Soil

The rapid expansion of urban areas, private country estates, and recreational parks has increased the flow of sewage and other wastes into streams and rivers in many parts of the U.S. This is particularly true in irrigation areas where the source of water used for such purposes is grossly contaminated with sewage. Obviously the growing of vegetables on irrigated land polluted with sewage water may be more of a public health problem than we are inclined to admit.

It is very difficult to trace any serious epidemics due to contaminated vegetables grown on polluted irrigated land. Common sense on the part of any public health official would discourage the growing of vegetables for human consumption under such conditions.

The time may come when it will be unlawful to dump raw sewage into any stream, river, or any body of water. Such a law is now in operation in certain parts of the country. Until we have the assurance that such practices are no longer permitted, the growing and consumption of vegetables should be looked upon as a potential public health hazard.

Presently there are no official national standards that may be applicable in controlling pollution in water used for irrigation.

The work of Mallmann and Litsky (1951) has revealed some interesting observations on the viability of selected test organisms in sewage polluted soil.

Four strains of *Salmonella typhi*, A, D, E, and F were used. Each culture contained Vi antigen.[1] The soil sample received one treatment of raw sewage and *S. typhi* suspension. The coliform indices ranged from 3680 to 30,200 per gm. of soil at the end of 40 days. The streptococci disappeared after the 40th day and the *S. typhi* did not survive beyond the 19th day in clay and muck soil. These results indicate that enterococci survive in the soil longer than did the typhoid bacilli. The authors state that *S. typhi* strains did not lose Vi antigen during their survival in the soil.

---

[1] An antigen found in strains of *Salmonella typhi* and some paratyphoid bacilli and believed associated with the virulence of the organism.

The longevity of *S. typhi* in the soil as determined by this experiment is comparable with the results of other workers who have studied the length of time these organisms may remain viable in the soil.

It may be concluded from this work that coliform organisms survive in polluted soil for a long time. Enterococci die out very rapidly in the soil, while virulent typhoid bacilli are the least resistant of the organisms studied. The latter organisms died out very quickly in the soil.

Since the growing period for most vegetables is much longer than the survival time of the selected organisms in the soil, a serious public health menace is removed from this viewpoint. But if polluted water is applied to the soil every day, the public health problem still remains with us.

The author has observed that coliforms can be isolated from many kinds of vegetables obtained from market stands. One should always keep in mind that the human element is a very important factor in contaminating vegetables. A good example is the continuous handling of vegetables in a public market where the operator and customer are involved. The public health dangers are greatly multiplied since many of the vegetables are consumed in the raw state.

Microbiological Analysis of Foods

Selective groups of micro-organisms are omnipresent in many kinds of foods regardless of the manner in which they are processed. It would appear as essential to recognize the sources of contaminating organisms and also to understand the selective effect of temperature, moisture, pH, and processing procedures.

The human being may be the ultimate source of pathogenic organisms in foods, although *Salmonella* are naturally present in some foods, such as frozen eggs and meats. Fortunately the low incidence of enteric disease is due to cooking of foods prior to eating. Federal inspection of meats eliminates many potential infections in man caused by such contaminated meat.

The coliform tests used in water analysis are not applicable to foods, except where these organisms are found in foods previously heated to temperatures sufficient to destroy vegetative cells. Total bacterial count does not measure safety of foods but should be a part of the quality control program.

There is no relationship between the bacterial counts in processed foods and those processed by the consumer. High counts may be due to improper storage temperatures. The research on chicken pies stored at $-13°F$ ($-25°C$) for 3 months showed no increase in psychrophilic or mesophilic counts. However, when pies were stored at 32°F (0°C) the bacterial counts increased appreciably. At 41°F (5°C) the psychrophilic count increased slowly for the first 5 days, then increased very rapidly. At 20°C similar products spoiled in 2 days with mesophilic bacteria predominating.

When 2.8 billion *Escherichia coli*, 15 billion *Streptococcus faecalis* and 15 million *Staphylococcus aureus* were inoculated into chicken pies, there were no appreciable increases in the counts after freezing for 24 hours.

Selective culture media may give erroneous results in determining the quality of food from the bacteriological standpoint. The selective culture media used in water analysis for detecting lactose fermenting organisms are not applicable when applied to foods. Ice-cream and citrus juices containing sucrose or dextrose will give a large number of false positive tests. Samples of food tested for *Salmonella* may appear negative when large quantities of food material are inoculated into selenite F, tetrathionate or other selective media, yet the results may be positive if small inocula are used. The removal of soluble materials in the supernatant by centrifuging is an erroneous factor interfering with the specificity of the selective medium.

There are a few common foods for which there are no recognized methods of control and these foods may contain *Salmonella, Micrococcus*, or *Clostridium* groups which can produce typical gastrointestinal syndromes, if certain numerical levels are reached.

The three genera mentioned are introduced by (a) human carriers, (b) live animal carriers, and (c) animal products used as foodstuffs. Human carrier rates of *Salmonella* are not known but outbreaks from this source occur each year, and this in turn increases the number of carriers since *Salmonella* organisms may be harbored for from several weeks to several years. Coagulase positive staphylococci are present in the nasal tracts of 50 to 60 per cent and on hands of 15 to 20 per cent of the general population. Approximately 10 to 20 per cent are the bacteriophage and serological types associated with food poisoning. *Clostridium perfringens* associated with food poisoning outbreaks is carried by only 2 to 5 per cent of the normal population. Strains of *C. perfringens* are present in 15 to 20 per cent of dogs, cats, and hogs. It is well to measure total anaerobic as well as aerobic flora. *C. perfringens* poisoning may take place in the presence of low aerobic and high anaerobic counts.

Animal products such as milk, eggs, and meat are likely to contain *Salmonella* which may be associated in some way with manufacturing processes.

Staphylococci are more intimately associated with the flora of the normal and abnormal udder. One should keep in mind the concept that if foods contain certain pathogens or indicator species they do not necessarily cause disease. Food with *Salmonella, C. perfringens, E. coli,* fecal streptococci and staphylococci may be found on the market with no associated outbreaks. However, foods of this type are usually dirty and are more likely to cause disease than clean foods.

Microbiological standards should be used to indicate levels of contamination so that corrective measures can be applied in order to improve sanitation and hygiene at the factory.

It is obvious that there is a need for a bacteriological procedure that would include aerobic plate count in tryptone dextrose yeast extract agar; proteolytic aerobic counts by drop plates on tryptone yeast extract gelatin agar; anaerobic counts by two methods; coliform counts in crystal violet-neutral red bile-lactose mannitol agar; or McConkey's bile lactose peptone water with subsequent confirmation; fecal streptococci in Packer's crystal violet sodium azide blood agar at 103°F (39.4°C) with subsequent confirmation; *Salmonella* by enrichment in both selenite and tetrathionate broths followed by confirmation; *Staphylococcus aureus* on 7.5 per cent NaCl agar followed by confirmation and detection of illegally added preservatives and antibiotics by the *Saccharomyces cerevisiae* fermentation test.

Errors of sampling and failure to revive the organisms injured by processing must be recognized. Interpretation of data can only be made after careful study of all factors concerned with survival of organisms in foodstuffs.

BIBLIOGRAPHY

Anon. 1953. When In Doubt Throw It Out. Ohio Dept. of Health, Columbus, Ohio.

Anon. 1960. Mold Counting of Tomato Products. Continental Can Co., New York.

Appleman, M. D., Hess, E. P., and Rittenberg, S. C. 1949. An investigation of a mayonnaise spoilage. Food Technol. *3,* 201–203.

Ascherhoug, V., and Jansen, E. 1950. Studies on putrefactive anaerobes as spoilage agents in canned foods. Food Research *15,* 62–67.

Bilenker, E. N., and Dunn, C. G. 1960. Growth of food spoilage bacteria in banana puree. Food Research *25,* 309–320.

Cameron, E. J. 1938. Recent developments in canning technology with reference to spoilage control. Food Research *3,* 91–99.

Fabian, F. W. 1951. Food preservation by the use of micro-organisms. *In* The Chemistry and Technology of Food and Food Products, Vol. 3, M. B. Jacobs (Editor). Interscience Publishers, New York.

Fabian, F. W., and Wethington, C. 1950. Spoilage in salad and french dressing due to yeasts. Food Research *15,* 135–137.

Fuller, G. W., Elbisi, H. M., and Francis, F. J. 1965. Microbial spoilage of prepeeled potatoes. Food Technol. *19,* No. 6, 103–107.

Goldblith, S. A., Joslyn, M. A., and Nickerson, J. T. R. 1961. An Introduction to the

242   PRACTICAL FOOD MICROBIOLOGY AND TECHNOLOGY

Thermal Processing of Foods. Avi Publ. Co., Westport, Conn.

Jacobs, M. B. 1951. Spoilage of Canned Foods. The Chemistry and Technology of Food and Food Products, 2nd ed. Interscience Publishers, New York.

Jones, A. H., and Lochhead, A. G. 1939. A study of micrococci surviving in frozen-pack vegetables and their enterotoxic properties. Food Research 4, 203–216.

Kaufman, A. W. 1947. Deteriorative Changes in Some Food Specialties. Proceedings of the Subsistence Research and Development Laboratory. Quartermaster General, U. S. Army, Chicago, Ill.

Mallman, W. L., and Litsky, C. 1951. A survival of selected enteric organisms in various types of soil. J. Public Health, 41, 38.

McCullough, E. C. 1945. Disinfection and Sterilization. Lea and Febiger Publishers, Philadelphia.

Mundt, J. O. 1956. The direct microscopic enumeration of bacteria in the washings of green beans. Food Research 21, 21–26.

Mundt, J. O., McCarty, I. E., and D. B. Williams. 1966. The safety of home-made pickles and relishes. Tenn. Farm Home Research 57, 6–8.

Pivnick, H., and Bird, H. 1965. Toxinogenesis by Clostridium botulinum types a and e in perishable cooked meats vacuum-packed in plastic pouches. Food Technol. 19, 132–140.

Rushing, N. B., and Senn, V. J. 1962. Effect of preservatives and storage temperatures on shelf life of chilled citrus salads. Food Technol. 16, No. 2, 77–79.

Samish, Z., Etinger-Tulczynska, R., and Bick, M. 1961. Microflora within healthy tomatoes. Appl. Microbiol. 9, 20–25.

Samish, Z., Etinger-Tulczynska, R., and Bick, M. 1963. The microflora within the tissue of fruits and vegetables. J. Food Sci. 28, 259–266.

Smart, H. F. 1939. Microbiological studies on commercial packs of frozen fruits and vegetables. Food Research 4, 293–298.

Splittstoesser, D. F., and Wettergreen, W. P. 1964. The significance of coliforms in frozen vegetables. Food Technol. 18, No. 3, 134–136.

Splittstoesser, D. F., Wettergreen, W. P., and Pederson, C. S. 1961A. Control of microorganisms during preparation of vegetables for freezing. I. Green Beans. Food Technol. 15, 329–331.

Splittstoesser, D. F., Wettergreen, W. P., and Pederson, C. S. 1961B. Control of microorganisms during preparation of vegetables for freezing. II. Peas and corn. Food Technol. 15, 332–334.

Tischer, R. G., and Esselen, W. B. 1945. Home canning: 1. Survey of bacteriological and other factors responsible for spoilage of home-canned foods. Food Research 10, 197–214.

Townsend, C. T. 1939. Spore-forming anaerobes causing spoilage in acid canned foods. Food Research 4, 231–237.

Williams, O. B. 1956. Canning experiments with non-sporeforming bacteria. Food Research 21, 502–504.

Wolford, E. R., and King, A. D., Jr. 1965. Variations in bacterial count in commercial corn freezing. J. Milk Food Technol. 28, 183–187.

CHAPTER 15

Sugar and Salt in Food Preservation

EFFECT OF SALT ON MICRO-ORGANISMS

Historical

The use of salt was one of the first methods used to preserve food. Preservation of meats and vegetables with salt brine or by dry salting is one of the oldest processes known to man. No doubt in early times salt was added to the food as a seasoning agent and by accident was observed to exert preservative properties.

Salt was an important article of trade at one time. Definite routes were established for its transportation, for instance, the Salarian way to Ancient Rome. Roman soldiers were given a *salarium* or money allowance to buy salt. The Latin "salarium" is the root of our word "salary." Marco Polo spoke of the salt coins used in the Orient.

Salt in solution exerts a certain degree of osmotic pressure and in this way affects the growth of micro-organisms. Osmotic pressure depends upon the number and size of molecules in solution. Compounds such as sugar with large molecules have a low osmotic pressure, while salt has relatively small molecules and thus an equal concentration exerts a greater osmotic pressure than sugar.

There are three conditions which may influence the activity of micro-organisms. The most favorable environment containing the ideal concentration of food nutrients is called "isotonic" meaning the bacterial cell contents have the same concentration as the surrounding medium or food material. If other environmental conditions are favorable, the organism grows very rapidly. However, if the concentration of the medium changes from that of the cell, then conditions may not be favorable for growth and the organism may die.

Plasmoptysis (hypotonic) is a condition in which the medium has a lower density than the cell, hence water passes from the less dense to the more dense medium. The cell actually bursts because water flows into it. This condition has very little application to food preservation.

However, plasmolysis (hypertonic) has a practical application to foods. In this case, the medium or food is more dense than the cell and since water passes from the less dense to the more dense, water passes out of the cell and it shrivels. The use of sugar and salt in preserving foods is a well known example of this. The bacterial spoilage of butter is inhibited in part by the salt incorporated in the small globules of water dispersed throughout the butter.

Salt, sugar, and spices act very much in the same way upon micro-organisms. If the salt concentration is sufficiently high it acts as a preservative by increasing the osmotic pressure. The moisture content of the food is withdrawn and the tissues are plasmolyzed thus there is insufficient moisture for the growth of micro-organisms.

Salt plays an important role in food preservation. It is added to many foods, such as butter, cheese, cabbage, cucumbers, green tomatoes, eggs, meat, fish, and bread to partially control microbial activity as well as give a characteristic flavor to the food. The concentration of salt will in turn determine what type of organisms will grow, which in turn influences the type of fermentation. In many cases undesirable organisms are held in check thus favoring a desirable fermentation.

The Effect of the Concentration of Salt on Micro-organisms

Many micro-organisms are salt tolerant. Some organisms may tolerate a salt concentration up to 25 per cent. Micro-organisms which require a high salt concentration for optimum growth are called "halophilic bacteria." Some molds are more resistant than bacteria to high concentrations of salt. Yeasts as a rule are very susceptible to salt, except certain species in the genus *Torula* which are comparable to bacteria and molds in their ability to tolerate salt. As a rule the common varieties of molds are inhibited in salt concentrations ranging from 20 to 25 per cent. The U.S. Department of Agriculture suggests a brine strength from 18 to 25 per cent to check microbial growth.

There are some bacteria and many types of molds that can grow in the presence of high concentrations of sugar or salt. Many bacilli are not able to grow in salt concentrations over 10 per cent although a few can tolerate concentrations much greater than this.

According to Nunheimer and Fabian (1940), staphylococci are killed in 20 per cent salt and inhibited by 15 per cent.

Several studies by different workers may be summarized by indicating the effect of salt upon micro-organisms. A study of 36 non-pathogenic bacteria studied showed that none of them grew in concentrations of over 16 per cent salt. Out of 31 pathogenic organisms none grew in 10 per cent salt, while members of the genus *Torula* were the most resistant of all the yeasts studied. *Clostridium botulinum*, an anaerobic bacterium, was inhibited under certain conditions in 10 per cent salt concentration.

Tanner and Evans (1934) showed that the growth of *Clostridium botulinum* in different culture media all containing the same concentration of NaCl was different depending on the medium. Glucose agar with 6.5 per cent salt inhibited the growth of this organism, while in 6.7 per cent salt in nutrient broth there were visible signs of growth for one culture and 5 strains of *Cl. botulinum* were able to produce toxin. The addition of 7.8 per cent salt to the broth was necessary to completely inhibit growth. These workers also observed that 7.3 per cent salt in dextrose broth and 7.8 per cent in pork infusion broth allowed growth and toxin production to take place. It finally required 12 per cent NaCl in dextrose broth to completely inhibit growth. When the pork was cooked and 5 per cent NaCl added, toxin production was checked.

According to Jensen (1954) many species of aerobes, facultative anaerobes, and true anaerobes are able to grow in high concentrations of salt brines containing large pieces of animal tissues. However, the growth is largely confined to the interfaces of brine and tissue, and not in the brine itself. In 15 to 20 per cent brines, the growth of salt tolerant micro-organisms was stopped even if whole blood was added. If pieces of meat were substituted for the blood, growth took place at the interfaces.

Chemical and Physical Effects of Salt on Micro-organisms

Organisms may be sensitive to the toxicity of the sodium. Winslow and Falk (1923) concluded that the sodium actually combined with protoplasmic anions of the cell and thus exerted a toxic effect upon the organism.

Another concept is the toxicity of the chlorine ion. Although the chlorine ion is firmly bound to the sodium and the amount of chlorine liberated is very small unless a great deal of energy is exerted to break the bond between the sodium and chlorine ions, if free chlorine is liberated, it may combine with the cell protoplasm and thereby cause death of the cell.

On the other hand, salt may interfere with the enzyme systems. This concept is not well understood but since enzymes are affected very much in the same manner as the living cell, it is only fair to assume that any alteration in the normal functioning of the enzymes is directly associated with the viability of the cell.

Obviously, salt has a marked effect in suppressing the growth of many undesirable organisms in food products. The micro-organisms may grow but their enzyme systems may be altered in such a way that no noticeable changes take place in the food. The whole system or mechanism is not well understood.

Kluyver and Baars (1931) proposed the theory that halophilism is the result of a physiological faculty by which certain organisms can adapt themselves to artificial culture saline media resulting from a pre-potency latent in the cell in the saltless environment. Hence, one may conclude that halophilic organisms are growth or mutant forms of ordinary soil bacteria adjusting themselves to a new environment.

Salt in low concentrations may accelerate the growth or favor certain physiological activities of certain organisms. Esty and Meyer (1922) reported that 0.5 to one per cent salt increased the thermal resistance of *Clostridium botulinum* spores, if the salt was increased to two per cent this effect was lost.

Sodium chloride has a very definite lethal action in the presence of heat against many kinds of micrococci. Likewise, alkaline solutions of salt tend to reduce the thermal death times of spores. It is the opinion of several investigators that NaCl in concentrations used in food preservation is not a bactericide but serves as a bacteriostatic agent against most varieties of micro-organisms.

The Effect of Salt on the Keeping Quality of Cream and Other Food Products

Thompson and Macy (1940) stated that 7.5 to 10.0 per cent salt added to cream retarded bacterial growth and acid development. No appreciable off-flavors were observed in the cream as compared to the control cream sample which turned cheesy and yeasty.

Castell and Garrard (1939) claimed that cream was very satisfactory after being stored for 8 days at 77°F (25°C) when 7 per cent salt was added. No cheesy or rancid flavors were observed due to the inhibition of certain oxidizing bacteria which were largely responsible for these defects. These authors found that cream stored for 8 days at 60° to 77°F (15.5° to 25°C) was still satisfactory for the making of good quality butter.

Some Disadvantages of Salt as Used in the Food Industry

Salt brines as used in the food industry are not free of halophilic bacteria, molds, and yeasts. Moreover many of these micro-organisms may be responsible for undesirable changes in the food product. Dry salt is not free of organisms and the microflora present may result from unsanitary practices used in salt processing, the impurities present, and the conditions under which the salt is stored.

Preservation of Meat by Salt

The use of sodium nitrate prior to salting of hams tends to increase the permeability of the muscle fibers.

Rockwell and Ebertz (1924) state that the preserving effect of NaCl implies more than its dehydrating action on the meat. For instance, many other dehydrating salts are more effective than common salt such as magnesium sulfate which will dehydrate proteins very rapidly. They conclude that there are four factors that contribute to this preserving action of the salt: (1) direct effect of the chloride ion, (2) removal of oxygen from medium, by reducing the solubility of the gas, (3) sensitization of the test organism to CO_2, and (4) interference with rapid action of proteolytic enzymes. It has been observed that dehydrogenases (citric, malic, and succinic) in pork show an impaired activity in the presence of salt.

Impurities in Salt as They Affect Meat Spoilage.—A few investigators believe that calcium and magnesium in the salt affect the meat by inducing deterioration, others are of the opinion that the salt penetrates into the meat more rapidly with these elements present. Recent studies show no appreciable differences in the rapidity of penetration of the meat due to these impurities, as compared with that of juice.

However, the toxic action of the chlorine ion may exert some effect upon the micro-organisms. It is known that a monovalent salt like sodium chloride can be neutralized by the presence of a divalent salt like calcium chloride.

The presence of calcium and magnesium compounds in salt increases the salt fish odor and taste of salted fish. Without these compounds, this taste and odor was not noted.

Hess (1942) observed that a culture medium not containing calcium and magnesium ions (prepared from dialyzed drip of fish muscle, washed agar, and pure NaCl) did not support the growth of red halophilic bacteria. When calcium and magnesium were added to the salt, good microbial growth took place.

The custom of rubbing sodium nitrate over the ham is practiced in the curing of southern style hams. The nitrate tends to increase permeability, so that by the time salt, or salt and sugar are applied to the ham and repeated at intervals over a 7 week period, the ham after smoking very rarely shows any sign of spoilage. In fact, it has an unusually good flavor.

Impurities in Salt Affecting Microbial Activity.—It is the opinion of several authorities in the field of meat curing that the impurities in the salt (calcium and magnesium) can affect the quality of the meat during the curing process. According to Moulton and Lewis (1940), the toxic effect of a monovalent salt can be neutralized by a divalent salt in certain concentrations. The work of Winslow and Falk (1923) showed that 0.145 molar solution of $CaCl_2$ mixed with 0.290 M NaCl was toxic to *Escherichia coli* while a solution of 0.145 M $CaCl_2$ + 0.680 M NaCl was non-toxic. These workers concluded that the sodium actually combined with protoplasmic anions of the cell and thus exerted a toxic effect upon the organism.

The salty fishy odor and taste of salted fish was accelerated by the presence of calcium and magnesium compounds as impurities in salt. Tressler (1920) believes the salt has a depressing action on the permeability of cell walls thus slowing down the penetration of salt into the muscle tissue. He noted less spoilage in cod press juice containing about 80 per cent pure salt as measured by an increase in bacterial count and the formation of trimethylamine.

The salt concentration is also important in preserving meat.

Halophilic Organisms

The term halophilic implies that certain micro-organisms grow well in high concentrations of salt and in brines, while salt-tolerant organisms can grow in high or low concentrations of salt.

The genera *Micrococcus, Halobacterium, Pseudomonas, Flavobacterium, Sarcina,* and *Leuconostoc* are representative of a few bacteria that may be classified as salt-tolerant.

Halophilic organisms are resistant to varying concentrations of salt. It is thought that these organisms contain hydrophobic substances although this idea is still debatable.

Another hypothesis suggested by Lamanna and Mallette (1953) is that halophiles can maintain a low intracellular salt concentration as compared to an extracellular environment. For example, recently the enzyme nitratase of *Micrococcus halodenitrificans* was found to be salt sensitive in the cell-free state and appeared to be salt tolerant in the intracellular state. However, when respiratory inhibitors were added to destroy resting cell suspensions at high salt concentrations, the reaction stopped. It has been postulated that interference with metabolism prevents or blocks the energy necessary for maintaining a low intracellular concentration of salt in the presence of high extracellular concentrations of salt.

The principles of food preservation by salting or the use of sugar solutions emphasizes the maximum limit for osmotic concentration for many kinds of micro-organisms. Obviously the effectiveness of food preservation will depend very largely upon the presence of osmophilic[1] organisms naturally present in the food. The molecular weight of salts and their ability to ionize will determine the critical osmotic concentration. Within certain concentrations of solutes a toxic reaction may take place which is entirely independent of osmotic pressure.

In the food industry it may be difficult to separate chemical effects and osmotic effects. In the case of sugars definite osmotic pressures can be observed for many kinds of micro-organisms. On the other hand varying concentrations of salt will support many kinds of organisms even though the compositions of the salts vary widely. According to Lamanna and Mallette (1953) Na^+, K^+, Li^+, Mg^{++}, and Ca^{++} all supported growth in a decreasing minimum total ionic concentration when an obligate anaerobic[2] halophile, isolated from salted anchovies, was grown in the presence of these ions.

During the early stages of the growth phase of bacteria the osmotic concentration of intracellular material is high, and the new protoplasm of the bacterial cell is actively synthesizing new compounds which may be rich in low molecular weight intermediates involved in respiration. This may be the starting point for the synthesis of carbohydrate, lipid, nucleic acid and protein molecules in the bacterial cell.

However, salt-tolerant or halophilic bacteria, molds and yeasts have been associated with food spoilage. They are widely distributed in nature according to Stuart and Swenson (1934) and can be cultivated from sources other than salt or brines when incubated for a long time. The authors noted the red discolorations, after a lag period, on old salted hides known to have been salted with uncontaminated salt. Micro-organisms isolated from sea water where the salinity is about 5 per cent, will not grow on culture media unless a high concentration of salt is added.

The author has incompletely studied the longevity of *Staphylococcus aureus*, food poisoning strain, in table grade salt as it is commonly used in the kitchens of the home and public refectories. Obviously the salt was contaminated from a human source, presumably the cook or chef. It is common knowledge to any one observing the routine habits of an individual engaged in the routine preparation of foods how convenient it is to use the hand in applying the salt from the salt container for seasoning purposes. The organism in question can be isolated from the surfaces of the skin, the throat, and nasal passages of nearly every normal person. However, the potential source of

---

[1] Adapted to high osmotic pressure.

[2] Obligate anaerobic: Absence of oxygen is necessary for survival.

Staphylococcus is no criteria that this organism is capable of producing enterotoxin. As a matter of fact a high percentage of staphylococci isolated from the human source are non-enterotoxin producers, meaning of course, that they are not responsible for the symptoms of *Staphylococcus* food poisoning.

THE ROLE OF SUGAR IN THE PRESERVATION OF FOODS

Sugar may alter the growth of micro-organisms in foods by the process of plasmolysis. It may be added to foods in a dry form, as in jellies and preserves; or, in the form of syrup with different degrees of concentration. Sugar is also added to foods to help maintain the appearance of the product and improve the flavor of the material.

The kind of sugar and its concentration will determine its ability to accelerate or stop the growth of micro-organisms. Usually a concentration from 1 to 10 per cent sugar will materially influence the growth of certain kinds of organisms, whereas a strength of 50 per cent sugar will stop the growth of most yeasts. It is generally thought necessary to have approximately 65% and 80% sugar to inhibit the growth of bacteria and mold, respectively.

Sugar is not a sterile product. However, strong sugar solutions usually have a bacteriostatic effect. A 60 per cent sucrose concentration in a food product invariably inhibits many types of food spoilage organisms. There are many types of sugar-tolerant organisms; of these, yeasts are very resistant to high sugar concentrations. The spoilage of honey is often due to sugar-tolerant yeasts. The work of Nunheimer and Fabian (1940) showed that different sugars exert a different bacteriostatic effect in different concentrations. For instance, 35 to 45 per cent dextrose or 50 to 60 per cent sucrose were bacteriostatic against food poisoning staphylococci. This organism was killed in 40 to 50 per cent dextrose or 60 to 70 per cent sucrose. Erickson and Fabian (1942) investigated the germicidal action of various sugars and they found that dextrose and fructose were more effective than sucrose or lactose. They gave the following explanation: "The difference in the germicidal effect of the different sugars may be due in part to plasmolysis of the microbial cell." This effect will depend upon the number of particles present in solution. Since dextrose and fructose each have a molecular weight of 180 they would contain more molecules per unit weight than sucrose or lactose with molecular weights of 342. Therefore, the biochemical activity would decrease as the molecular weight increases.

However, the reactivity of dextrose and fructose with respect to bacteria may be explained on a chemical rather than on a physical basis.

While fructose is a keto sugar, dextrose is an aldehyde sugar. Moreover, fructose is very active, while dextrose requires heat to accelerate the reaction as revealed by chemical tests.

Fellers, Miller, and Onsdorff (1937) stated that glucose syrups were more effective than sucrose in the inhibition of micro-organisms. No spoilage occurred in the fruit products containing glucose as compared to sucrose.

Some authorities maintain that heating the glucose solution for 15 minutes at 212°F (100°C) and then cooling brings about marked inhibition of the growth of yeasts. Molds, on the other hand, were not affected.

A 40 per cent glucose solution inhibits the growth of yeasts in apple, grapefruit, and pineapple syrups and was more effective than 40 per cent sucrose.

According to Tarkow, Fellers and Levine (1942) an equal concentration of glucose is more inhibitory than sucrose to *Saccharomyces cerevisiae* and *Aspergillus niger*. Equal mixtures of glucose and sucrose inhibited growth equally with either sugar alone at the same concentration. Glucose solution heated for 15 minutes at 212°F (100°C) and cooled, markedly inhibited the growth of yeasts as compared with unheated sugar. The heat treatment of the sugar had no noticeable affect upon mold growth, especially with respect to *Aspergillus niger*.

Sugar occupies an important place in cooking, nutrition and preservation of foods in our daily life. Sugar in many respects, like salt, will support the growth of many kinds of micro-organisms, depending, of course, on the concentration of sugar. The role of sugar as a sweetening agent in cooking and in the processing of many foods is well known to everyone. The term "saccharolytic" is widely used to designate those organisms capable of growing in high concentrations of sugar. There are a few varieties of bacteria that have a high sugar tolerance and are classified as saccharolytic bacteria. Molds and yeasts are capable of surviving in much higher concentrations of sugar than bacteria.

Sugar beets, cane and maple sap are the principal sources of our sugar supply. The latter being somewhat a luxury is not an important source of our potential sugar supply. The raw sugar from these sources is not free of micro-organisms. Naturally the purification of the sugar for human consumption removes large numbers of organisms but saccharolytic types of bacteria are usually present.

Unfortunately, many of these resident bacteria can be a contributing cause of spoilage in certain foods, especially if the concentration of sugar ranges from 20 to 30 per cent.   The genus *Leuconostoc* seems to be more involved in many foods with high concentrations of sugar than most other bacteria.

As a rule, granulated sugar has a low microbial content, usually in the neighborhood of a few hundred organisms per gram.   However, as would be expected the surviving organisms are spore forming organisms, due to the method of processing the sugar.   The raw product may be contaminated with spores of thermophiles and organisms such as *Leuconostoc mesenteroides*, *L. dextranicum*, and *Bacillus mycoides*. Molds usually include species of the genera *Aspergillus*, *Cladosporium*, *Penicillium* and *Monilia*.   *Schizosaccharomyces* and *Zygosaccharomyces* as well as *Asporogenes* are species of yeasts usually found in commercial sugar.

In syrups *Clostridium butyricum* and asporogenous yeasts have been involved in spoilage.   Osmophilic yeasts have been involved in molasses and syrup because of their heat tolerance.

The microbial content of frozen fruit juices will depend upon the contamination of the fruit prior to freezing and unsanitary practices in the processing of the juice.   A variety of organisms may be present including yeasts and molds.   The bacteria may include *Lactobacillus*, *Achromobacter* and coliforms.

Cellulose

Cellulose is a complex carbohydrate and its chemical composition is not clear.   Cellulose is an important substance in nature; nearly all cell walls of plants as well as the stems contain this material.   It is not available as food for human consumption, although certain kinds of micro-organisms possess cellulase with which they are able to bring about hydrolysis of cellulose.   The decomposition of cellulose, in nature or in the rumen of certain animals, results in several kinds of simple sugars.   These sugars are then available as a source of energy for many varieties of micro-organisms.   Indirectly the decomposition of cellulose by organisms makes the product available as a source of energy in human digestion.

There are some micro-organisms that play an important role in cellulose decomposition.   Even protozoa that live in a symbiotic relationship with other organisms in ruminants aid in breaking down low energy feeds.   Their presence along with certain varieties of bacteria vary in numbers according to the type of feed the animal is consuming.

The role of these organisms in breaking down cellulose in the soil, septic tanks and in marsh lands is not well known.   Methane, hydrogen and hydrogen sulfide gases are present during the decomposition of organic matter in the soil. The same reaction takes place in sewage treatment. Methane is formed together with other gases in the intestinal tract by cellulose splitting bacteria. It has been predicted that cellulose fermentation may be our principal source of fuel for internal combustion engines when our gasoline becomes too expensive. These are indications that micro-organisms may play an important role in the formation of natural gas, which contains an average of about 85 per cent methane.

BIBLIOGRAPHY

Anderson, E. E., Esselen, W. B., Jr., and Fellers, C. R. 1949. Effect of acids, salt, sugar, and other food ingredients on thermal resistance of *Bacillus thermoacidurans*. Food Research *14*, 499–510.

Castell, C. H., and Garrard, E. H. 1939. Preserving cream with salt. The Can. Dairy Ice Cream J. *18*, 19.

Caulfied, W. J., Nelson, F. E., and Martin, W. H. 1940. Effect of salt on the keeping quality of cream. J. Dairy Science *23*, A139 (ABS).

Clark, F. M., and Tanner, F. W. 1937. Thermophilic canned-food spoilage organisms in sugar and starch. Food Research *2*, 27–39.

Dunn, J. A. 1947. Salt and its place in the food industry. Food Technol. *1*, 415–420.

Erickson, F. J., and Fabian, F. W. 1942. Preserving the germicidal action of various sugars and organic acids on yeasts and bacteria. Food Research *7*, 68–79.

Esty, J. R., and Meyer, K. F. 1922. The heat resistance of the spores of *B. botulinus* and allied anerobes. J. Infectious Diseases *31*, 650–663.

Fabian, F. W. 1951. The preservative action of salt. *In* The Chemistry and Technology of Food and Food Products, Vol. 3, M. B. Jacobs (Editor). Interscience Publishers, New York.

Fabian, F. W., and Graham, H. T. 1953. Viability of thermophilic bacteria in the presence of varying concentrations of acids, sodium chloride and sugars. Food Technol. *7*, 212–217.

Fellers, C. R., Miller, J., and Onsdorff, T. 1937. Dextrose in the manufacture of fruit and vegetable products. Ind. Eng. Chem. *29*, 946–949.

Hess, E. 1942. Studies on salt fish. J. Fisheries Res. Board Can. *6*, 1–23.

Hohl, L. 1938. Further observations on production of alcohol by *Saccharomyces ellipsoideus* in syruped fermentations. Food Research *3*, 453–465.

Hucker, G. J., and Pederson, C. S. 1942. A review of the microbiology of commercial sugar and related sweetening. Food Research *7*, 459–480.

Jensen, L. B. 1954. Microbiology of Meats. Garrard Press, Champaign, Ill.

Kluyver, A., and Baars, S. 1931. Konenk Akod. Wetenschappen, Amsterdam Proc. *35*, 370.

Lamanna, C., and Mallette, M. F. 1953. Basic Bacteriology. Williams and Wilkins, Baltimore.

McFarland, V. H., and Goresline, H. E. 1943. Microbial destruction in buffered water and in buffered sugar sirups stored at −17.8°C (0°F). Food Research *8*, 67–77.

McRay, G. A., and Vaughn, R. H. 1957. The fermentation of glucose by *Bacillus stearothermophilus*. Food Research *22*, 494–500.

Moulton, C. R., and Lewis, W. L. 1940. Meat Through the Microscope. Inst. of Meat Packing, Univ. of Chicago, Chicago, Ill.

Nunheimer, T. D., and Fabian, F. W. 1940. Influence of organic acids, sugars and sodium chloride upon strains of food poisoning staphylococci. Am. J. Public Health *30*, 1040–1049.

Rockwell, G. E., and Ebertz, E. G. 1924. How salt preserves. J. Infectious Diseases *35*, 573–575.

Schuette, H. A., and Ihde, A. J.   1939.   Honey and the lead contamination problem.   Food Research 4, 555–562.

Stuart, L. S., and Swenson, T. L.   1934.   Halophilic organisms in nature.   J. Am. Leather Chem. Assoc. 28, 142.

Tanner, F. W., and Evans, J. B.   1934.   Effect of sodium chloride in meat curing solutions on anaerobic bacteria.   Zenthl. F. Bakt., Abt. 11, 91, 44–45.

Tarkow, L., Fellers, C. R., and Levine, A. S.   1942.   Relative inhibition of micro-organisms by glucose and sucrose syrups.   J. Bacteriol. 44, 367.

Thompson, W. A., and Macy, M. C.   1940.   Effect of salt on the microflora and acidity of cream.   Natl. Butter Cheese J. 31, 12–14.

Tressler, D. K.   1920.   Some Considerations Concerning the Salting of Fish.   U. S. Bureau of Fisheries.   Doc. 884, 1–55.

Willits, C. O., and Tressler, C. J., Jr.   1938.   Sources of lead in maple syrup and a method for its removal.   Food Research 3, 449–452.

Winslow, C. E. A., and Falk, I. S.   1923.   Studies on salt action.   J. Bacteriol. 8, 215–236.

Wolk, J., and Smith, W. W.   1944.   Bacteriological studies of refined sugars on the retail market.   Food Research 9, 115–120.

CHAPTER 16

Organic and Inorganic Acids and Alkalies in Food Preservation

The Use of Acids in Food Preservation

Food has been preserved since early history by acids. The normal fermentation that usually takes place in a food rich in carbohydrates results in the production of sufficient acid in the product to suppress further microbial activity. The souring of milk is a normal fermentation with the formation of appreciable amounts of lactic acid. This acid helps to preserve the milk from further decomposition so that it usually remains sour for a long time without spoiling. However, if the acid is neutralized by the addition of an alkali, mold growth is encouraged. Molds have the ability to utilize the acid as a source of energy, thus reducing the pH nearly to the neutral point. Under these conditions the milk may be then spoiled by bacteria. This is due primarily to the growth of many kinds of micro-organisms that cannot survive in an acid evironment. The fermentation of sauer-kraut and of pickles are examples of food preserved by biological fermentation.

It has been observed that the addition of certain chemicals delay the action of spoilage organisms. Unscrupulous food dealers have taken advantage of this situation. In the past they have been guilty of adding formaldehyde to poor quality milk to preserve it from further decomposition. In some instances catsup canneries used sodium benzoate. The use of sodium benzoate was cheaper than cleanliness and good quality tomatoes. Laws have been enacted to protect the consumer against "embalmed" foods. However, a few preservatives are permitted by law to be used under certain selected conditions. McCullough (1945) summarizes the types of preservatives that may be added to foods and drinks as follows:

1. Acetic acid used as vinegar in pickling.
2. Benzoic acid in the form of the acid or as benzoates.
3. Sulfur dioxide (SO_2) in which the foods are exposed to the sulfur fumes, forming sulfurous acid.
4. Carbonic acid in the form of CO_2 maintained under pressure.
5. Propionic acid in the form of calcium and sodium salts is used to delay mold growth.
6. Sorbic acid as a fungistat in bread and cheese wrappers.
7. Antioxidants are effective in delaying oxidation thus preventing off-flavors and rancidity.

The work of Levine and Fellers (1940) showed that acetic acid adjusted to a certain hydrogen ion concentration was more toxic to bacteria, molds, and yeasts than was lactic acid or hydrochloric acid of the same pH.

The addition of sugar syrups or salt brines did not appreciably alter the toxicity factor of the acids studied. It appeared that acetic acid was inhibitory to selected micro-organisms in direct proportion to the amount of acid used.

Corper and Cohn (1938) demonstrated that the incubation time of *Mycobacterium tuberculosis* was increased when exposed to a 2.5 per cent of acetic acid for 30 minutes, while 90 minutes' exposure killed the test organism.

Acetic Acid.—According to Levine and Fellers (1940) the toxicity of acetic acids and other organic acids seems to be due to other factors than pH alone. The idea of the undissociated molecule which is toxic to many organisms associated with food spoilage seems to be an acceptable explanation.

When different concentrations of acetic acid were prepared and various test organisms were exposed, the following results were observed. Acetic acid in a 2 per cent solution destroyed *Pseudomonas aeruginosa* in 15 minutes, likewise 3 per cent solution killed *Salmonella typhi;* 4 per cent destroyed *Escherichia coli* and 9 per cent concentration completely destroyed the viability of *Staphylococcus aureus.*

Commercial strength vinegar is usually less than 5 per cent acetic acid. A normal solution of acetic acid is approximately 6 per cent which results in a pH of 2.36. Table 23 shows the effectiveness of acetic acid in inhibiting and destroying micro-organisms.

TABLE 23

THE INHIBITING ACTION OF DIFFERENT CONCENTRATIONS OF ACETIC ACID ON MICRO-ORGANISMS[1]

Organism	Inhibiting pH[2]	Inhibiting Acidity	Lethal pH[3]
Salmonella aertryche	4.9	0.04	4.5
Micrococcus aureus	5.0	0.03	4.9
Phytomonas phaseoli	5.2	0.02	5.2
Bacillus cereus	4.9	0.04	4.9
Bacillus mesentericus	4.9	0.04	4.9
Saccharomyces cerevisiae	3.9	0.59	3.9
Aspergillus niger	4.1	0.27	3.9

[1] From Levine and Fellers (1940).
[2] The pH at which no visible growth occurred yet the organisms remained viable.
[3] The pH at which the organisms were destroyed.

It appears that acetic acid showed more germicidal properties against *Staphylococcus* food poisoning strains than any of the acids studied when added to foods. Nunheimer and Fabian (1940) have studied the dissociation of many organic acids in relation to food spoilage organisms. They observed marked variation with the different acids in their dissociation constants and on a variety of microorganisms involved in undesirable biological changes in foods.

Nunheimer and Fabian (1940) concluded that organic acids have a germicidal and antiseptic effect not in a direct relationship to the hydrogen ion concentration produced. Hence, the observed effects are due to factors in addition to the hydrogen ion, perhaps either the undissociated molecule or the effect of the characteristic anion. The following summary in Table 24 of these authors results shows the relative antiseptic and germicidal effects of the different acids.

TABLE 24

THE DECREASING ORDER OF ANTISEPTIC AND GERMICIDAL VALUE OF THE DIFFERENT ACIDS TOGETHER WITH THEIR DISSOCIATION CONSTANTS

Acid	Germicidal pH	Inhibiting pH	Dissociation Constants
Acetic	4.37	4.59	1.86×10^{-5}
Citric	3.87	4.06	8.00×10^{-4}
Hydrochloric	3.80	4.27	9.6×10^{-1}
Lactic	2.43	2.94	1.38×10^{-4}
Malic	3.74	3.98	4.00×10^{-4}
Tartaric	3.65	3.92	1.10×10^{-3}

[1] From Nunheimer and Fabian (1940).

Table 25 shows the relations between lethal temperatures and pH values at a constant (10 minute) time period.

TABLE 25

EFFECT OF PH ON THE THERMAL DEATH TIME OF MICRO-ORGANISMS WHEN EXPOSED FOR 10 MINUTES[1]

Organism	pH Value	Lethal Temperature	
		C°	F°
Salmonella aertrycke	6.0	55	131
	5.0	50	122
Micrococcus aureus	6.6	65	149
	5.5	60	140
Bacillus cereus	6.6	100	212
	5.5	60	140
Bacillus mesentericus	6.6	100	212
	6.6	60	140
Saccharomyces cerevisiae	6.8	60	140
	4.5	60	140
Aspergillus niger	6.8	60	140
	6.0	60	140
	4.5	60	140

[1] From Levine and Fellers (1940).

Apparently the action of the highly dissociated mineral acid is due to the hydrogen ion concentration while the organic acids do not show their germicidal and antiseptic action in a proportionate relationship to the pH produced. Perhaps the un-ionized molecule or the anion or both are additional factors that affect the survival of micro-organisms.

Vinegar added to foods prior to heat treatment is very effective in destroying the organisms. Table 21 shows the effectiveness of acetic acid upon heat resistant bacilli. Acid producing organisms are more difficult to destroy.

Levine and Fellers (1940) concluded that at the same hydrogen ion concentration, acetic acid is more toxic to bacteria, molds, and yeasts than lactic or hydrochloric acid.

Moreover, the addition of sugar syrups or salt brines did not appreciably alter the action of acetic acid. These investigators found that acetic acid inhibited bacterial growth in direct proportion to the amount present.

Benzoic Acid.—This acid has been used in food preservation for a long time, especially the salts of this acid. Herter (1910) clearly showed that 0.2 per cent sodium benzoate retarded the growth of *Escherichia coli* in glucose broth, but was ineffective when calcium carbonate was added. According to Perry and Beal (1920) *Saccharomyces cerevisiae* failed to grow in the presence of 0.5 per cent sodium benzoate and was completely destroyed in a 3 per cent solution.

The results obtained by various workers all seem to show that sodium benzoate can be safely added to acid fruit juices and other acid foods to retard fermentation without being harmful to human nutrition. In the case of low acid foods this procedure will not work. However, sorbic acid and sorbates can be used in these type foods.

Preservation of Fish.—A mixture of borax and sodium benzoate has been used for many years in the salting of cod fish with good results. The Canadian Pacific Fisheries use a 15 minute dip of the fillets in 20 per cent salt brine plus 0.1 per cent benzoic acid as a routine procedure in handling their fish in storage. This treatment definitely prevents the formation of trimethylamine, an objectionable bacterial decomposition product.

The Canadian Government now permits the addition of chlortetracycline (aureomycin) to ice in order to preserve the fish during transportation. The antibiotic is used to destroy or inhibit undesirable micro-organisms on the surface of the fish.

The level of antibiotics presently incorporated in commercial poultry feed supplements for growth ranges from 4 to 20 gm. per ton and for the control of diseases in birds, 200 gm. per ton has been recommended. The use of antioxidants is important in delaying undesirable changes such as rancidity due to oxidative changes in mackerel, herring, and salmon. These fish have appreciable amounts of unsaturated fatty acids in their body fats, which readily undergo biochemical changes. To prevent these changes various methods may be used such as storage of the fish in carbon dioxide, or the addition of ascorbic acid and finally ice glaze coating on the fish.

According to Fellers and Harvey (1940) benzoate offered greater effectiveness in controlling the taste and odor rather than suppressing the total number of bacteria. Perhaps benzoic acid affects only certain kinds of bacteria or the acid may regulate their metabolism.

The use of benzoate in various foods, like many other chemical preservatives, should be carefully regulated. Otherwise, the procedure of adding preservatives to unwholesome foods can lead to unscrupulous practices by the food industry. Good clean food produced, processed, and handled in a clean sanitary manner rarely requires the addition of preservatives. For example, it used to be a common practice to add chemical preservatives to milk in order to prolong its sweetness. At the present time this practice has almost disappeared.

Boric acid has been used in the preservation of milk samples for bacteriological examination. However, in most instances a one per cent boric acid solution failed to prevent most non-spore forming organisms from growing. Dunham and MacNeal (1942) found that the borate anion is less toxic than the benzoate and more toxic than the salicylate anion.

Citric Acid.—This is a tribasic acid whose normal solution of around six per cent has a pH of 1.73. Obviously the acidity of this acid is more effective than either acetic or lactic acid, even though the citrate anion is thought to be less toxic to most bacterial cells.

It has been known for a long time that citrates are an excellent source of carbon for many kinds of bacteria. In fact non-fecal types of coliform bacteria are differentiated from the fecal forms such as *Escherichia coli* by their ability to use citrates as their sole source of carbon.

Some observations by the author show that orange juice (pH 3.7) and grapefruit juice (pH 3.2) were not effective in destroying bacteria in the mouth, however, a mixture of saliva and these juices was effective in reducing the microflora normally found in the mouth after 90 minutes' exposure.

Formic Acid.—The germicidal action of formic acid is due primarily to the hydrogen ion concentration. McCullough (1945) found that it is not an efficient germicide. However, it has been used as a food preservative. When *Salmonella typhi* was exposed to 0.5 per cent concentrations of formic acid the organisms were killed in 25 minutes while 0.1 per cent strength required 205 minutes according to Norton and Hsu (1918).

Lactic Acid.—McCullough (1945) summarizes the germicidal properties of lactic acid as follows. He states that this acid is less active as a germicide than acetic or citric acids and much more active than malic, tartaric, or hydrochloric acids. Lactic acid at pH 5.2 was effective in destroying *Salmonella aertrycke* and at pH 4.27 inhibited the growth of food poisoning staphylococci. A normal solution of lactic acid is around nine per cent and has a pH of 1.9.

Everyone interested in food microbiology is familiar with the production of lactic acid in milk by lactic acid producing bacteria. Lactic acid exists in milk partly as lactate and partly as a free acid. The buffering action of the milk makes it difficult to appraise the true effect of lactic acid upon the survival of micro-organisms.

Reid (1932) observed that 0.3 per cent lactic acid destroyed *Pseudomonas aeruginosa,* while *Salmonella typhi* required almost twice this concentration. *Escherichia coli* required 2.25 per cent and *Staphylococcus aureus* 7.5 per cent lactic acid.

Moreover, not all the varieties of milk souring organisms are tolerant to the acids they produce. As a matter of fact the acids formed are toxic to most organisms after sufficient intervals of time. However, the buffering action of the milk helps to prolong the viability of these bacteria.

Salicylic Acid.—Since salicylates have been widely used to inhibit the growth of bacteria, salicylic acid has been suggested as a germicidal agent in the control of food spoilage organisms. Birkhaud (1931) in his studies on salicylic acid found it to be a very weak germicide. However, it is effective as a bacteriostatic agent.

The author has received suggestions from a few enthusiastic housewives relating their experience in canning peaches with aspirin. The fantastic idea spread from one household to another resulting in specific directions as to the use of aspirin. "Slice the peaches into a quart jar, fill with water, drop two aspirin tablets in the jar and tightly seal the container." Obviously such a procedure is not economical nor practical and such practices or fads should be discouraged. This use of aspirin would not be permitted by the U. S. Food and Drug Administration.

Hydrochloric Acid.—Burrell, Johnson, Rice, and Sohn (1945) studied the effects of hydrochloric acid on the preservation of certain vegetables. The authors selected this acid since, in the subsequent preparation of the canned product for the table, the addition of a little baking soda can be used to remove the sour taste, thereby producing a little more salt as the result of such neutralization. It was found that 25 ml. of 0.5 N hydrochloric acid added to one pint of snap beans gave a pH of around 3.6, likewise in a vegetable mixture a pH range of 3.5 to 3.7 was obtained. Obviously, such pH values are unfavorable for growth of bacteria and most enzyme activity.

One quarter of a teaspoon of baking soda was found to be adequate to remove the sour taste and yet not completely neutralize the product, which would tend to destroy vitamin C during the heating preliminary to serving. The beans after neutralization by baking soda had a pH of 6.2, and the vegetable mixture, 4.9 to 5.0.

Forty cans of snap beans and 50 cans of vegetable mixture were stored for six months to one year without any appreciable spoilage occurring in the products.

Pyroligneous Acid.—This "acid" is formed and absorbed by meat during the smoking process. Although the underlying principle involved in the smoking of meats is not well understood, it is known that a dehydration process takes place during the smoking of meat and a hard rind is formed, all of which are unfavorable to microbial growth. In addition, the absorption of formaldehyde by the meat and the formation of other chemical compounds play an important role in preservation by smoking.

There are certain commercial preparations on the market as substitutes for smoking, such as smoked salt and smoking liquids. They are mixtures containing pyroligneous "acid" while other preparations are made from the condensation of hickory wood smoke upon salt.

Sulfurous Acid.—In the early days of bacteriology, sulfur fumigation was used following outbreaks of contagious diseases, because the burning of sulfur was considered an excellent germicide. Later sulfur dioxide was used to kill insects. It is not effective against microorganisms unless moisture is present to form a film around the cell. The moisture and sulfur dioxide combine to form sulfurous acid which is a fairly effective germicide. Its effectiveness is thought to be due primarily to its hydrogen ion concentration.

Sulfurous acid is not widely used as a food preservative agent except in wineries. Sulfur dioxide is objectionable because it attacks metals very readily. There are many other more effective germicides that have fewer disadvantages.

However, the sulfuring of certain kinds of dried fruits is being done at the present time. The formation of sulfurous acid on the sulfured fruits enhances the keeping quality of these products.

Monochloracetic Acid.—This acid is used for a preservative for foods and beverages, such as fruit juices, soft drinks, beer and wine, although it possesses certain disadvantages over sodium benzoate that may limit its acceptance. In concentrations about 5 per cent, local irritation of mucous membranes or skin was noted. When used as a beverage stabilizer in concentrations of 0.05 per cent, no significant public health hazard was observed. At the present time monochloracetic acid is prohibited by the Food and Drug Administration.

This acid is comparable with benzoic acid in its preserving action. Both chemicals are more effective against yeasts than acid producing bacteria.

Propionic Acid.—Sodium or calcium propionate are salts of propionic acid and are available under the trade name of "Mycoban." These compounds have an inhibitory effect upon molds and many undesirable bacteria found in food products and are widely used.

A few examples will suffice to indicate their widespread use. Butter wrapping paper and butter tubs treated with calcium or sodium propionates helped to protect the butter against mold growth. Smoked fish fillets, smoked meats, and many other foods have been similarly treated with good results.

A concentration of 0.1 per cent propionic acid was sufficient to protect fruit fillings from mold growth for long intervals, due to a pH of about 3.5.

Smoked fish fillets dipped in 6 per cent propionic acid showed marked ability to inhibit mold growth. However this practice would not be permitted by the U. S. Food and Drug Administration.

Propionic acid as a rule is non-toxic since it is a normal constituent present in the body resulting from the metabolism of fatty acids. Approximately 2 to 3 ounces of calcium propionate is added to each 100 lbs. of wheat flour used for breadmaking. The amount is usually double in dark bread.

Sorbic Acid.—Sodium, calcium, and potassium salts of sorbic acid are used as fungistats in apple cider, cheese, cakes, dried fruits, macaroni salads, and similar preparations.

Public Health Aspects of Fermented Milks

For many years food sanitarians have considered fermented milks safe for human consumption. However, the U. S. Public Health Service has assembled sufficient evidence during the past few years to show that some disease outbreaks can be traced to the consumption of fermented milks.

Wilson and Tanner (1945) have made an extensive review of the literature on this subject and found that there were many contradictory reports. The growth of acid forming bacteria, usually found in milk, and selected pathogenic organisms were studied by comparing the rate of growth of each group in milk by the addition of acid as compared to milk fermented by the acid forming bacteria.

These investigators also studied the survival of *Salmonella typhi*, *S. paratyphi, S. schottmulleri, Shigella dysenteriae,* and *Shigella paradysenteriae* (Flexner), when grown in sterile skim milk acidified with lactic acid, naturally fermented milks, and milks inoculated with lactic acid-producing bacteria and these pathogens.

The results of the study are summarized as follows:

1. The amount of acid produced by lactic acid bacteria in sterile skim milk varies widely. This variation in acidity may contribute to the survival of many pathogenic organisms.
2. The pathogenic test bacteria were destroyed more easily in acidified milk than in milk allowed to undergo natural fermentation.
3. Larger numbers of pathogenic organisms survived in milk when the biological acidity increased gradually as compared to a rapid increase in acidity. The presence of acid tolerant strains of the pathogens may account for their resistance to biological acidity.
4. The authors concluded that the acidity of naturally fermented milks is not sufficient to destroy all pathogenic organisms.
5. An acidity of 0.95 to 1.15 per cent (pH 3.9 to 4.2) in milk failed to destroy the pathogens after an incubation period of seven days.
6. Likewise, an acidity ranging from 0.50 to 0.86 per cent (pH 4.3 to 5.0) in the milk showed many viable organisms after 9 weeks' incubation.

Preservatives for Food

The food industry has an acute need for non-toxic preservatives to be used in preserving perishable food products not stored under refrigeration. Sodium benzoate has long been used for this purpose but certain factors limit its use.

Workers at the Institute of Paper Chemistry (Pearl 1945) developed a process for the quantitative transformation of vanillin to vanillic acid and its esters. It was found that these esters have inhibiting properties. Vanillic acid is a derivative of p-hydroxybenzoic acid and esters formed from the latter acid are known to have the properties of an acceptable preservative.

Salt fish, fresh fruit juices, vegetable juices, cheese spreads, and bread are being tested using vanillic acid esters as the preservative.

The toxicity of ethyl vanillate as compared to benzoate was studied in rabbits, guinea pigs, and rats by the Kettering Research Laboratories of Applied Physiology of the University of Cincinnati.[1]   When administered in olive oil, the two agents had about the same lethal effect on the test animals.   However, in aqueous suspension, the vanillate was less toxic than the benzoate.

Alkali Producing Organisms

According to Ayers *et al.* (1923), alkali-forming bacteria in milk and other food products may be defined as bacteria which produce an alkaline reaction in litmus milk in 14 to 18 days, with no visible evidence of peptonization.   This author believes that the alkalinity is due to the fermentation of citric acid salts in milk to alkali carbonates. Perhaps other salts of organic acids may cause an alkaline reaction if they are present in milk.   Apparently, ammonia was not involved in producing this reaction.

Stock (1936) concluded that the alkali-forming bacteria belong to a large group of organisms normally found in milk.   The ability of many kinds of micro-organisms to attack proteins thus liberating basic products must be considered along with the true alkali-forming bacteria.   A few species of molds are capable of forming basic products when permitted to grow in certain foods.

The presence of alkali-forming organisms in foods is undesirable, especially when they gain the ascendancy over the acid-forming microorganisms.   Several investigators state that these bacteria may be desirable in the soft cheese industry because they can break down the casein, a desirable function in the making of cheese.

The Role of Alkalies in Food Preservation

The action of strong alkalies upon micro-organisms has been recognized for a long time.   The use of lye made from wood ashes for scrubbing contaminated objects dates back to antiquity.

The germicidal efficiency of an alkali will depend upon the presence or absence of organic matter which has the ability to neutralize part of the alkalinity.

Gram-positive bacteria are very resistant while bacterial spores are extremely resistant to the action of alkalies.   Gram-negative nonsporulating organisms are very susceptible to alkalies.

---

[1] Private communication.

A pH of from 10 to 12 was lethal for most organisms with the exception of bacterial spores. McCullough (1945) found household lye to be effective in destroying streptococci, even in the presence of five per cent skim milk as shown in Table 26.

TABLE 26

THE EFFICIENCY OF LYE AGAINST MASTITIS STREPTOCOCCI AT 40 °C IN THE PRESENCE
OF FIVE PER CENT SKIM MILK

Household Lye (97.5% Sodium Hydroxide)	pH	5 Per Cent Skim Milk Was Added to the Cultures Subcultures after:			
		1 Min.	2 Min.	5 Min.	10 Min.
1:300	11.22	+	−	−	−
1:350	11.21	+	−	−	−
1:400	11.20	+	+	−	−
1:500	11.18	+	−	−	−

NOTE: + indicates growth in subculture; − indicates no growth in subculture.

The sanitary code of the Manufacturers of Bottled Carbonated Beverages states, "Unclean bottles shall be exposed to 3 per cent alkali solution of which not less than 60 per cent is caustic (sodium hydroxide), for a period of not less than 5 minutes at a temperature of not less than 130°F (55°C) or to an equivalent cleansing and sterilizing process." Thirty-two states require the use of from 2 to 5 per cent caustic soda. The strength of the caustic soda solution in pasteurizing milk plants is important in order to maintain the sanitary quality of the milk.

Topley and Wilson (1946) claimed that a 5.6 per cent solution of potassium hydroxide was required to kill the spores of *Bacillus anthracis* in 10 hr. This concentration of hydroxide would be equivalent to a four per cent solution of sodium hydroxide. Potassium hydroxide has been recommended as an effective disinfectant against anthrax organisms when used as a five per cent solution.

A Washington State College Extension Bulletin (1938) recommends household lye as a practical and economical disinfectant to use around the farm. A can of lye, containing 13 ounces, dissolved in 1 pail of water, will make a solution that will kill germs except members of the acid fast group and spore-forming organisms.

There are many alkalies that have been recommended with varying degrees of effectiveness as a disinfectant. Perhaps trisodium phosphate should be mentioned since it is widely used as a detergent in the dairy industry and for washing dishes and glassware where a bright, shiny surface is desired.   The compound will destroy the less resistant pathogens.   Time of exposure and concentration are two important factors in determining the potency of trisodium phosphate.

How Alkalies Exert Germicidal Action.—The hydroxyl ion concentration, or the degree of alkalinity is largely responsible for the germicidal action of the strong alkalies.   However, other factors may modify the germicidal action such as cell permeability, surface tension, oxidation-reduction potential and osmotic pressure.   The work of Myers (1929) on the action of various alkalies and their combinations on spores at 140°F (60°C) can be stated as follows: "The death rate was increased by an increase in the hydroxyl ion concentration of the solution when the buffer index and the osmotic pressure were kept constant.   The death rate was increased by an increase in the buffer index of the solution when the pH and the osmotic pressure were kept constant."

McCullough (1945) concluded that the dissociation of hydroxyl ions of sodium hydroxide was the most important factor in the destruction of micro-organisms.   Also he concluded that different concentrations of sodium hydroxide, with the same pH, due to the addition of different amounts of peptone, had about the same germicidal value.

Prucha (1934) compared the germicidal properties of household lye with a specially prepared lye plus salts to increase the amount of undissociated sodium hydroxide.   He found the special mixture slightly less effective than the household lye in destroying very resistant bacterial spores.

It is also believed that neutral salts tend to suppress the dissociation of sodium hydroxide and may alter the resistance of the bacterial cell to the hydroxyl ions, or that these salts may influence the permeability of the cell wall.

If sodium chloride is added to a sodium hydroxide solution the germicidal efficiency is not appreciably increased at ordinary temperatures but at higher temperatures the action is much greater.   This may be due to the increased permeability of the bacterial cell walls according to McCullough (1945).

If a weak alkali is added to a sodium hydroxide solution, the germicidal efficiency is increased, especially in the presence of organic matter.

The work of Levine, Toulouse, and Buchanan (1928) found that the addition of sodium chloride or sodium carbonate to sodium hydroxide solutions increased the destruction of bacterial spores at 122° and 140°F (50° and 60°C).   The sodium chloride reduced the killing time by 28 per cent, the sodium carbonate by 30 per cent. The 140°F (60°C) temperature was much more effective than the lower temperatures.

The presence of organic matter reduces the efficiency of alkalies.

Tilley and Schaffer (1931) found that weak solutions of sodium hydroxide are effective against non-sporulating bacteria. However, the cocci were much more resistant than the rod forms.

Temperature in relation to germicidal action: Myers (1929) showed that as the temperature increased from 77° to 104°F (25° to 40°C) no appreciable increase in the germicidal efficiency of sodium hydroxide was noted.

The Effect of Alkalies on Gram-Positive and Gram-Negative Bacteria.—It is generally agreed that gram-negative bacteria are very susceptible to the action of strong alkalies. Filtrable viruses are equally susceptible. The cocci and non-spore forming organisms are more resistant to the strong alkalies. Tilley and Schaffer (1931) found the acid fast group of organisms to be very resistant. They reported that *Mycobacterium tuberculosis* withstood a 2 hr. exposure in 2 per cent sodium hydroxide and the same length of time in 10 per cent calcium hydroxide. Protozoan parasites seem to be very resistant to alkali solutions.

BIBLIOGRAPHY

Ayers, S., Rupp, P., and Johnson, W. T. 1923. The influence of surface tension depressants on the growth of Streptococci, J. Infect. Diseases *33*, 202–216.
Birkhaud, K. E. 1931. Detoxifying and disinfecting properties of sodium salicylate. J. Infect. Diseases *48*, 212–225.
Burrell, R. C., Johnson, J. R., Rice, B., and Sohn, J. 1945. Canning vegetables with hydrochloric acid. J. Chem. Ed. *22*, 8–10.
Corper, H. J., and Cohn, M. L. 1938. Some fundamental investigations on the resistance of tubercle bacilli. J. Bacteriol *35*, 223.
Dunham, W. B., and MacNeal, W. J. 1942. Culture of the *Chick Chorie allantois* as a test of inactivation of *Vaccinia* Virus. J. Bacteriol. *44*, 413–424.
Fabian, F. W., and Bloom, C. 1945. The chloracetic acids as preservatives for apple juice. Fruit Products J. *21*, 292–296.
Fellers, C. R., and Harvey, E. W. 1940. Effect of benzoated brine dips on keeping quality of fish fillets. Food Research *5*, 1–12.
Herter, C. A. 1910. The action of sodium benzoate on the multiplication and gas production of various bacteria. J. Biol. Chem. *7*, 59–67.
Jay, J. M. 1970. Modern Food Microbiology. Van Nostrand Reinhold Co., New York.
Levine, A. S., and Fellers, C. R. 1940. Action of acetic acid on food spoilage micro-organisms. J. Bacteriol. *39*, 499–515.
Levine, A. S., Toulouse, R., and Buchanan, R. E. 1928. Effect of addition of salts on the germicidal efficiency of sodium hydroxide. Ind. Eng. Chem. *20*, 199.
McCullough, E. C. 1945. Disinfection and Sterilization, 2nd ed. Lea & Febiger, Philadelphia.
Myers, R. P. 1929. The germicidal properties of alkaline washing solutions. J. Agr. Research *38*, 521–563.

268   PRACTICAL FOOD MICROBIOLOGY AND TECHNOLOGY

Norton, J. F., and Hsu, P. H.   1918.   The physical chemistry of disinfection.   J. Infect. Diseases *18*, 180.

Nunheimer, T. D., and Fabian, F. W.   1940.   Influence of organic acids, sugars and sodium chloride upon strains of food poisoning staphylococci.   Am. J. Public Health *30*, 1040.

Pearl, I. A.   1945.   Vanillic acid esters as preservatives.   Food Industries *17*, 1173.

Perry, M. C., and Beale, G. D.   1920.   The quantities of perservatives necessary to inhibit and prevent alcoholic fermentation and the growth of molds.   J. Ind. Eng. Chem. *12*, 253–255.

Prucha, M. J.   1934.   Germicidal Properties of Alkaline and Chlorine Solutions.   Dairy Short Course Manual.   Univ. of Ill.

Reid, J. D.   1932.   The disinfectant action of certain organic acids.   Am. J. Hyg. *16*, 540–566.

Shrader, J. H., Wilson, E. L., and Tanner, F. W.   1945.   The acid milks; their potential hazard.   J. Milk Technol. *8*, 127–128.

Stock, V.   1936.   Alkali-forming bacteria.   Zeullet. Bakt. Pt. Z. *94*, 295–330.

Tilly, F. W., and Schaffer, J. M.   1931.   Germicidal efficiency of sodium hydroxide, sodium carbonate and trisodium phosphate.   J. Agr. Research *42*, 93–106.

Topley, W. W. C., and Wilson, G. S.   1946.   The Principles of Bacteriology and Immunity, 3rd ed.   The Williams and Wilkins Co., Baltimore.

Washington State College.   1938.   Extension Bulletin *245*.

Wilson, F. L., and Tanner, F. W.   1945.   Behavior of pathogenic bacteria in fermented milks.   Food Research *10*, 122–124.

CHAPTER 17

Radiation in Food Preservation

THE NATURE AND SOURCES OF RADIATION

Although preservation of selected food products by radiation has been successful, there are still some questions concerning the safety of these products which need to be resolved before such foods are made available to consumers. A summary of the work of several investigators follows.

Radioactive substances give off rays which are invisible to the naked eye but can be detected by a photographic plate. Modern X-ray machines make use of such rays. Three kinds of rays are emitted from radioactive substances. They are alpha and beta particles and gamma rays.

Alpha particles consist of positively charged pieces of matter, traveling at a velocity of about 20,000 miles per second. Such particles are readily stopped by material substances. The beta particles, on the other hand, carry a negative charge and travel at a much higher rate of speed. Some of them move with a velocity of over 170,000 miles per second and can penetrate several millimeters of iron. The beta particles are about $\frac{1}{1800}$ of the size of a hydrogen atom nucleus. The gamma rays are able to pass through several inches of iron or lead and several feet of water. They carry no electrical charge. These rays have the property of neutralizing an electrified body and they produce a large number of positively and negatively charged ions in a neutral substrate. This latter property is of the utmost importance in the processing of food.

The expulsion of these rays results from an explosion of the particles which proceeds at a definite rate. The rate is expressed as half-life (the time in which one half of the substance will have been radiated). This value varies for different radioisotopes. Such atomic reactions give off a tremendous amount of energy. Most of the heating effect of an element such as radium is directly due to alpha rays. These rays are emitted with a considerable energy of motion, which is transferred into heat when it strikes other matter. Because these rays are stopped easily by matter, very few escape the radium and, therefore, radium is heated by the unceasing self-bombardment of alpha rays.

By reversing this process and adding energy, atoms can be made unstable. This is the basis of a chain reaction in which alpha, beta, and gamma rays release energy. By controlling such a reaction and applying a magnetic field to the rays given off, the three can be separated.

Many variations have been applied in the last few years and there are many problems in physics and engineering involved in the practical application of the rays to useful purposes.

Heating of food products often brings about undesirable changes in the food. The dosage of radiation necessary for complete sterilization of a product usually does not raise the temperature more than 50°F (28°C). Thus, packaging would be much simpler and more economical. Radiation may also produce physical or chemical changes in the food, causing alteration of flavor, color, and sometimes texture of the food. The packaging, storage life, and toxicity of foods treated by radiation involve problems that have not been solved, nevertheless, some foods can be successfully preserved by radiation (Desrosier and Rosenstock, 1960).

As previously mentioned, alpha particles are positively charged particles which carry most of the energy from the fission process. Such rays emit large amounts of energy and, therefore, would readily destroy bacteria. However, alpha rays are readily stopped by material as thin as a sheet of paper. For this reason, such rays would not be useful in food processing.

Gamma rays are electrically neutral particles which have a much greater power of penetration than beta rays. Gamma rays are by-products of atomic fission. They are actually a type of X-ray. By bombarding a heavy metal target with cathode rays, X-rays can be produced. Only 3–5 per cent of the electron energy is used in this procedure, the remainder of energy is released as heat on the target. Thus, continuous use of such units would require extensive cooling attachments. In medical X-ray equipment, the actual exposure time is seldom over a second or so and therefore, the target is cooled between exposures by a fan-type cooler. Because of the low efficiency, a number 2 can of food would require from 10 to 20 minutes' exposure. Because of these technical difficulties, the use of X-rays in food processing remains a possibility only when improved equipment is developed.

Gamma rays obtained from radioactive fission products would improve the efficiency if an adequately low cost source of material were available. Such material is rapidly becoming available. Cobalt 60 has been the principal source of these rays.

All kinds and types of micro-organisms can be destroyed by irradiation, but the degree of sensitivity varies with different species. Resistance of an organism to radiation seems to parallel the resistance to heat. That is, spore forming bacteria are more resistant to irradiation than non-spore forming species. In general, the lower the order in the plant and animal kingdom, the greater the resistance to radiation.

Insects then, could easily be killed in food products such as dried grains, but considerable irradiation would be required to destroy bacteria or fungi. Studies on the radiation resistance of the natural bacterial flora of canned ham show that most strains of bacteria are sensitive to irradiation and are destroyed at low levels. Spores isolated from bacteria in the ham are resistant to 0.5 megarad irradiation when incubated at 80°F (27°C) for two months. No differences were found in the destruction of organisms when gamma rays or an electron beam were the source of irradiation.

Destruction of single-celled organisms is effected by the passage of a single ionizing particle through or near the cell. Such a "hit" causes ionization and subsequent death of the organism.

The direct hit explains bacterial death by a direct mechanism, brought about by the passage of a radiation particle directly through the cell. Such a theory is supported by the fact that survival curves are exponential. That is, the number of viable organisms decreases in geometric progression as the dose of radiation increases. The dose rate is independent of the amount of destruction, therefore, the effect of a given dose is the same regardless of the period of time involved. Destruction is independent of temperature. The percentage of survival is not affected by the concentration of organisms. Such facts support the "direct hit" theory but some destruction may be attributed to other effects.

Some lethal action may be attributed to chemical effects caused by free radicals produced in the solvents. For example, irradiations of water may be illustrated in the following manner. When ionizing radiations bombard water, a positive water ion is formed and an electron is liberated. This electron reacts with another water molecule and thus produces a negative water ion. Cathode rays are negatively charged electrons and may directly combine with water molecules without this first step. These positive and negatively charged molecules then dissociate into free hydrogen and hydroxyl radicals.

$$H_2O \rightarrow H_2O^+ + e^-$$
$$e^- + H_2O \rightarrow H_2O^-$$
$$H_2O^+ \rightarrow H^+ + OH^-$$
$$H_2O^- \rightarrow H^+ + OH^-$$

These hydroxyl ions are strong oxidizing agents and will oxidize an oxidizable substance in solution. The hydrogen ions are strong reducing agents and will reduce any reducible substance in the solution. If no oxidizable or reducible solute is present, these free radicals may combine to form water peroxides or other radicals. Such reactions are important in understanding certain side-effects produced in the irradiated product.

Oxidizing or reducing compounds may alter flavor compounds in the food. This can be alleviated by adding a substance with a greater affinity for the radical involved than the flavor compounds. Many attempts have been made to find such compounds which do not alter the product. Some of the results have been encouraging. For example, vitamin C and its analogues will act as free-radical acceptors in many cases. Ascorbic acid would also help prevent flavor changes and would have no toxic effects. By freezing the food before it is irradiated the diffusion rate of the free radicals produced is lowered and the off-flavors can be minimized.

The degree of off-flavor produced in foods increases generally as the dosage of the ionizing radiations is increased. The off-flavor development is definitely noticeable at dosages far below those necessary to sterilize many kinds of foods. Some foods, because of their chemical composition, may be able to withstand a complete sterilization dosage with little or no off-flavor development.

Because of the chemical composition of different foods, the reaction to ionizing radiation will be different. Because of this, each product requires individual evaluation.

Somewhat related to the development of off-flavor is the effect radiation may have on the storage life of the product. The storage life of foods sterilized by irradiation might be markedly different from that of foods sterilized by heat.

Enzymes catalyze chemical transformations of the foods, which may result in changes in taste, appearance, odor, or texture. A great deal more energy is necessary to inactivate enzymes completely than for the destruction of food-spoiling organisms. Ten times more radiation is needed for inactivation of enzymes in certain food materials. In many cases, the doses necessary to inactivate enzymes may make irradiation processing too expensive and may be sufficiently high to cause marked side effects in the product. Since most enzymes can be readily inactivated by low heat, a blanching process might be combined with the radiation treatment. Blanching would consist of a very rapid exposure to a moderate temperature and therefore would not have the harmful effects that occur with heat sterilization.

Packaging of foods plays an important role in the final product. Steel and glass containers would minimize the effect of a given dose of radiation because of their thickness and density. Aluminum or plastic containers would readily transmit the electrons or X-rays. Recent advancements in plastics make this a very desirable method of packaging. Vacuum packaging has been developed in the past few years. It has been suggested that such packaging be used in conjunction with radiation. Another similar method packs the food in an inert gas. By eliminating the oxygen from the foods, radiation side effects may be reduced. However, it has been shown that bacteria are more radio-sensitive in the presence of oxygen. Therefore, the sterilization dose may have to be increased considerably in the absence of oxygen.

Investigations carried out at Massachusetts Institute of Technology and elsewhere have shown that all kinds of micro-organisms can be killed by radiation, in any type of container provided that it is not too large, and in any menstruum. This can be carried out if the dimensions of the container are within practical limits for penetration of the particular type of radiation used.

Radiation has been successfully applied to the processing of several foods such as meat, fish products, vegetables, and spices. Milk and milk products, however, appear to be extremely sensitive to ionizing radiations and undesirable changes in flavor frequently follow. Research at the University of Michigan has shown that potatoes can be preserved at 48°F (8.8°C) for one year, whereas they usually sprout or rot after 6 months. A test panel compared irradiated potatoes with untreated potatoes and found a slightly different taste. The flavor of irradiated potatoes was actually preferred by some panel members.

The Use of Cathode Rays in the Food Industry

The reduction of the microflora in food products by various methods has been a fertile field for investigations for many years. Recently, cathode rays (electrons) have served as a quick and practical way of sterilizing dairy and other food products. Already investigations have shown that these rays are very effective in killing insects which infect grain thus reducing a big waste in this raw food product.

Cathode rays are actually artificially accelerated electrons which are analogous to the beta rays. Cathode ray production is relatively efficient since approximately 75 per cent of the energy emitted in the electron beam can be utilized. Such efficiency would effect sterility in a matter of seconds, an important consideration in production line processing. The range of penetration of these rays warrants consideration of their use if the food product can be processed in fairly thin containers. The larger bulk packaging could not be readily used in such processing and thus the cost of packaging is increased. Such cathode ray irradiation equipment uses one tube of a single generator and requires somewhat elaborate facilities for use in a production setup. At least two such processing units have been devised and tested on a large scale. The Van de Graff generator is built by the High Voltage Engineering Corporation of Cambridge, Mass. The Capacitron is being adapted for the food industry by the Electronized Chemical Corporation of Brooklyn, N.Y. The General Electric X-ray Corporation Laboratories in Milwaukee, Wis., have been carrying out intensive research on the development of electron bombardment apparatus.

Proctor (1952) has compared the results of ultraviolet light, infrared rays and X-rays on the destruction of micro-organisms. The X-rays require from 15 to 30 minutes to destroy bacteria in food whereas cathode rays will do the job in a few seconds. However cathode rays will not penetrate to a depth much beyond one inch.

Perhaps in the future cathode rays may play an important role in the destruction of spoilage organisms in foods in any type of container. One advantage of this kind of sterilization is that it does not increase the temperature of the product. Also the nutritive value, the vitamin content and the flavor of the food are not altered as much as with other types of radiation.

One of the disadvantages in the use of these rays is that the composition of the food is slightly changed. The fats and oils have a tendency to turn rancid and the carbohydrates are slightly modified. Proteins, vitamins, and enzymes are not affected to any great extent. Vitamin A, carotene, vitamin C, and several components of the vitamin B complex are not appreciably affected by this process, although if these vitamins are irradiated in solution instead of in the food these constituents suffer severe damage.

Proctor (1952) reports that vitamin C is relatively sensitive and niacin more resistant to radiation. When the two vitamins are mixed and irradiated the niacin protects the ascorbic acid, hence there appears to be a greater destruction of niacin and a sparing of ascorbic acid. Other vitamin combinations seem to behave very much in the same way.

The application of ionizing radiation is opening up new possibilities in the development of physical and electrical equipment applicable to the food industry. This is truly a new field that should be given serious attention by many investigators.

The Role of Ultraviolet Light in Food Preservation

The effectiveness of any type of radiation depends very largely on the kind of radiation, its intensity, and the efficiency of its absorption.

In order to have a practical concept of radiation we must think of radiation as a part of a series of light rays which make up the spectrum.

The spectrum may be natural radiation as coming from the sun or artificial radiation as produced by electrical energy.

Moreover, the spectrum may be divided into visible light rays and invisible rays. Whether the light rays are visible or not will depend upon each individual wave length. The wave lengths are measured in terms of angstrom units.

Micron = $\frac{1}{1,000}$ of a millimeter or $\frac{1}{25,400}$ of an inch.

Millimicron = $\frac{1}{1,000,000}$ of a millimeter.

Angstrom unit = $\frac{1}{10,000,000}$ of a millimeter or 254,000,000 angstrom units = 1 in.

In the visible light range, the colors are violet, blue, green, yellow, orange, and red. The wave lengths range from 3900 to 8,000 angstrom units and are considered as long rays as compared with the invisible spectrum in which no light rays are visible; the latter are short rays as shown in Table 27.

Since the spectrum is composed of several light rays they can be broken up into component rays of varying wave lengths by passing the light through a prism. Hence some of the light rays are deflected, absorbed, or filtered out. This has a practical significance in the destruction of micro-organisms. Usually the short rays between 2,540 and 2,800 angstrom units are the most effective. Moreover, it is the short rays that are absorbed when passed through glass, yet they have the highest germicidal power. In general the visible spectrum has very little germicidal power while the invisible one has a marked effect upon micro-organisms. The ultraviolet is the most destructive light

TABLE 27

BACTERICIDAL EFFECTS OF DIFFERENT WAVE LENGTHS OF RADIANT ENERGY

Classification	Wave Length Angstroms	Germicidal Effects
A. *Invisible Long*		
Radio	Very long	None
Infrared heat	8,000 and longer	Temperature may be raised
B. *Visible*		
Red, orange, yellow, green, blue, violet	4,000 to 8,000	Little or none
C. *Invisible Short*		
Ultraviolet total range	136 to 4,000	
	3,200 to 4,000	Photographic and fluorescent range
	2,800 to 3,200	Human skin tanning Antirachitic-vitamin D
	2,000 to 2,800	Maximum germicidal power
	1,500 to 2,000	Shuman region
	1,000	Ozone forming germicidal in proper concentration
X-rays	1,000 to 1,500	
Alpha, beta, and gamma rays	Less than 1,000	Germicidal
Cosmic rays	Very short	Probably germicidal

ray.   It extends beyond the violet at the blue end of the spectrum. Infrared is beyond the red end of the spectrum.

Sunlight is germicidal but it will vary with the climate, season, time of day, wave length, intensity of rays, angle of incidence, and length of exposure.

An electric light bulb has about the same germicidal properties as sunlight passed through the ordinary window glass.

Table 27 shows the different wave lengths of radiant energy and their bactericidal effect upon micro-organisms.

THE ACTION OF ULTRAVIOLET LIGHT IN FOOD PRESERVATION

The maximum lethal effects of ultraviolet lie between 2,000 and 2,800 angstroms.   However, the mechanism of destruction of micro-organisms is not well understood.   A few factors may be considered pertinent in arriving at a modest explanation.   They are: (1) Ultraviolet light has a very low penetrating power, (2) ordinary window glass or even a thin cover slip will filter or retard the penetrating power of these light rays, and (3) certain proteins act very much like glass in this respect.

A few observers believe that a chemical change is induced in the medium or in the cell protoplasm itself.   For instance, if a nutrient agar medium is exposed to ultraviolet rays a chemical change seems to take place in the medium.   If a culture of any common bacterium is seeded on this medium, usually a poor growth results as compared with a control preparation.   It is assumed that some toxic substance develops in the medium that is inimical to the growth of the organisms. The change in the medium may be of a photo-electric character, since the highly lethal waves seem to have enough energy to displace some electrons in the cell protoplasm.   Perhaps there is a displacement of certain molecular groupings in the cell which may have a high specific absorption spectra for these rays.

Likewise, ultraviolet light may produce some oxidizing substances, such as ozone which has a marked germicidal effect.   Recently, it has been shown that these light rays are destructive in the absence of atmospheric oxygen.   It is known that a consumption of oxygen takes place when tetani and cholera cultures were irradiated in the sun in the presence of air.

A few chemical compounds such as formaldehyde are capable of bringing about a coagulation of the cell protoplasm, which is largely protein.   This phenomenon is widely accepted as being responsible for the destruction of many kinds of micro-organisms.   When various albumins and globulins are exposed in thin layers to ultraviolet rays, a similar coagulation of these proteins takes place and they are no longer soluble in weak acids or alkalies.

Fundamental Principles of the Germicidal Action of Different Rays

In order for any ray to be germicidal it must be absorbed. Most proteins that may constitute the microbial cell are transparent, therefore, they do not absorb and the cell is not affected. However, there are a few amino acids that will absorb ultraviolet light which thus becomes effective in destroying the cell. These amino acids are alanine, tryosine, and tryptophane. If a dye such as eosin is added to the protein upon exposure to ultraviolet light, the absorption power of the protein is enhanced.

If the ultraviolet light is directed against a white object the rays are reflected and not absorbed. The procedure alters the germicidal effect. Passing these rays through window glass will filter out the ultraviolet rays thus rendering them ineffective.

Similarly, when eggs of sea urchins were stained with neutral red and exposed to ultraviolet rays, a deep yellow color developed within a few hours, thus indicating the presence of alkali in the egg cell.

Recently, a theory was presented stating that the light rays induced some chemical action on the superficial membrane of the cell. This action made the cell more permeable to the hydroxyl ions of the medium thus coagulating its colloids.

The Use of Ultraviolet Light in the Control of Food Spoilage by Micro-organisms

Although a number of attempts have been made to control food spoilage micro-organisms by the use of ultraviolet light, the only practical application has been to reduce the number of organisms in the air. The chief limitation for sterilization has been the inability of the rays to penetrate liquids and solids.

Ultraviolet light is used in meat coolers primarily to reduce the numbers of micro-organisms in the air. Because of the reduced microbial population it is possible to hold meat at higher temperatures and speed up the aging and tenderizing process considerably.

Ultraviolet light is used to maintain a relatively microbial free air in food handling establishments. These rays have been used with a high degree of success in bakeries especially in controlling the spores of *Bacillus mesentericus* which is largely responsible for ropy bread. Mold spores on the other hand are very resistant to ultraviolet radiation.

Cathcart, *et al.* (1942) showed that ultraviolet rays ranging from 2,000 to 2,950 A. were effective in reducing the numbers of *Staphylococcus aureus* and *Salmonella enteriditis* when they were sprayed into the air and inoculated on to smooth hard surfaces. However, when these organisms were added to custard-like foods they were not effectively destroyed.

Bacterial spores may require five to ten times as much exposure as vegetative cells. Bacteria and yeasts are comparable as far as their resistance to ultraviolet light, while molds are much more resistant, especially if they are pigmented.

Effects of Ultraviolet Light on Foods

There are reports that undesirable changes take place such as off-colors, odors, and tastes. The sterilization of fresh pork and pork products has been partially successful. The sterilization of certain vegetables, milk, and eggs has been encouraging.

Undesirable Biochemical Changes in Foods From Radiation

1. Rise in pH of meats.
2. Destruction of glutathione.
3. Increase in H_2S.
4. Destruction of natural antioxidants in fats.
5. Destruction of thiamine, ascorbic acid, riboflavin, niacin, and other vitamins in addition to many endogenous enzymes.

The Application of Ultraviolet Light in the Tenderization of Meat

The aging of meat is due primarily to the action of certain inherent enzymes present in the meat. Cold storage of meat retards the activity of enzymes. However, if the temperature of storage is raised, the enzymes are activated, and many undesirable contaminating bacteria become active and may bring about undesirable changes. This is where ultraviolet light can be effective in controlling the bacteria on the surface of the meat but not those organisms beneath the surface. Meat that has been exposed directly to ultraviolet light sometimes develops certain off-flavors such as a cooked or rancid taste. Fats in the meat are susceptible to the rays and often an oxidation of the fat occurs because of the ozone from the ultraviolet light.

Pasteurization of Milk.—Supplee (1930) showed a 90 per cent reduction in bacteria counts on market milk supplying the New York area. They found radiation at 2,537 Å. to be more effective than shorter wave lengths between 2,200 and 2,300 Å. There is very little bactericidal action in milk when it is irradiated to activate the precursor of vitamin D because the use of shorter wave lengths and a minimum degree of exposure has very little germicidal action.

Sanitization of Glassware.—Water or drinking glasses can be effectively sterilized by ultraviolet light providing they are clean. Mechanical difficulties in applying ultraviolet radiation has not made this method of sanitization very popular with efficient restaurant management.

Irradiated Oils.—Ross (1932) irradiated a mixture of two parts petrolatum and one part lanolin and found that this mixture killed *Staphylococcus aureus* within 24 hr. Harris, Bunker, and Milas (1932) showed that certain oils can be made actively germicidal due to the formation of peroxides which are poisons to many kinds of bacteria. However, these authors found that some oils do not respond to irradiation and consequently are ineffective germicides. At present, irradiated fats form the basis for "germ free" cold creams.

Supersonic Vibrations

Supersonic waves are inaudible, "super" meaning above, and "sonus" is the Latin word for sound. The threshold of audibility for the human ear depends on the pressure and the frequency. The lowest frequency audible to the human ear is about 31 cycles per second at a pressure amplitude of one dyne. The highest audible frequency is around 14,000 cycles per second with a pressure of 0.05 dyne. The human ear distinguishes variations in frequency most readily when the frequency of the sound lies between 1,000 and 4,000 cycles.

The Physical Field of Application

It has been found also that immiscible liquids, such as oil and water, or water and mercury, are transformed into remarkably stable emulsions by supersonic vibration. Long chain molecules have been depolymerized; dispersions in water, alcohol, and oil have been made with many of the metallic elements, as well as with fusible alloys.

Various frequencies have been found to cause accumulation and coagulation of precipitates in liquids, suggesting application to the filtration field. Other supersonic waves cause smoke or dust particles to agglomerate, suggesting applications in the smoke prevention field. Some frequencies produce colloidal suspensions of solids in liquids; others break up suspensions, yielding precipitated lumps.

Biological Applications.—The biological field for research with supersonics is one of the most fascinating, promising, and unexplored in all of sound science. Protozoa, bacteria, and small animals are all affected by the waves, some adversely and some beneficially.

Yeast cells lose their reproductive ability when exposed to supersonic waves; luminous bacteria lose their luminosity. Still other bacteria, far from being adversely affected, are stimulated to increased activity and virulence.

An attempt to produce sonic-soft-curd vitamin D milk has met with partial success. The milk is pumped in a thin film between two stainless steel circular plates. Behind one of the stainless steel plates is an oscillating electrical magnet of high voltage that sets up a vibration in the diaphragms, resulting in intense waves of energy at the rate of 360 per second. This breaks up and disperses the fat globules to form a product similar to homogenized milk.

The lethal effect of supersonic vibrations depends on the volume of cells being vibrated, the number of organisms per unit of volume, and the shape and the size of the micro-organisms.

Bacilli are more easily killed than cocci, large bacilli are more quickly destroyed than small. A suspension of *Escherichia coli* containing 3,000,000 organisms per ml. was sterilized in 20 minutes, while 45,000,000 per ml. required 38 minutes.

Large micro-organisms are more susceptible to lower frequencies of sound and ultrasonic frequencies. Beckwith and Weaver (1936) concluded that in a grape juice suspension *Saccharomyces ellipsoideus*, a wine yeast, was killed promptly by supersonic treatment. They observed that a strain of bacteriophage was not inactivated by supersonic effect. Moreover, the presence of protein in solution blocks the germicidal activity of supersonic treatment. The supersonic treatment of milk is less efficient bactericidally when small amounts of protein are added.

Supersonic vibrations of 300,000 to 1,000,000 cycles per second reduced a viable culture of *Escherichia coli* from 70,000,000 to 20,000 per ml.

Vibrations Create Great Pressure

It may be explained that the transfer of supersonic energy from a vibrating crystal is somewhat like that of a boxer striking a punching bag. As the frequency of his punches becomes more and more rapid, the bag strikes the board more quickly and the speed of the bag becomes greater and greater—until finally the bag seems to be motionless and the "pressure" against the board seems to be constant.

Small gas bubbles under the action of alternating sound pressure undergo local mechanical stress which may rise to 15,000 times the hydrostatic pressure. It is not improbable that the phenomenal effects of supersonic waves are due at least in part to this great concentration of energy. The formation of H_2O_2 is believed to be responsible for many of the chemical changes by a supersonic generator since most of these changes have been noted when the solutions are saturated with oxygen or air, and small gas bubbles form.

It is believed that the motion of the gas bubbles causes oxygen molecules to be ionized at the comparatively large boundary between liquid and gas, perhaps by the action of electric charges. The oxygen atoms thus liberated are then absorbed by the water with formation of hydrogen peroxide. Dissolved nitrogen has been found to react similarly.

Underlying Principle Involved in the Operation of Ultrasonic Waves

The ultrasonic waves are usually produced by the means of a piezo-electric oscillator. It was invented by a French physicist named Langevin and consists of a mosaic made up of quartz crystals held between two plates. It is based on the fact that quartz has the property of piezo-electricity. This simply means that it is capable of creating an electrical impulse or potential when pressed or squeezed; or vice versa, of vibrating (creating a changing pressure) when subjected to an alternating current. The crystal possesses a natural frequency that is determined by its elasticity and density.

Table 28 shows the bactericidal efficiency of ultrasonic treatment under various conditions.

TABLE 28

EFFECTS OF ULTRASONIC VIBRATION ON BACTERIAL COUNTS IN MILK[1]

Expt. No.	No. of Organisms Before Treatment	Time of Treatment, Min.	After Treatment	Efficiency
1	1,390,000	5.0	26,000	98.9
2	26,200,000	15.0	21,000,000	19.8
3	2,200	8.5	50	97.7
4	60,000	10.0	7,000	88.3
5	3,500,000	10.0	1,040,000	70.3
6	14,500	6.0	5,800	60.0

[1] From Beckwith and Weaver (1936).

It has been claimed that these waves may be beamed from the oscillator and that the beam may be confined within a relatively small angle and so can be made directional. Thus the supersonic waves can be controlled much better than ordinary sound waves.

The Use of Electrons to Preserve Foods

An "Electron Gun" has been used to sterilize fresh meats and vegetables. There was no apparent change in the natural flavor of the food product even after four years of storage in sealed containers. The so-called gun fires electrons which are negatively charged particles. The bombardment of the food molecules by the electrons occurs within a millionth of a second. The apparatus is called a Capacitron. According to Huber and Brasch (1946), the process may have wide application in the preservation of many kinds of foods.

BIBLIOGRAPHY

Beckwith, T. D., and Weaver, C. E.   1936.   Sonic energy as a lethal agent for yeast and bacteria. J. Bacteriol. *32*, 361–373.

Brown, W. L., Vinton, C., and Gross, C. E.   1960.   Radiation resistance of the natural bacterial flora of cured ham. Food Technol. *14*, 622–625.

Cathcart, W. H., Ryberg, R. E., and Merz, A.   1942.   Staphylococcal and Salmonella control in foods. Food Research *7*, 1–9.

Desrosier, N. W., and Rosenstock, H. M.   1960.   Radiation Technology in Food, Agriculture, and Biology. Avi Publ. Co., Westport, Conn.

Harris, R. S., Bunker, J. W. M., and Milas, N. A.   1932.   The germicidal activity of vapors from irradiated oils. J Bacteriol. *23*, 429–435.

Huber, W., and Brasch, A.   1946.   The Use of Electrons in Food Preservation. Electronized Chemicals Corp., Brooklyn, N. Y.

Larson, B. L.   1960.   Significance of strontium in milk. J. Dairy Sci. *43*, 1–21.

Proctor, B. E.   1952.   Cathode rays and the food industry. Certified Milk *27*, 15–16.

Proctor, B. E., and Goldblith, S. A.   1951.   Electromagnetic radiation fundamentals and their application in food technology. Advances in Food Research *3*, 157–167.

Robinson, H. E., and Urbain, W. M.   1959.   Radiation preservation of foods. J. Am. Med. Assoc. *174*, 1310–1311.

Ross, A. T.   1932.   Bactericidal property of ultraviolet irradiated petrolatum-lanolin mixture. Proc. Exp. Biol. and Med. *29*, 1265.

Supplee, A. R.   1930.   The effect of ultraviolet radiation on market milk. J. Milk Technol. *16*, 251.

Wishnetsky, T., Livingston, G. E., Francis, F. J., and Fagerson, I. S.   1959.   Effect of gamma ray irradiation on color and chlorophyll retention in green beans and broccoli. Food Technol. *13*, 352–357.

CHAPTER 18

Antibiotics in The Food Industry

THE NATURE OF THE ANTIBIOTICS

Dunn (1953) and Nickerson (1963) reported that the use of antibiotics has been greatly extended. An antibiotic is a chemical substance produced by micro-organisms which has the capacity of inhibiting growth or destroying other kinds of micro-organisms. Numerous antibiotics have been isolated, and some have been crystallized and chemically defined and others have been chemically modified.

Their use and application in medicine is well known in controlling certain "disease producing" organisms in the body. However, many antibiotics are limited in their use because of their toxicity to animals, or because of the possibility that residues will remain in food after cooking.

A significant characteristic of the antibiotics is their relative selective action against specific bacteria. According to Waksman (1946) tyrothricin and pencillin are effective against many gram-positive bacteria but they have little effect upon selected gram-negative organisms. Streptomycin is equally effective against many gram-positive and gram-negative bacteria. Obviously, these three antibiotics differ in their chemical properties and their antibacterial activities.

Tyrothricin is produced by *Bacillus brevis,* a spore-forming aerobic bacillus. This substance is a polypeptide and is soluble in water. Selected strains of the mold, *Penicillium notatum* are used in the production of penicillin. It is a ring compound, containing nitrogen and sulfur. Five or more different penicillins have been isolated and each varies in chemical structure and antibacterial potency. Some are now modified chemically to extend their activity spectrum. *Streptomyces griseus,* a member of the higher bacteria, produces a compound known as streptomycin. Apparently this substance is a glucoside containing a guanidine-like group and a nitrogenous carbohydrate base. In animals, penicillin is the least toxic of the three while tyrothricin is the most toxic.

In the production of antibiotics, various agricultural by-products are used. These products supply a culture medium favorable for the growth of the organisms. Corn steep liquor and lactose are used in the production of penicillin, and casein is used for streptomycin. Perhaps many other agricultural products will be used in the future.

Biochemists have been quite successful in synthesizing or rearranging the structural formulas of some of the antibiotics. A few antibiotics have been limited in their use because of their extreme toxic properties. Now the toxicity may be modified by removing the toxic radical or substituting another, thus reducing the toxicity of the antibiotic but still retaining its effectiveness in controlling the growth of selected micro-organisms.

Use of Antibiotics in Fruits and Vegetables

Andersen and Michener (1950) propose the use of subtilin, an antibiotic obtained from certain strains of *Bacillus subtilis,* to facilitate preservation of asparagus, corn, and peas. Subtilin is most effective against gram-positive and spore-forming organisms. It has very little antibiotic effect against gram-negative bacteria. Moreover, this antibiotic has the remarkable characteristic of being heat stable. Its use to supplement a mild heat treatment of food would be most desirable since application of extensive heat in preserving food may cause changes in the appearance, and the chemical and physical characteristics of the food.

These investigators state that *Bacillus stearothermophilus,* the organism responsible for flat sour spoilage in the canning industry, can be inhibited in nutrient dextrose broth by adding 0.004 p.p.m. of subtilin. The addition of 0.5 p.p.m. of subtilin to brain heart infusion broth containing *Clostridium botulinum* (62A) spores and heated for 5 minutes at 212°F (100°C) inhibited the growth of these organisms after 7 months' incubation.

More experimental data is necessary in order to establish firmly the efficacy of subtilin in the preservation of foods.

Shiveler and Weiser (1951) were able to preserve peas, green beans, and tomatoes by using a mild heat treatment and varying concentrations of subtilin. A pure culture of *Bacillus stearothermophilus* was added directly to the product prior to the treatment.

Results Obtained on Peas and Tomatoes.—All of the control samples (those heated but receiving no subtilin) spoiled within one week as indicated by an increase in the thermophilic count and a change in the pH to approximately 5.0. Spoilage by the test organism was not prevented in the cans in which 5 p.p.m. of subtilin was added, although the various samples showed less change than the control series. The pH of these samples ranged from 5.2 to 5.8. A slight turbidity of the brine was evident although the appearance and odor of the samples were only slightly altered.

All the cans containing 10 and 20 p.p.m. subtilin were free of the test organisms and there was no noticeable change in the pH as compared with the controls.

The beans inoculated with *Bacillus stearothermophilus* and containing no subtilin showed evidence of flat-sour spoilage within 3 days.   A marked increase in the bacterial count of the test organism occurred and a change in pH ranging from 5.0 to 5.3.   All the cans that were inoculated with the test culture containing 5, 10, and 20 p.p.m. of subtilin showed no evidence of spoilage and no apparent change in pH.   In fact, all the cans were sterile regardless of the concentration of subtilin used.

All of the tomato samples which were inoculated with *Bacillus thermoacidurans* but received no subtilin appeared to have about the same counts as the control samples.   After 3 months' incubation no viable test organisms could be demonstrated.   There was no noticeable change in the pH values between the control samples and the inoculated series with different concentrations of subtilin added.

Campbell et al. (1959) have shown that subtilin and nisin effectively reduce the thermal process requirements necessary to control the spoilage of several food products inoculated with spores of food spoilage bacteria.

The freshness of leafy vegetables may also be prolonged slightly by antibiotic treatment.

Antibiotics in Feeds and Foods

The role of antibiotics used in the medical field as a therapeutic agent has been widely recognized.   Antibiotics in the food industry have been used in the following ways.

1.   The incorporation of low levels of antibiotics into feed supplements, especially poultry feed, has been a common practice by feed manufacturers.   Somehow the presence of antibiotics influences the physiology of the birds so that they utilize the feed more efficiently and this results in more rapid growth.   This idea is now being used in other feed supplements for feeding hogs.

2.   The use of antibiotics to control mastitis in dairy cows has been a remarkable success.   The dosage is on a therapeutic level and is infused into the teat canal in order to destroy the organisms responsible for mastitis.

Unfortunately, a residue of the antibiotic is built up in the udder of the cow and eventually is eliminated into the milk supply.   Therefore, the human being consuming the milk may inadvertently acquire the antibiotic.   This can be a serious public health problem from the standpoint of developing pathogens resistant to therapeutic doses of antibiotics.

3. Antibiotics have been used successfully to delay food spoilage. However, it is illegal to add antibiotics to food used for human consumption, at levels high enough to prevent food spoilage.

According to Sir Alexander Fleming, the discoverer of penicillin, ". . . there may be more antibiotics used for the feeding of animals than for medicinal purposes." However, the question still remains in the feeding of antibiotics to meat animals whether resistant strains of pathogenic bacteria may be passed on to man.

Therein lies one of the major problems. The mechanism by which the antibiotics affect growth is not yet understood, but it has been shown that in fowl fed antibiotics, there is a rapid development of resistant staphylococcus organisms potentially harmful to man.

Another danger is that the feeding of antibiotics may encourage the growth of yeast-like organisms in the livestock, and if these are passed on to man they are likely to be quite troublesome, inasmuch as the existing antibiotics are relatively ineffective against fungus organisms.

A third potentially dangerous effect is concerned with the still unanswered question as to whether the antibiotics in the feed might accumulate in the flesh of the animals. If there is such accumulation, the continued ingestion of the meat from such animals would sensitize some persons so that subsequent use of the antibiotics might cause severe allergic reactions.

The Use of Antibiotics in the Preservation of Fish and Meat

Antibiotics were used first on fish by Tarr and only later applied to flesh foods. A limited amount of work has been done on the effect of certain antibiotics on flesh food. Goldberg, Weiser, and Deatherage (1953) have selected beef as an ideal food to test the success of antibiotics in food preservation. Beef has a relatively high spoilage rate where proper refrigeration is lacking; since it is a highly suitable medium for microbial growth, the efficacy of the antibiotics·could be determined accurately. Jensen (1949, 1954) reported the isolation of antibacterial substances from plants. He added them to brine in which the meat was being cured. The results of this study were encouraging. Goldberg, Weiser, and Deatherage (1953) tested six antibiotics for their preserving action in fresh ground beef. Penicillin, streptomycin, bacitracin, chloromycetin, terramycin, and aureomycin were selected. Chloromycetin, terramycin and aureomycin successfully lengthened the keeping quality of the beef and also showed a higher activity against pure cultures of microflora isolated from deep tissues of beef.

The disc assay technique showed that aureomycin could not be detected after 72 hours. It would appear that the antibiotic begins to disappear within 24 hours and after 72 hours is no longer detectable. This suggests that the action of the antibiotic may be bacteriostatic, and when it disappears the organisms begin to grow and ultimately a delayed spoilage occurs.

Lepovetsky, Deatherage, and Weiser (1953) reported on the examination of lymph nodes, bone marrow, and muscle tissues from chicks and rounds of beef. Most of the organisms were found in the lymph nodes, as might be expected, since these tissues serve a phagocytic

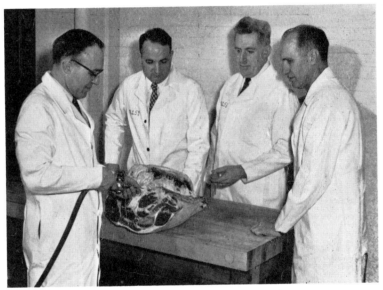

FIG. 28.   INFUSION OF BEEF ROUND WITH ANTIBIOTIC

function. This finding seemed to confirm observations on "sour"[1] rounds where deep spoilage often appears to propagate from lymph nodes. Since lymph nodes have excellent blood supplies, it seemed that deep spoilage might be controlled by infusing solutions into these tissues (see Figs. 28 and 29). The use of acidic buffers has been tried as a method for retarding bacterial growth because several investigators have reported slower bacterial growth in muscle tissue than in tissues with a higher pH (lymph nodes, bone marrow, fat, and connective tissue).

However, Husaini (1950) infusing calves with pH 4.7 lactate buf-

---

[1] The term "sour" is applied to meat infected with streptococci and certain gramnegative bacteria that attack the protein causing unpleasant acid odors.

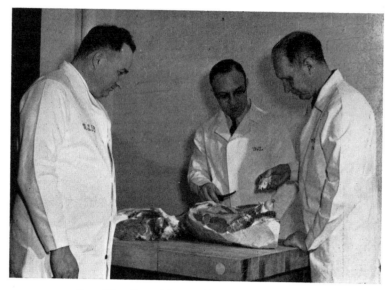

FIG. 29.   BEEF ROUND SHOWS NO SPOILAGE

The same beef round, infused with antibiotic as shown in Fig. 28, and stored at 80° F, shows no spoilage after 72 hours.

fers, encountered some problems which indicated that other types of infusates might be desirable.   For this work antibiotics might be used, since they are effective in small amounts and would impart little or no flavor to the meat.

Goldberg, Weiser, and Deatherage (1953) added 0.0, 0.5, 1.0, 1.5, and 2.0 p.p.m. respectively of penicillin, bacitracin, streptomycin, chloromycetin, aureomycin, and terramycin to ground beef and stored the samples at 40°F (4.4°C).   The last three antibiotics definitely delayed spoilage of the beef.   This work confirmed completely the work of Tarr (1952).   In order to select the most effective antibiotic, Lepovetsky et al. (1953) screened aureomycin, terramycin, and chloromycetin against 93 strains of organisms from 492 isolates from meat.   These organisms represented 12 genera.   Aureomycin inhibited growth in 81 strains, terramycin in 77, and chloromycetin in 74.   Nine strains were unaffected by all three antibiotics.   Aureomycin was finally selected for the exploratory work on processing fresh meat by infusion.

A solution of 55 p.p.m. of aureomycin in physiological saline was prepared.   A Griffith curing pump was used for the infusion.

Following the infusion both control and infused rounds were refrigerated at 37° to 38°F (2.7° to 3.3°C) for 48 hours.   No color or flavor changes were noted. All the infused rounds were in excellent shape. Seven out of ten control rounds showed some evidence of spoilage. The bacterial counts on the infused rounds were as follows: (organisms per gram), popiteal lymph nodes 300 to 130,000; top rounds 800 to 26,000; and knuckle 4,200 to 61,000. The corresponding controls ranged from 10,000 to 21,000,000; 12,000 to 12,000,000; 20,000 to 12,000,000.

In order to rule out the possibility that infusion *per se* was causing the lowered counts, several rounds were infused with saline only. No differences were noted between the bacterial populations of the saline infused and control rounds.

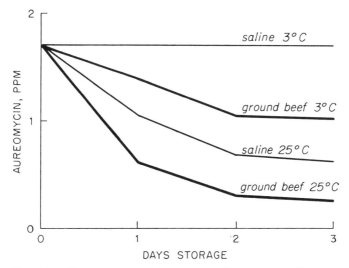

FIG. 30. DECREASE OF AUREOMYCIN CONTENT OF GROUND BEEF ON STORAGE

The relative rates of disappearance of aureomycin from physiological saline and ground beef at the same pH, at 3° and 25°C.

Whole beef animals, ranging from 700 to 1,250 lbs. were infused. The animals were killed and carotid arteries were partially severed to prevent retraction, and the jugular veins were cut completely.

After infusion the animals were dressed in the usual manner. One side was placed in the cooler and the other was held at room temperature 68° to 69°F (20° to 20.6°C) for 48 hours before refrigeration. At 120 hours post mortem, the sides were cut down and examined for general appearance, flavor, tenderness, bacterial populations, and residual antibiotics.

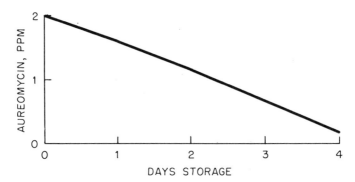

FIG. 31.   AVERAGE AUREOMYCIN CONTENT OF
GROUND BEEF ON STORAGE

Eleven samples held at 10°C for four days.   When ground,
2 ppm aureomycin was added to each sample.

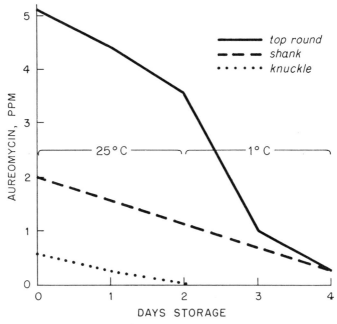

FIG. 32.   DISTRIBUTION OF AUREOMYCIN IN
BEEF ROUND ON STORAGE

The rounds were held at room temperature (25 °C) for 48 hours
and then placed in refrigeration at 1 °C.

Figure 30 shows the relative rates of destruction of the aureomycin
in saline and in ground beef at the same pH and at 38 °F (3.3 °C) and
at 77 °F (25 °C).   The antibiotic was less stable in the meat than in the

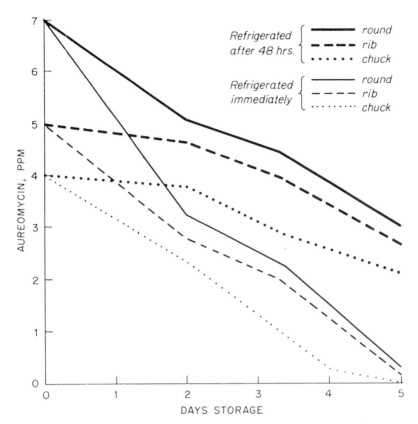

FIG. 33. DISTRIBUTION OF AUREOMYCIN IN INFUSED WHOLE ANIMALS

The upper curve (heavier) of each pair represents the aureomycin content of the side held at room temperature 48 hours and then refrigerated.

saline. For 11 samples of ground beef initially containing 2 p.p.m. aureomycin, the decrease in the antibiotic at 50°F (10°C) storage is shown in Fig. 31.

The distribution of the antibiotic in the infused rounds is shown in Fig. 32. This is the average of ten rounds and the individual variations from the curves were insignificant. The amount of aureomycin in the different parts of the rounds reflects the blood supply to these parts. Whereas the top rounds averaged about 5.1 p.p.m., the knuckle contained only 0.5 p.p.m. These rounds were kept at 77°F (25°C) for 48 hours after slaughter and then placed in a cooler at 34°F (1.1°C). No aureomycin was present after 4 days.

Similar data on six infused whole animals appear in Fig. 33. The rounds received more antibiotic than the rib or chuck. One side was held at room temperature for 48 hours and then moved to the cooler, whereas the control side was placed in the cooler from slaughter. The upper three curves when compared with the lower three show the effect of retarded refrigeration on the disappearance of the antibiotic. From the data on the rounds, it may be presumed that no antibiotic remained in the meat after 4 days when refrigeration was delayed. Yet, in the refrigerated sides some antibiotic was present after 5 days.

These data indicate that if this meat had gone through customary commercial channels little or no aureomycin would have remained in the meat when it reached the dinner table. Even if freshly treated raw ribs were eaten, approximately three-fourths pound of lean meat would give only $^1/_{1,000}$ of the minimum recommended daily therapeutic dose for a 70-kg. man. This amount is far below pharmacological interest. It must be kept in mind, however, that the aureomycin was determined by biological assay and this does not tell precisely what happened to the antibiotic in terms of its decomposition products nor of their toxicity. Since these decomposition products were ineffective in retarding the growth of the test organism, it is quite probable that they are ineffective in the life processes of higher animals, particularly in the amounts which were present.

During these investigations the question arose concerning whether antibiotics modified the general flora in meat. This is a difficult question to answer, yet some information was obtained. Earlier work of Goldberg *et al.* (1953) indicated that chloromycetin might modify the kinds of organisms in meat. An experiment was set up whereby the relative numbers of gram-positive cocci, gram-positive rods, and gram-negative rods were determined in ground beef and in the same food treated with 2 p.p.m. penicillin, chloromycetin, and aureomycin. No gram-negative cocci were found in the beef. The experiment was done in triplicate holding all samples at 50°F (10°C). It is worthy of note that in untreated beef the general microflora showed only gram-negative rods. Penicillin which inhibits gram-positive cocci tends to promote this condition. With chloromycetin and aureomycin the relative numbers of gram-negative rods decreased during the earlier part of the storage period and the absolute numbers of organisms were far less in these samples than in the control. The aureomycin-treated samples tended to develop a gram-negative flora more quickly than the samples treated with chloromycetin. This is what might be expected since aureomycin would be dissipated after about 3 days at 50°F (10°C) (Fig. 30). Difco discs were used to determine the sensitivity of the organisms remaining in the meat at various intervals of time to the various antibiotics. The bacteria in the chloromycetin and aureomycin-treated meat were all sensitive to the respective antibiotics. Resistant organisms did not appear to develop in the meat. This finding might be due to the bacteriostatic nature of the antibiotics, the instability of the antibiotics, or the fact that the amount of antibiotics used to delay spoilage in ground beef was insufficient to stop development of all sensitive bacteria and to permit rapid development of truly resistant organisms. In the case of penicillin-treated meat, the general flora were not sensitive to penicillin, since it is generally ineffective in retarding meat spoilage.

The study on ground beef suggested that aureomycin might be effective in retarding spoilage in fresh pork sausage which has a somewhat shorter shelf life than ground beef. Samples of fresh pork sausage were taken from one of the largest markets in Columbus. Samples were purchased as the sausage was made available to the public. Cased sausage showed 1,500,000 organisms whereas freshly made bulk sausage contained 25,000,000 organisms per gram. One may draw his own conclusions from this comparison. Certainly antibiotics would have no place in the freshly made bulk sausage as sampled. However, to determine if aureomycin might retard spoilage, duplicate experiments were conducted using good, fresh pork trimmings as starting material and incorporating two p.p.m. aureomycin in the finished product. Both heated and unheated spices were used. Aureomycin lowered the count in all.

The work discussed here is exploratory in nature. It points to two possibilities: first, antibiotics may be used in meat processing, and second, whole animals may be processed by infusion prior to dressing out. Results obtained offer an explanation for deep spoilage in meat and offer some information on some of the quality attributes of meat such as color and tenderness.

Tarr (1952) has studied a number of antibiotics with reference to flesh food preservation. Subtilin, circulin, polymixin B, neomycin, gramicidin, bacitracin, tyrothrycin, penicillin, streptomycin, rimocidin, terramycin, aureomycin, and chloromycetin were investigated. The last three antibiotics have proved effective as bacteriostats for fish and meat at 32° to 38°F (0° to 3.3°C) and for fish at 68°F (20°C). Aureomycin had the most pronounced bacteriostatic action and was effective in 1 to 2 p.p.m. concentrations. Bacterial spoilage of fish fillets immersed in an aureomycin solution containing 10 mg./ml. was studied. The treated samples were stored for several days at 32° to 38°F (0° to 3.3°C) with no noticeable bacterial spoilage although molds and yeasts were not inhibited, but they were eliminated by rimocidin at 10 mg./gm. level.

Aureomycin is not heat stable, therefore the usual cooking temperature may destroy this antibiotic.

Effects of Antibiotics and Drugs on the Microflora and Enzymes of Milk and Milk Products

Antibiotics and sulfa drugs commonly used as effective therapeutic agents against bovine mastitis are reported to appear in the milk from treated cows. While the antibiotics have been shown to impede lactic acid fermentation desired in the manufacture of cheese and cultured dairy products, certain of these antibiotics have shown promise as preservatives in the dairy industry. Although these antibiotics are known to occur in milk, they have not been studied adequately with respect to their effect on the naturally occurring microflora and enzymes in milk, and also with respect to their stability in milk as affected by processing and aging.

Shahani, Gould, Weiser, and Slatter (1956) observed that when milk containing 0.13 to 0.53 units penicillin per ml. was pasteurized at 143°F (61.6°C) for 30 minutes, 0.0 to 18.2 per cent with an average of 8.2 per cent penicillin was inactivated. Four to 16.0 per cent with an average of 10.1 per cent penicillin potency was lost when milk was pasteurized at 160°F (71.1°C) for 30 minutes, whereas, when milk was autoclaved at 15 lbs. for 15 minutes, 45.5 to 69.0 per cent with an average of 59.7 per cent penicillin was inactivated.

Storage of the milk samples for 7 days at 36° to 41°F (2.2° to 5°C) showed 34.8 per cent loss of potency in milk pasteurized at 143°F (61.6°C) for 30 minutes; 20.6 per cent inactivation occurred when the milk was pasteurized at 160°F (71.1°C), and 9.9 per cent loss of potency when the samples were autoclaved.

Likewise, when raw milk containing 0.13 to 0.53 unit of penicillin per ml. was stored at 36° to 41°F (2.2° to 5°C), an average of 46.6 per cent penicillin potency was lost during 6 days.

These authors concluded that when penicillin was added to raw and pasteurized milks and both samples stored in a refrigerator, the quality of the raw milk was not acceptable within 10 days, whereas the pasteurized milk developed a rancid flavor after 17 to 30 days. Obviously penicillin in combination with regular pasteurization did not appreciably increase the keeping quality of the milk.

Studies on streptomycin were comparable to the results obtained with penicillin under similar conditions. Approximately 14 per cent streptomycin was lost from the milk when pasteurized at 143°F (61.6°C) for 30 minutes. At 160°F (71.1°C) 22.8 per cent disappeared and at 167°F (75°C) within 15 minutes 20.6 per cent loss of potency. However, when the milk was autoclaved at 15 lbs. for 15 minutes no trace of streptomycin could be detected.

Similarly, the storage of raw milk containing streptomycin showed an average of 18.0, 27.4, and 35.1 per cent inactivation during the first, second, and third week respectively.

These authors concluded that in milk, streptomycin was comparatively more heat-labile than penicillin, when subjected to various heat treatments. However, during the same period of storage of raw and processed samples, streptomycin was inactivated to an appreciably less extent than penicillin.

Inhibitory Substances in Milk.—Several antibiotic agents may be found in milk. They are sanitizers, antibiotics, and bacteriophages all of which, in certain concentrations, tend to cause lowered plate counts and retard lactic acid development. However, none of these agents are satisfactory as milk preservatives, and none are effective against all types of organisms.

To avoid starter difficulties due to bacteriophage action, one should follow recommended practices for the handling of starters.

Probably the best way to avoid the accidental entry of objectionable levels of antibiotics in milk is to properly inform the dairy producer and insist he comply with the accepted recommendation of the Committee on Antibiotics of the Federal Food and Drug Administration.

There is no doubt about the success of antibiotics in treatment of mastitis, but such agents should not be used unless they are needed.

The harmful effects of antibiotics or other inhibitory substances on human beings has not been determined although it is known that some people show violent and dangerous allergic reactions to certain of them. Until such information is available, milk used for human consumption should be kept as free as is practical of any bacterial growth inhibitors.

Boyd, Weiser, and Winter (1960) have studied the influence of high level antibiotic rations with terephthalic acid on the antibiotic content and keeping quality of poultry meat. They observed that feeding broilers and laying hens high levels (1,000 gm./ton of feed) of chlortetracycline (CTC) and oxytetracycline (OTC) resulted in storage of the antibiotics in the serum, liver and dark and white meat.

Feeding terephthalic acid (TPA) at 0.05 per cent level in the high CTC and OTC rations resulted in a substantial increase of the antibiotics in the tissues.

Feeding a low calcium ration during the time of use of high level CTC or OTC with TPA resulted in much greater storage in the tissues.

High level CTC feeding with TPA resulted in a longer keeping time for eviscerated chickens held at 96°F (35.5°C).

Frye, Weiser, and Winter (1958) fed 1000 p.p.m. of chlortetracycline, oxytetracycline, penicillin, bacitracin, and streptomycin respectively to groups of laying hens. Chlortetracycline was the only one of the five antibiotics studied that could be detected in the eggs from the hens fed antibiotics.

The addition of antibiotic to liquid eggs at higher levels (5 p.p.m.) than that found in eggs from hens fed antibiotic did not prolong the keeping time appreciably.

The liver, dark meat, and light meat from chlortetracycline, oxytetracycline, and bacitracin fed hens contained detectable amounts of the antibiotics. It was highest in the liver and lowest in the white meat. Cooking destroyed the antibiotic.

Suggested Mode of Action of Antibiotics

Jay, Weiser, and Deatherage (1957) studied the mode of action of chlortetracycline in the preservation of beef. Both organic and inorganic compounds were tested for their ability to reverse the (CTC) inhibition of (CTC)-resistant *Proteus sp.* in beef. None of the organic compounds which included B-vitamins, amino acids, purine and pyrimidine bases, and Kreb's cycle intermediates were effective. The following inorganic compounds were effective and are listed in the order of their effectiveness: tungstate, molybdate, magnesium, calcium, borate, silicate, strontium, and barium. The molar ratios of ion to antibiotic ranged from 8:1 for $WO_4^=$ to 1660:1 for Ba^{++} as determined in 0.5 per cent proteose-peptone broth. The molar ratios were much higher in beef. These findings appear to have supported an earlier hypothesis that the effectiveness of (CTC) against chlortetracycline-resistant *Proteus* in beef is due to its ability to compete with the organisms for essential ions.

Antibiotics as Food Additives

The addition of an antibiotic to a food brings to focus the basic questions of additives to foods which come under the jurisdiction of the Food and Drug Administration. When one inspects the retail market's uncooked ground beef and pork products, or at times even packaged cut meat, it is not difficult to see that much improvement is possible in getting quality fresh meat to the consumer. There is no doubt that antibiotics can help do this job. However, one must keep in mind that an antibiotic cannot make tainted meat fresh. It would be effective only in preserving clean and fresh meat. Also, it is necessary to know that the added compound will not be a hazard to the consumer. Obviously, the consumer must be assured that the material added is not acutely toxic on usage over an extended period of time. Second, he must be assured that general usage of antibiotics in foods will not give rise to large numbers of resistant organisms which in turn may be harmful to the individual. These problems require the most thorough study. Fundamental research on the intermediary metabolism of antibiotics and the elucidation of their mode of action could help answer these problems. Micro-organisms and some insects seem to develop resistance to certain toxic compounds and not to others. In this connection, it has been reported that flies develop resistance to D.D.T., yet lose their resistance if grown for several generations without being exposed to it. Is this true in the case of certain antibiotics? An understanding of why these things happen would do much to clear up these two basic considerations confronting the Food and Drug Administration and the public.

Thatcher (1958) summarizes the use of antibiotics in foods as follows:

(a) Must be effective under commercial conditions and storage methods.
(b) Must be stable in foods for certain periods to exercise effective bacteriostasis.
(c) Must have a "broad-spectrum" antibacterial action.
(d) Must be non-toxic within limits of safety.
(e) Must be non-carcinogenic.
(f) Must be non-allergenic.

BIBLIOGRAPHY

Anderson, A. A., and Michener, H. D. 1950. Preservation of foods with antibiotics. 1. The complementary action of subtilin and milk heat. Food Technol. *4*, 188–189.

Bing, F. C. 1950. Chemicals introduced in the processing of foods. Am. J. Public Health *40*, No. 2, 154–156.

Boyd, J., Weiser, H. H., and Winter, A. R. 1960. Influence of high level antibiotic rations with terephthalic acid on the antibiotic content and keeping quality of poultry meat. Poultry Sci. *39*, 1067–1071.

Campbell, L. L. Sniff, E. E. and O'Brien, R. T. 1959. Subtilin and nisin as additives that lower the heat process requirements of canned foods. Food Technol. *13*, 462–464.

Dunn, C. G. 1953. Food Preservatives. *In* Antiseptics, Disinfectants, Fungicides and Chemical and Physical Sterilization, 2nd ed. G. F. Reddish (Editor). Lee and Febiger, Philadelphia.

Frye, G. R., Weiser, H. H., and Winter, A. R. 1958. Influence of antibiotic feeding on the keeping quality and antibiotic content of poultry products. Poultry Sci. *37*, 633– 637.

Goldberg, H. S. 1959. Antibiotics; Their Chemistry and Non-Medical Uses. D. Van Nostrand Co., Princeton, N. J.

Goldberg, H. S., Weiser, H. H., and Deatherage, F. E. 1953. The use of antibiotics in preservation of fresh beef. Food Technol. *7*, 165–166.

Husaini, S. A.   1950.   Biochemical Studies Relating to Quality in Fresh Meat.   Ph.D. Dissertation.   The Ohio State University, Columbus.

Jay, J. M., Weiser, H. H., and Deatherage, F. E.   1957 A.   The Effect of Chlortetracycline on the Microflora of Beef, and Studies on the Mode of Action of This Antibiotic in Meat Preservation.   Antibiotics Annual 954–965.

Jay, J. M., Weiser, H. H., and Deatherage, F. E.   1957 B.   Studies on the mode of action of chlorotetracycline in the preservation of beef.   J. Appl. Microbiol. 5, 400–405.

Jensen, L. B.   1954.   Microbiology of Meats, 3rd ed.   The Garrard Press, Champaign, Ill.

Jensen, L. B.   1949.   Meat and Meat Foods.   The Ronald Press Co., New York.

Lepovetsky, B. C., Deatherage, F. E., and Weiser, H. H.   1953.   A microbiological study of lymph nodes, bone marrow and muscle tissue obtained from slaughtered cattle.   J. Appl. Microbiol. 1, 57–59.

Nickerson, J. T. R.   1963.   Preservatives and antioxidants.   In Food Processing Operations, Vol. 2, M. A. Joslyn, and J. L. Heid (Editors).   Avi Publ. Co., Westport, Conn.

Prescott, S. C., and Dunn, C. G.   1959.   Industrial Microbiology, 3rd ed.   McGraw-Hill Book Co., New York.

Shahani, K. M., Gould, I. A., Weiser, H. H., and Slatter, W. L.   1940.   Effect of selected antibiotics upon some micro-organisms associated with lactic acid fermentation in milk.   J. Dairy Science 1, 465.

Shahani, K. M., Gould, I. A., Weiser, H. H., and Slatter, W. L.   1956.   Observations on antibiotics in a market milk supply and the effect of certain antibiotics on the keeping quality of milk.   Antibiotics and Chemotherapy 6, 544–549.

Shiveler, G. C., and Weiser, H. H.   1951.   The effect of subtilin on the preservation of canned peas, green beans and tomatoes.   Canning Trade J. 26, 65–69.

Tarr, H. L. A.   1952.   Experimental Preservation of Flesh Foods with Antibiotics.   Food Technol. 9, 363.

Thatcher, F. S.   1958.   Antibiotics in Foods.   Can. J. Public Health, 49, 58–72.

Waksman, S. A.   1946.   Antibiotics and Medicine.   The Chemurgic Digest, National Farm Chemurgic Council, Columbus, Ohio.

Weiser, H. H., Goldberg, H. S., Cahill, V. R., Kunkle, L. E., and Deatherage, F. E.   1953.   Observations on fresh meat processed by the infusion of antibiotics.   Food Technol. 7, 495.

Weiser, H. H., Kunkle, L. E., and Deatherage, F. E.   1954.   The use of antibiotics in meat processing.   Appl. Microb. 2, 88.

CHAPTER 19

Food Additives

INTRODUCTION

A large number of food additives are used as preservatives in foods. In many cases additives perform functions other than preservation. For this reason food microbiologists are concerned with them. Acids, alkalies, sugar, salt, spices, and antibiotics are discussed in previous chapters.

Food additives include a wide range of chemicals, nutrients, and other substances. The term is defined under the 1958 amendment to the Federal Food, Drug and Cosmetic Act of 1938 as " . . . any substance the intended use of which results or may be reasonably expected to result, directly or indirectly, in its becoming a component or other-wise affecting the characteristics of any food (including any substance intended for use in producing, manufacturing, packing, processing, preparing, treating, packaging, transporting, or holding food; and including any source of radiation intended for any such use), if such substance is not generally recognized, among experts qualified by scientific training and experience to evaluate its safety, as having been adequately shown through scientific procedures (or, in the case of a substance used in food prior to January 1, 1958, through either scientific procedure or experience based on common use in food) to be safe under the conditions of its intended use."

The term GRAS refers to those food additives *generally recognized as safe* and recognized by qualified experts as safe for their intended use or used in foods prior to January 1, 1958. *Toxicity* is the capacity of a substance to produce injury while the term *hazard* refers to the probability that injury will result from the use of a substance in a proposed quantity and manner.

PROBLEMS ASSOCIATED WITH FOOD ADDITIVE LEGISLATION

One of the main problems involved in food additive legislation is to determine "What is safe" and "What is harmful." The following series of federal laws illustrates the attempt to define and regulate the use of food additives.

The Act of 1890 prevented importation of adulterated food.
The Federal Food and Drug Act passed in 1906 (Pure Food Law) broadly defines adulteration and misbranding and prohibits movement in interstate commerce of adulterated of misbranded food.
The Federal Food, Drug, and Cosmetic Act of 1938 added new provisions to the

1906 law such as defining the term "food," prohibits adulteration, requires truthful labeling and authorized definitions and standards for foods when necessary.

The Miller Pesticide Amendment to the Food, Drug, and Cosmetic Act of 1938 was passed in 1954. It sets up procedures for establishing tolerances for pesticide residues and for certification that the proposed chemical is useful for the purpose claimed.

The 1958 Food Additives Amendment to the Food, Drug, and Cosmetic Act makes it mandatory to show proof of safety before a substance may be added to a food and permits the use in food of substances which are safe for their intended use.

The Color Additive Amendments of 1960 brought together the regulation of all food colors under one regulation. The Food and Drug Administration must list the particular color as "harmless and suitable for use."

Other regulations are covered under the Federal Meat Inspection Act, The Imported Meat Act, The Poultry Products Inspection Act, and several other acts.

Many states, counties and municipalities also have laws governing the amounts and types of additives which can be used in foods and their conditions of use. With a few exceptions unless foods are transported across state lines they are not subject to federal laws. State and local laws vary greatly from state to state. There is a growing trend to adopt or revise state and local laws patterned after the federal laws.

Safety

The statement attributed to Dr. Miller, author of the Miller pesticide amendment illustrates the problem of evaluating the safety of an additive. He stated that "There are no harmless substances; there are only harmless ways of using substances." Toxicity depends on the level and frequency of use by the consumer. It can be immediate or acute such as in the use of silver, bismuth, cadmium, fluorine, mercury, lead, arsenic, antimony, barium, bromine, selenium, tellurium, molybdenum, vanadium, and thallium depending on the level of ingestion, or long range in the case where the effect is cumulative. Examples of long-range toxicity occur in lead and arsenic poisoning and from radioactive substances.

Effects of different additives vary with different segments of the population. The detoxification mechanisms of infants are not as well developed as those of adults; consequently they cannot stand as large an amount of some additives, for example, fluorine. Individuals suffering from various diseases may require limited intakes of certain common additives, such as sugar or salt. Excessive vitamin intake can also cause illness (hypervitaminosis). Vitamins A, D, and folic acid can be hazardous above certain levels.

Different combinations of nutrients and additives can be harmful. Phosphates, oxalates, and phytates react with calcium to form insoluble calcium salts. As a result, the calcium cannot be absorbed and utilized in the body. Mineral oil also inactivates nutrients needed in the diet.

In some cases additives may not be harmful, but they mask the true appearance of a product or give the appearance of high-quality ingredients which are not always present in the amounts indicated by the color of the product. Eggs give mayonnaise a desirable yellow color in proportion to the color of the yolks and the amounts used. Any other coloring material is illegal. Certified food colors are used in margarine to give it a yellow color to resemble butter.

Illegal Food Additives

Mineral oil is used to some extent as a mild cathartic but its use in food is sporadic. It has been used in salad oils, dressings, and in mayonnaise as a substitute for fats. Its use in foods is illegal. Although it is not absorbed from the digestive tract, its presence in foods causes the excretion from the body of excessive amounts of some of the fat-soluble vitamins which are soluble in mineral oil.

Saccharin, a substitute for sugar, has been used in soft drink beverages and other foods. Fluorides, used as preservatives, have been found in beer. The quaternary ammonium compounds have been found in a few foods either as contaminants left over from the sanitizing equipment or it may have been added as a preservative. They pose a particular problem in the dairy industry where these compounds are used to sanitize milk equipment on the farm.

The conditions of use also determine whether a particular chemical is legal or not. Ascorbic acid is a desirable vitamin supplement and antioxidant, but its use is prohibited in fresh meat because it also masks deterioration of the meat. Sulfites and red dyes are prohibited from use in meat for the same reason.

Nitrogen trichloride is a gas which at one time was used for bleaching and maturing flour. Experiments showed it could cause severe nervous disorders in animals. As a result, its use was prohibited August 7, 1949.

Boric acid or sodium salt borax was used frequently in bacon and margarine as a food preservative until its use was prohibited.

Other Chemical Compounds That Are Probably Deleterious in Foods

Parahydroxybenzoic acid has been used as a food preservative in place of benzoic acid. Dilute nitric acid is another compound which, when added to ordinary flour with the addition of a little soya flour and lecithin, conveys a deep yellow color similar to that produced by egg yolks. A bun or sweet roll made from such flour appears to have more consumer appeal. The effect on human metabolism of consuming nitric acid treated flour is unknown.

Emulsifying Agents in Bread and Other Foods

Certain surface active agents are called "bread softeners." Polyoxyethylene monostearate when added to the flour at the rate of 0.5 lb. to each 100 lbs. of flour precipitates the amylose fraction of the wheat starch leaving an excess of the amylopectin fraction in the bread which makes the bread soft when removed from the oven. It has been observed that such bread will go stale as rapidly as bread which does not contain the softener. The so-called emulsifiers are used to some extent in commercial cake baking, cake mixes, salad dressings, mayonnaise, and ice cream. They were used primarily as a substitute for eggs during a period when they were scarce. The egg yolk contains lecithin which is a good emulsifying agent and is soluble in fats and water. Moreover, eggs have a high nutritive value in any food. The question arises, should the newer or synthetic emulsifying agents adding no food value be permitted as a substitute for eggs? The question of possible harmful or deleterious effects of some of these substances must be considered. At the present, we do not know what the long-term results may be on the digestive system of the human being.

Synthetic Flavors

The use of synthetic flavors in foods is another area about which very little is known concerning the harmful effects upon the human being. Diacetyl is an organic compound which has the fine delicate flavor of butter and for this reason it has been added directly to butter. However, this flavoring agent is being largely replaced by starter distillate. This substance is prepared by steam distilling a good active butter culture starter, the diacetyl thus formed is a stabilized substance and then is added to the butter in the vat.

Non-intentional additives included in this category are: (1) pesticides, including insecticides, fungicides, and rodenticides; (2) plant growth regulators or hormones, such as stilbesterol used in poultry, defoliants, herbicides, and sprout inhibitors; (3) animal growth promoters include antibiotics, organic arsenicals and estrogenic substances; (4) veterinary drugs include coccidiostats, antibiotics, tranquilizers, and parasiticides; and (5) pieces of packaging materials including metals, plastics, paper, fabric, rubber, wood, and certain agents used to impart physical properties to the food such as pigments, adhesives, and lacquers used on wrappers.

During the past decade many new chemical components have by various methods been added to our foods. It is important to identify these compounds and to determine what physiological changes may be induced by continual lifetime ingestion. The wholesomeness of our food supply depends on more complete knowledge of these substances.

Radioactive Fallout

Recently the term radioactive fallout resulting from nuclear explosions has become a major concern for all forms of life. Radioactive particles produced by a hydrogen bomb may give off destructive rays injurious to health. This may be by blast heat, initial radiation, or residual radiation. The latter may have a delayed effect and usually covers a large area. When a bomb explodes close to the earth, soil and rock are drawn into the cloud. It is mixed with radioactive material and eventually drifts down to earth over a wide area.

Fallout may harm human beings, animals, and crops. It can also contaminate food, water, buildings, and fields. Some rays may penetrate the body causing burns on the skin. Radioactive strontium and iodine are extremely dangerous. Radioactive strontium, chemically like calcium, enters the bones and may cause cancer. It has a half-life of 28 years, while radioactive iodine has a half-life of 8 days. The latter may cause cancer of the thyroid gland. Larson (1960) reported that individuals who consume large amounts of milk are less likely to accumulate large levels of ^{90}Sr in their bones than non-milk consumers because the high calcium level in the milk reduces the absorption of ^{90}Sr in the body.

Antibiotics

Until recently the U.S. Food and Drug Administration permitted chlortetracycline and oxytetracycline to be added to the water in which poultry was chilled to extend shelf life. Although results in the laboratory were good and shelf life was extended several days as a result of the antibiotic inhibiting the growth of micro-organisms, these same benefits were not able to be duplicated in commercial production. There was also concern that resistant strains of micro-organisms might develop. As a result of these problems, the costs of using antibiotics were not justified by the slight increase in shelf life.

The antibiotic nisin produced by certain strains of *Streptococcus lactis* appears to offer some promise as a bactericidal agent in selected food products. More information must be made available before the potential use of this antibiotic can be evaluated. There appears to be no health hazard in the use of nisin in cheeses, nor canned fruit provided the pH of the product is below 4.5. Olives treated with nisin may not be free of botulinum toxin nor can certain meat products such as ham and sausages be assured freedom from *Salmonella* poisoning.

CLASSIFICATION OF FOOD ADDITIVES

Food additives can be broadly classified according to their functional properties in food. A general classification is as follows:

Nutritive Additives

Some examples are vitamins added to milk, both natural and synthetic, mineral salts added to produce fortified skim milk and the addition of certain amino acids. Vitamin enrichment of flour is a common practice; in fact, in some states it is required by law. Considerable progress is being made in developing nutritionally balanced vegetable rations with the addition of food additives for use in under-developed countries.

Iodine, in the form of potassium iodide, is added to table salt for nutritional reasons. However, traces of thiosulfate are usually added to stabilize the iodine content of the salt so that it will not be greatly reduced in storage.

Acids, Alkalies, Buffers, Neutralizing Agents

Some examples are chemical leavening agents which are used to produce carbon dioxide in doughs to produce baked goods of good quality and texture. Acids such as potassium acid tartrate, sodium aluminum phosphate, tartaric acid, monocalcium phosphate, and sodium acid pyrophosphate react with sodium bicarbonate, ammonium carbonate or bicarbonate in the presence of heat and moisture to form carbon dioxide.

Monocalcium phosphate added to flour will compensate for possible excessive use of baking soda in the preparation of sour milk biscuits. Calcium monophosphate is a common acidifying salt in self-rising flour and prepared pancake mixes while tricalcium phosphate serves to inhibit "caking" in powdered sugar. Molds in flour and in bread may be successfully controlled by the use of calcium or sodium propionate. Moreover, calcium salts are used as firming agents in the production of canned tomatoes as well as for nutritive purposes.

Bleaching and Maturing Agents, Bread Improvers

The oxides of nitrogen, chlorine dioxide, nitrosyl chloride and chlorine exert a whitening effect on flour and accelerate the aging process which improves baking properties. Other chemicals used are potassium bromate, potassium iodate, calcium peroxide and inorganic salts such as ammonium chloride, ammonium sulfate, calcium sulfate and ammonium and calcium phosphates.

Emulsifying, Stabilizing and Thickening Agents

Compounds in this group are used to create a uniform suspension among such hard-to-mix ingredients as fats, oils, and chocolates. Examples are lecithin, mono- and diglycerides and certain sorbitan and polyoxyethylene fatty esters. Stabilizers and thickening agents act as "bodying agents," improve the texture of ice cream and help keep chocolate in suspension in chocolate milk drinks. They also form gels in pies and puddings. Examples are gelatins, pectins, starches, marine polysaccharides, gum arabic and tragacanth, cellulose gum derivatives, and sorbitol.

Flavoring Materials

Examples of compounds included in this group are spices, natural extractives, oleoresins and essential oils as well as many synthetic flavors. Typical chemicals in this group are amyl acetate, benzaldehyde, carvone, ethyl acetate, ethyl butyrate and methyl salicylate. Salt, sugar, condiments, and certain organic acids have been used for seasoning foods since man became interested in processing and preserving foods.

Recently many new compounds have been introduced into the food industry for the purpose of duplicating or intensifying the natural flavor of the food product. Monosodium glutamate is one of these preparations. It is sold under the trade name of Accent or "MSG." The compound is noted on the labels of a long list of soups, meat products, and flavoring sauces. Chinese and Japanese cooks many centuries ago discovered the flavoring possibilities in soybeans fermented by traditional processes. Soy sauces which contain glutamate impart a characteristic and satisfying flavor to the monotonous plain dishes of Orientals.

Protein chemistry has been a fertile field for research, especially in studying the properties of amino acids, including glutamic, and their salts, such as monosodium glutamate. Glutamic acid is one of the amino acids or so-called "building blocks," that are so essential for growth and body repair. Many protein foods are rich in glutamic acid. Wheat gluten, the sticky part remaining after the starch is washed away, contains a very high concentration of glutamic acid. Certain levels of glutamic acid, as it naturally occurs in certain foods, have been reported to raise the I.Q. of low I.Q. children under observation. Whether eating extra glutamic acid makes us extra keen is still uncertain. However, the addition of small amounts of glutamate in meaty foods enhances the delicate flavor of the product. It also adds a meat taste to vegetarian dishes.

During the last 20 years about 6 plants manufactured glutamate from sugar beet waste or wheat gluten. Much of this pioneer work was done in Ohio, using sugar beet waste as a raw material. An Ohio by-product plant was able to recover this valuable by-product while solving a pollution problem caused by beet sugar mill waste.

Monosodium glutamate has no characteristic flavor of its own; however, it has an effect in the mouth that the chemists call the "glutamate taste." In solid form it is mildly salty and slightly sweet. In aqueous solution it assumes four taste components: bitterness, saltiness, sourness, and sweetness. Physiologically it produces a pleasant sensation in the mouth or what may be called a "sense of satisfaction."

Food processors and homemakers are using MSG as a flavor intensifier. It accentuates and blends the natural flavors of foods such as meats, poultry, seafood, stews, soups, gravies, and certain vegetables. It is now used in spaghetti to bring out the cheese flavor. One manufacturer of toothpaste sprinkles MSG on the paste to intensify the mint flavor in the product. Moreover, it has the ability to suppress many undesirable flavors. It was found to reduce the sharpness in onions, earthiness in potatoes, and bitterness in canned vegetables. How does monosodium glutamate intensify flavor? Biochemists believe it stimulates the taste buds or it may excite nerves in the mouth and throat to produce a feeling of satisfaction. It has been shown that MSG stimulates the flow of saliva in the mouth which produces a chemical-physical effect. The increase in saliva may help to release flavor from food and may serve as a contact between the food and the taste buds. Recently MSG was found to bring on an illness in a few people. The illness is referred to as the "Chinese restaurant syndrome."

Food Colors

Annatto, alkanet, carotene, cochineal, chlorophyll, saffron, and turmeric are examples of food coloring materials. These are used in confectionery, bakery goods, soft drinks, and some dairy products such as butter, cheese, and ice cream. The use of food colors for the purpose of concealing damage or an inferior product or for improving the appearance of a product is illegal.

Preservatives and Antioxidants

Preservatives are used to prevent the growth of micro-organisms and antioxidants to prevent off-flavors and odors in fats, oils, and some vitamins. Examples of preservatives are sodium diacetate, sodium and calcium proprionates, acetic acid, lactic acid and monocalcium phosphate. Sorbic acid, sodium benzoate, sugar, salt, and vinegar are also used for retarding spoilage. Examples of antioxidants include butylated hydroxyanisole, butylated hydroxytoluene, and propyl gallate.

Preservatives in Foods Under Selected Supervision

Sulfurous acid can be used as a food preservative in the form of sulfurous acid, sulfur dioxide, or as sulfites of sodium, potassium, or calcium. Sulfurous acid inhibits the growth of yeasts, molds, and aerobic bacteria. This acid disappears in foods upon storage or during processing. Upon ingestion, sulfurous acid and sulfites are rapidly oxidized and eliminated in the urine as sulfates. Sulfites may combine with aldehydes, ketones, or simple sugars containing these groups. In wines and dried fruits sulfites become fixed. There may be other combinations with other food constituents. It appears that the toxicity of sulfites with aldehydes and ketones is no greater than that of free sulfurous acid.

Sulfite preservatives can conceal incipient putrefaction by removing the odor of decay in meat and restoring a bright red color to discolored portions. Therefore its use in meat is not allowed. Sulfurous acid tends to inactivate the vitamin B group. Furthermore, it prevents darkening of pared fruit and vegetables due to enzyme action, and tends to conserve the vitamin C content. Grapes used for wine making are crushed and treated with sulfur dioxide (50–200 p.p.m in the juice) or an equivalent strength of potassium metabisulfite to inhibit undesirable yeast fermentation. The burning of sulfur to produce sulfur dioxide gas at levels ranging from 1,000 to 3,000 p.p.m. by volume in air is employed to preserve color and vitamin C, repel insects and destroy undesirable organisms in fruits and vegetables. It is used mostly in molasses, fruit juices, and wines.

Nitric oxide is bacteriostatic in acid solution. It is produced from sodium nitrate.

Benzoic acid is used in the form of sodium benzoate in concentrations of 0.1 per cent in fruit juices, margarine, and jellies. It is no longer permitted in catsup. The compound is more effective in an acid environment as compared to a neutral condition in foods. Benzoic acid or its sodium or potassium salts are permitted in coffee extracts, pickles and sauces, soft drinks, and in grape juice not intended for use as a beverage. The germicidal action of benzoic acid is due to the undissociated acid. The greater the acidity of the medium the smaller is the amount of benzoic acid required. The action is diminished markedly at pH 5. This is the reason why 350 p.p.m. sulfur dioxide and 600 p.p.m. of benzoic acid are permitted in soft drinks. In metabolism, benzoic acid is eliminated in urine after combination with glycine to form hippuric acid and glucuronic acid. Benzoic acid is not actively toxic to humans in doses of around 0.5 g. per day.

Nitrates and nitrites of sodium and potassium-nitrates are comparable to salt in germicidal action and can inactivate certain enzymes. Nitrates occur naturally in many foods. On ingestion, nitrates are absorbed and excreted unchanged but a small part may be converted to nitrite. The mechanism of toxicity of nitrates may depend on the rate of conversion to nitrite. In the digestive tract this process may be beyond the capacity of the elimination process and poisoning may be the result. For instance, cases of methemoglobinemia in infants have been shown to be due to the high concentration of nitrate in the water used to prepare infant food.

Sodium nitrite is readily absorbed from the intestinal tract and disappears in the blood stream. Nitrite can combine with the meat pigment, myoglobin to form nitrosohemoglobin, thus producing the red color found in pickled meats. It also oxidizes blood hemoglobin to methemoglobin which has no oxygen-carrying properties. The blood can function as a normal reducing system but increases in methemoglobin in the blood may upset the reducing mechanism thus causing cyanosis.

Nitrates by altering the oxidation-reduction potential, favor the growth of aerobic organisms and restrict the growth of anaerobes. Nitrates and nitrites are added in curing meats primarily to fix the red color. The red nitric oxide produced from myoglobin and hemoglobin, forms a purplish color in meats. In an acid environment these compounds may have a mild bacteriostatic effect especially on anaerobes. The U.S. Department of Agriculture permits the use of 200 p.p.m. of nitrites in cured meats.

Sorbic acid is a comparatively new fungistatic agent especially when it is impregnated into the wrapping material. Unfortunately, sorbic acid may impart an undesirable flavor and aroma or it may disturb the desirable fermentations in food products, especially in an alcoholic fermentation. Sorbic acid treated wrappers have proved their value as good fungistatic agents by increasing the shelf life of many food products, especially cheese. Sorbic acid has a low toxicity factor. It is metabolized to water and carbon dioxide much the same as is the natural saturated fatty acid analogue caproic acid.

Diphenyl is active against mold, but only mildly active against bacteria and yeasts. It is used on citrus fruits, although the odor and taste are objectionable.

BIBLIOGRAPHY

Anon. 1957. Radioactive Fallout on the Farm. U.S. Dept. Agr. Farmers Bull. 2107.
Anon. 1958. Food-Packaging Materials, Their Composition and Uses. Nat. Acad. Sci.—Nat. Research Council, Publ. 645, Wash. D.C.
Anon. 1959A. Principles and Procedures for Evaluating the Safety of Food Additives. Nat. Acad. Sci.—Nat. Res. Council, Publ. 750, Wash. D.C.
Anon. 1959B. Problems in the Evaluation of Carcinogenic Hazard from Use of Food Additives. Nat. Acad. Sci.—Nat. Res. Council, Publ. 749, Wash. D.C
Anon. 1960. Food Additives. Manufacturing Chemists Assoc., Wash. D.C.
Anon. 1961. The Use of Chemicals in Food Production, Processing, Storage, and Distribution. Nat. Acad. Sci., Nat. Res. Council, Publ. 887, Wash. D.C.

Anon. 1962. Committees Intern. Assoc. Milk and Food Sanitarians, Inc. for 1962.

Anon. 1965A. Feed Additives. Veterinary Drug Encyclopedia and Therapeutic Index, 13th ed., 189–200.

Anon. 1965B. The Safety of Monoglycerides and Diglycerides for Use as Intentional Additives in Foods. Nat. Acad. Sci.—Nat. Res. Council, Publ. *1271*, Wash. D.C.

Anon. 1966. Food Chemicals Codex. Nat. Acad. Sci.—Nat. Res. Council, Publ. *1143*, Wash. D.C.

Baier, W. E. 1961. Pros and cons of food additives. Food Technol. *15*, 5–9.

Bing, H. 1950. Chemicals introduced in the processing of foods. Am. J. Public Health *40*, 618-620.

Desrosier, N. W., and Rosenstock, H. M. 1960. Radiation Technology in Food, Agriculture and Biology. Avi Publ. Co., Westport, Conn.

Dove, W. F. 1948. Flavor and Acceptability of Monosodium Glutamate. Proceedings of the Symposium. QM Food and Container Institute, Chicago, Ill.

Frazer, A. C. 1960. Control of food additives. Lab. Pract. *9*, 651–654.

Frazier, W. C. 1967. Food Microbiology, 2nd ed. McGraw-Hill Book Co., New York.

Frye, G. R., Weiser, H. H., and Winter, A. R. 1958. Influence of antibiotic feeding on the keeping quality and antibiotic content of poultry products. Poultry Sci. *37*, 633–637.

Furia, T. E. 1968. Food Additives. Chemical Rubber Co., Cleveland.

Goldberg, H. S. 1959. Antibiotics. Their Chemistry and Non-Medical Uses. D. Van Nostrand Co., Princeton, N.J.

Ives, M., and Nagler, E. M. 1960. Biological screening techniques for food additives. Food Technol. *14*, 499–502.

Judge, E. E. 1960. The almanac of Canning, Freezing, and Preserving Industries, Edward E. Judge, P.O. Box 248, Westminster, Md.

Larrick, G. P. 1961. Operations of the Food and Drug Administration. Presented before the Medical Advisory Committee Session held in conjunction with the 41st Annual Meeting of the American Petroleum Institute, Conrad Hilton Hotel, Chicago, Ill., Nov. 13, 1961.

Larson, B. L. 1960. Significance of strontium in milk. J. Dairy Sci. *43*, No. 1, 1–21.

Newton, R. C. 1953. Viewpoints on the problems of chemicals in foods: the viewpoint of a food manufacturer. Am. J. Public Health *44*, 985–987.

Oser, B. L. 1953. Viewpoints on the problems of chemicals in foods: laboratory problems in establishing the safety of food additives. Am J. Public Health *44*, 979–984.

Smith, D. P., and Rollin, N. J. 1954. Sorbic acid as a fungistatic agent for foods. Food Technol. *8*, 133-135.

Yeary, R. A. 1914. Medicated Feed Additives: A Handbook on the Safe Use of Feed Additives and Drugs for Livestock and Poultry. Cooperative Exten. Serv., The Ohio University Bull. *474*.

CHAPTER 20

Food Poisoning

The so-called "food poisoning" in man dates back to the early history of man. Various agents in food can be responsible for illness in the human being. We are primarily concerned with the role of certain micro-organisms capable of causing food poisoning. However, there are other agents besides organisms that may be involved. Perhaps a classification of the various causes would help to clarify the importance of the different etiological agents.

Allergy or food idiosyncrasies are well known to many individuals. These are hypersensitivities or reactions which some people show toward proteins. The protein may be injected into the tissues or taken in with the foods we eat. The latter is more striking in food idiosyncrasies. A variety of foods are known to cause a hypersensitive response while the symptoms will vary with each individual from a slight reaction to a severe shock. These idiosyncrasies are due to anaphylaxis, based on the fact that an animal may be sensitized against a foreign protein in such a way that when the protein is introduced later a violent reaction takes place, sometimes resulting in death. This phenomenon is comparable to that which takes place in man. Many individuals are sensitive to different protein foods. The reactions may occur in the form of skin rashes, bronchial asthma, or intestinal disturbances.

Such foods as whole wheat bread, eggs, strawberries, cheese, tomatoes, and other foods are often involved in food idiosyncrasies. The only remedy for this unpleasant discomfort is to avoid eating foods known to contain an allergic factor. In some cases individuals allergic to wheat flour, or handling of flour may be "desensitized" by being given small injections of wheat protein. Eventually the person may reach a condition whereby he can eat modest amounts of wheat bread daily. This same phenomenon occurs with eggs, strawberries, cheese, milk, and other foods. If the protein which is objectionable is essential food, the problem of desensitization is more complicated. Desensitization is absolutely necessary if the food cannot be eliminated from the diet.

THE ROLE OF MICRO-ORGANISMS IN FOOD POISONING

There are two ways in which bacteria may cause illness in human beings. The organisms may enter the host by being present in the food and establish "food borne infections." When contaminated food is eaten, the organisms enter the alimentary tract. Sometimes they enter the blood stream and are carried to other organs in the body, although ordinarily this does not occur. Dysentery, scarlet fever, brucellosis, hepatitis, and typhoid fever are typical food-borne infections. Usually no symptoms appear in the individual until the bacteria have had time to localize and grow in the host, although this phenomenon is debatable. This is called the incubation period. After a period of incubation, symptoms may appear that may serve to identify typical food poisoning.

The second method of food poisoning is known as food-borne intoxication. Toxin from the bacteria involved are present in the food before it is consumed. During the growth of the organisms an exotoxin or "poison" is formed and liberated in the food. It is the toxin that causes the symptons of food poisoning in the individual. Although an incubation period is required for exotoxins before illness occurs, the symptoms occur in a very short time. Herein lies a marked distinction between food-borne infection and intoxication. The former depends upon a varying period of incubation of the organisms in the host before any characteristic symptoms are observed, while in the latter method since the toxin is already in the food before it is consumed food poisoning symptoms appear earlier.

Food is essential for all animal and plant life. No living cell can exist indefinitely without food. However, certain foods may be deleterious to health especially in man. The subject of food poisoning and food-borne infection can be very misleading to the layman. Perhaps a classification would help to clarify the misconceptions about food poisoning. (1) Some foods are poisonous to humans such as clams during certain seasons of the year, toadstools which are confused with edible mushrooms and certain weeds which when consumed by the cow impart a poison to milk, yet the animal sometimes suffers no ill effects. (2) On the other hand wild snake-root may cause trembles in the cow. The addition of chemicals purposely or inadvertently may cause serious illness. Sometimes sodium fluoride or other insecticides are accidentally added to foods for human consumption. Many of these compounds resemble flour or salt in appearance so these materials can be added by mistake if they are not properly labeled. (3) The presence of toxins or poisons formed by microorganisms, especially certain types of bacteria, play a significant role in food poisoning. (4) Food-borne infection by selected types of bacteria which are present in the food prior to its consumption may cause a typical gastrointestinal disturbance.

Staphylococcal Food Poisoning

A high percentage of food poisoning is due primarily to *Staphylococcus aureus.* Staphylococci liberate a soluble toxin in the food before it is eaten. This toxin is called an enterotoxin (entero means intestine). The toxin may produce a marked irritating effect on the gastrointestinal tract. It is still quite difficult to detect the different strains of enterotoxin-producing organisms even by cultural, biochemical, and serological tests. Enterotoxin formed by these organisms is solely responsible for staphylococcal food poisoning. It has been determined that staphylococcus enterotoxin B is a simple protein with a molecular weight of about 35,000 which is very soluble in water and dilute salt solutions.

Perhaps one unique feature of staphylococcal food poisoning is the short incubation period, usually 3 hours after the infected food is consumed. The typical symptoms of this kind of food poisoning are: nausea and vomiting followed by abdominal cramps, severe diarrhea, and prostration. The mortality rate is very low. Fortunately the symptoms are of short duration and in most instances recovery occurs within 20 to 48 hours.

Conditions Favorable for Staphylococcal Food Poisoning.—Food rich in carbohydrates serves as an excellent medium for the growth of these organisms, provided no acid producing bacteria are present to furnish acids that may inhibit the growth of the Staphylococci. Bakery products such as custards and cream fillings as found in eclairs, cream puffs, custard filled doughnuts, and cream and custard pies are examples of such food. Some states and cities have laws forbidding the sale during the warm months of the year of eclairs and the custards which are used in baked goods. Meat products of various kinds are potentially dangerous, especially left over roast turkey and chicken improperly refrigerated. Also precooked hams can be involved in this type of food poisoning. Various dairy products such as milk, cream, cheese, and ice cream have been reported as dangerous if they aren't properly handled. Foods may be contaminated with staphylococci which can multiply and form toxins before freezing. Thawing of the frozen food and holding it at room temperature for several hours is a dangerous procedure, since staphylococci will grow at such temperatures.

Many outbreaks of staphylococcal food poisoning are due to unrefrigerated foods especially custard-filled bakery products. Food held at temperatures below 45°F (7.2°C) is usually safe because enterotoxin is not formed. However, an infected cow's udder or an infected person who has handled the milk may cause an outbreak. The presence of enterotoxin in food cannot be detected since it does not impart an odor which is usually associated with spoilage and there is no alteration in the normal taste of the food.

The author has studied the epidemiology of *Staphylococcus* associated with food handlers. Over 1,000 persons were studied in a survey to detect the presence of staphylococci in the throat and nasal passages. Approximately 60 per cent of the individuals examined harbored staphylococci and 20 to 25 per cent of the 60 per cent carried coagulase positive staphylococci.

These results are significant from the standpoint of food handlers. It is not difficult to follow the course of contamination from the potential carrier of staphylococci to the various food he may come in contact with.

Salmonella

The *Salmonella* group of organisms has been isolated from many outbreaks of food poisoning. Probably all serotypes of *Salmonella* are pathogenic for man, some for animals and a few for both man and animals. Over 1000 serotypes are known at the present time.

The term *Salmonella* gastroenteritis implies an infection rather than a poisoning like that due to preformed toxins produced by certain varieties of staphylococci. However, members of the *Salmonella* group are capable of multiplying very rapidly in certain kinds of foods, before the food is consumed by man. In this case, the organisms find their way into the intestinal tract and in a short time produce symptoms usually associated with typical food poisoning. The mechanism of food poisoning by members of the *Salmonella* group is not well understood.

The onset of the symptoms of food poisoning or the incubation period varies from 12 to 36 hours; this will vary with the number of *Salmonella* organisms present in the food. The greater the number of organisms, the more severe the infection and the shorter the time before symptoms appear.

Salmonella food infection is usually characterized by severe headache followed by chills. As the symptoms progress, vomiting, abdominal pain, diarrhea, rise in temperature, and prostration usually follow. The symptoms and effects are much more pronounced in young children than in adults. Fortunately with proper medical care the infection lasts only about a week. However, weakness may persist for 2 or 3 weeks.

The human element plays an important role in the contamination of foods. A food handler may be a carrier of *Salmonella typhi, S. typhimurium, S. schottmuelleri, S. enteritidis, S. newport,* and *S. choleraesuis.* Unclean personal habits, especially after visiting a rest room, can be the vehicle which contaminates food. Since these organisms are frequently present in the intestinal tract of some individuals it is very easy to understand the way in which the organisms gain entrance to food during its preparation, handling, and serving. Infected rats and mice may be involved as well as cockroaches and flies. Salads, especially where eggs are used, and pastries are frequently responsible for *Salmonella* food poisoning as well as nonfat dried milk solids.

Salmonella can be destroyed by thorough cooking. The greatest danger involves uncooked foods or food prepared and contaminated by food handlers. Also a lack of refrigeration of prepared foods enables the organisms to increase in large numbers. As already mentioned high doses of *Salmonella* in foods are almost necessary to induce a severe case of food poisoning.

Miscellaneous Food Poisoning Organisms

Streptococcus faecalis or alpha type, causes a greenish discoloration when grown on blood agar. Like Salmonella, no toxins are formed during the growth in foods. An infection type of food poisoning is manifested when a large number of *S. faecalis* is ingested. The organisms grow at 55°F (12.7°C) to 115°F (46°C) and show a high degree of salt tolerance. Pasteurizing temperatures will destroy a high percentage of the streptococci.

The sources of *Streptococcus faecalis* are usually the intestinal contents of man, mammals, and birds. Jensen (1954) has reported that poultry dressings which had been incubated and not properly cooked after being stuffed into the bird have been involved. Adequate heating of the food, followed by refrigeration is necessary in order to destroy the organisms. Food-borne outbreaks are due largely to infected food handlers, since staphylococci, salmonellae, and streptococci are ubiquitous. Again, the symptoms are comparable to other types of food poisoning. Usually large numbers of organisms must be ingested with the contaminated food. The period of incubation ranges from 2 to 20 hours and includes nausea, abdominal pains, diarrhea, and vomiting, but no appreciable rise in temperature.

Proteus vulgaris and *P. mirabilis* have been isolated in cases of food poisoning traced to fish, ham, and sausage.

Glasser (1895) stated that *Bacillus subtilis* could form toxins when grown in meat. Hauge (1955) reported that *Bacillus cereus* caused four outbreaks involving 600 persons, after eating custard made from commercial cornstarch, containing large numbers of *B. cereus*.

The Escherichia-Aerobacter group have been suspected in food poisoning outbreaks. However, at the present time there is no convincing evidence that they are directly responsible for food poisoning. They have been isolated and identified from characteristic cases of food poisoning but the role they play is not well understood.

Botulism Poisoning

Botulism (in Latin, *botulus* means sausage) poisoning as it was commonly called, was first reported in sausage. Fortunately, there is now very little sausage poisoning in the U.S.

Clostridium botulinum is an anaerobic organism. When favorable conditions exist, it produces an exotoxin resulting in an acute toxemia when the food containing the toxin is consumed. The organism is a typical saprophyte, and it is assumed that it is responsible for all types of botulism found in man.

The physiology of *Cl. botulinum* is unique in that it is a spore bearing organism whose spores are extremely resistant to heat. The spores may remain viable after they have been exposed to boiling water for several hours. However, a temperature of 249°F (121°C) will destroy the spores in 10 to 15 minutes. If the spores are consumed in the food, they will not reproduce. Similarly the organism will not multiply in the intestinal tract nor will they cause any ill effect in the human. The toxin produced can easily be destroyed at a temperature of 212°F (100°C) within a few minutes. This phenomenon is very fortunate since the toxin in food can be inactivated by heating or cooking the food within reasonable temperature ranges.

At least six types of exotoxin may be produced by *Cl. botulinum* and are designated as A, B, C, D, E, and F. Types A and B toxins are chiefly responsible for human cases of botulism, while types C and D affect cattle, horses, sheep, and goats. It appears that type C is responsible for "limber neck" a term used to designate botulism in domestic fowl and wild ducks.

The exotoxin formed by *Cl. botulinum* is absorbed from the intestinal tract into the blood stream. The toxin has a specific affinity for the nervous system and is often called neurotoxin. Biochemists have obtained type A toxin in the form of pure white needle shaped crystals. One gram of the crystal form of this toxin would furnish about 8,000,000 lethal doses. About 68 per cent of humans ingesting the toxins do not survive.

Distribution in Foods.—*Clostridium botulinum* is widely distributed in the soil. Hence it is found on fruits and vegetables grown in or near soil. Although the number of organisms will vary with different types of soil and climatic conditions, soil in the Great Plains area contain type A toxin producing *Cl. botulinum,* whereas in the Great Lakes region and the Atlantic States, type B organisms are the principal form.

The organism can grow in canned foods providing the pH is near the neutral point. Low acid foods such as string beans, corn, beets, and meats serve as excellent food material for the growth of *Cl. botulinum.* The number of cases of botulism reported in the U.S. are usually due to inadequately processed home-canned foods which are consumed without cooking after removal from the jar.

There is very little danger of botulism from fresh foods, cooked or raw, because the spores are harmless when present in the food. The exotoxin is formed only under anaerobic conditions or reduced oxygen tension as one would find in sealed containers.

Symptoms of Botulism.—The time it takes for symptoms to occur after ingestion of the toxin will vary from 20 hours to several days. The onset of the symptoms are in many cases the opposite of those for staphylococcus or salmonella food poisoning. Usually fatigue and muscular weakness are the first symptoms followed by double vision (diplopia), drooping of the upper eye lids, dilated pupils, dryness of the mouth, swelling of the tongue, persistant constipation and, finally, difficulty in swallowing and speaking. There is usually no gastrointestinal disturbances and death results from a paralysis of the respiratory muscles. Consequently, in fatal cases the victim suffocates because of his inability to breathe.

The studies of Esty and Myers (1922) show the heat resistance of *Clostridium botulinum* spores at different time intervals and temperatures.

4 minutes exposure at 248°F (120°C)
10 minutes exposure at 239°F (115°C)
32 minutes exposure at 230°F (110°C)
100 minutes exposure at 221°F (105°C)
330 minutes exposure at 212°F (100°C)

It has been observed by several investigators that young spores of *Cl. botulinum* are more resistant to heat than old spores. No doubt this observation may be applicable to all spore forming bacteria.

The inactivation of *Cl. botulinum* toxin by heat varies according to different workers from 175°F (79.4°C) for 30 minutes to 176°F (80°C) for 8 minutes. Dack (1956) reported the results of several studies by Bengston; Schoenholz and Myer; and Seddon.

Clostridium Perfringens

The presence of *Clostridium perfringens* in many kinds of foods along with *Cl. botulinum* suggest a practical method of differentiation, from other non-motile clostridia. Lewis and Angelotti (1964) have suggested a procedure they have used with reasonable success (see Appendix).

Many investigators have reported that both staphylococcus and botulinum toxins are not easily destroyed by heat. Since heat stability of all these toxins has not been determined any suspected food should be discarded. Preparing and cooking foods far in advance of the time they will be eaten is a dangerous practice unless adequate safeguards are taken to protect the food. Many foods held at room temperature, especially during the summer months, present ideal conditions for the growth of most food poisoning organisms.

Communicable Diseases Transmitted Through Food

Many foods during harvesting processing, handling, and distribution may become contaminated from intestinal discharges of infected persons or even carriers. Human carriers are far too numerous as far as food handlers are concerned. Typhoid fever and dysentery are typical examples of bacterial diseases transmitted through food contaminated by human carriers. Milk and other dairy products may be involved in the transmission of pathogenic bacteria from an infected cow, human beings, or carriers who handle the food product before it reaches the ultimate consumer. The cow may harbor certain species of streptococci which may be largely responsible for septic sore throat or other streptococcal infections in man. Certain species of *Mycobacterium tuberculosis,* especially the bovine type, may be responsible for a high incidence of tuberculosis in children, since children are large consumers of milk. Fortunately, the detection and elimination of the infected cow and the universal pasteurization of milk, have practically eliminated the dairy cow as a source of this disease. This observation does not imply that tuberculosis is no longer a dangerous disease. It is still an important disease in man, but modern medical science has made remarkable strides in controlling it.

Causative organisms of the disease brucellosis or undulant fever in man belong to the genus *Brucella. Brucella abortus* causes contagious abortion in cattle and swine and undulant fever in man. Likewise, *Brucella suis* affects swine, chickens, horses, dogs, cows, monkeys, and man, and *Brucella melitensis* goats and man.

All three species of *Brucella* are pathogenic for man, goats, swine, horses, and other animals. However, the symptoms of brucellosis in various animals are different. The swine species may also affect cattle and together with the other species may be transmitted to man in milk and milk products.

Like tuberculosis in cattle, brucellosis can be detected in dairy cows and the infected animal may be eliminated. The Brucella organisms are easily destroyed when exposed to sunlight. Studies show that these organisms may remain viable in cream stored at 50°F (10°C) for several days. They also resist drying and remain alive in dust for long intervals of time. Likewise, the pasteurization of milk makes it safe from brucellosis.

There is evidence to show that the causative organisms of scarlet fever, tuberculosis (human type), typhoid fever, and certain kinds of dysenteries may come from human sources and thus be a potential source of danger in foods from the public health standpoint.

Tularemia, an infection produced by *Pasteurella tularensis*, can be transmitted to man by direct contact or by the ingestion of uncooked tissues of rabbits and squirrels. Infection through the alimentary tract is not common and it produces a syndrome similar to typhoid fever without localized lesions.

Many human intestinal infections may come from water polluted with raw sewage; oysters, clams, and many kinds of shell fish may be contaminated as they grow in this environment.

Many insects, rodents, cats, and dogs may be implicated in the contamination of foods. The habitat of the carriers makes the problem rather complicated as a public health problem.

Infections That May Be Confused with Bacterial Food Poisoning

There are four types of infections that may be confused with food poisoning. According to Dack (1956) they are classified as follows. *Bacillary dysentery* is caused by a bacillus. Little is known about the natural habitat of the organism. However, in areas where typhoid fever and cholera are controlled, bacillary dysentery remains endemic. The infection appears to be common where people are closely associated as in prisons, army camps, asylums, and summer resorts. The isolation and identification of dysentery bacilli from feces is difficult due primarily to the rapid disappearance of the organisms from the stools during convalescence. Undoubtedly many individuals are undetected carriers. *Bacillary dysentery* may be spread by food contaminated with feces from carriers or from those suffering from the disease.

One of the outstanding symptoms of the disease is the shorter incubation period extending several days in most cases as compared to *Salmonella* infections. Also the recovery and identification of the bacilli from stools is usually sufficient to differentiate the disease from typical food poisoning. Fortunately, there are not many food poisoning cases due to *bacillary dysentery*. At least they are not identified as such in public health reports.

Cholera in man is acquired by the ingestion of a spirillum (*Vibrio comma*), usually found in food or water contaminated by fecal material. The ingested organisms multiply in the small intestine and after 2–5 days cause a sudden onset of nausea, vomiting, diarrhea, and abdominal cramps.

The third disease that may be confused with food poisoning is *amoebic dysentery*. Its insidious and chronic nature usually differentiates it from bacterial food poisoning.

The incubation period after the ingestion of the amoeba varies from a few days to 3 or 4 months. The symptoms of amoebic dysentery in man vary from a mild diarrhea to an acute bloody flux.

Endamoeba histolytica, a protozoan, is the causative agent of amoebic dysentery. It is good laboratory procedure to identify the protozoan, if possible, and exclude it before making a final diagnosis of food poisoning. Its presence in stools should be interpreted with some reservation because about 10 per cent of the population are known to be infected, while a high percentage of these persons suffer no noticeable symptoms.

The disease usually occurs sporadically and may continue to occur over a long period of time. Dack (1956) relates that the Chicago epidemic in 1933 was waterborne and was due primarily to faulty plumbing and back siphonage of sewage which occurred in water lines in certain hotels. Amoebic dysentery may also be food borne. Usually the disease is endemic and spread by intimate personal contact.

Again, like bacillary dysentery, the infection is not a major cause of food poisoning. Where good sanitary practices are followed in processing and handling food, little fear should arise from the dangers of food borne infections.

Trichinosis is another disease that may be confused with food poisoning. The causative agent is *Trichinella spiralis*, a nematode, which is usually obtained by man from poorly cooked and infected hog meat. When the encysted larvae are eaten, the cysts are digested in the patient's stomach, whereupon the larvae enter the duodenum. Finally they localize in the duodenal and jejunal mucosa, then the symptoms are manifest as nausea, vomiting, diarrhea, dysentery, colic, and profuse sweating. It is important that the infection should be recognized about 48 hours after the ingestion of the larvae and it must be differentiated from food poisoning. Again a case history of eating uncooked pork and the finding of encysted nematodes in the food is important in a diagnosis.

Apparently there is no way to exclude trichinella from pork at the time of slaughter, but one sure safeguard is the thorough cooking of the meat.

Diagnosis is very important and this depends on the stages of the disease. Dack (1956) states that eosinophilia is suggestive of trichinosis. However, during the intestinal phase, adult worms are usually recovered from the feces. During and after larval migration, the larvae localize in muscle strips removed at biopsy.

One should bear in mind that it is very important to establish a correct diagnosis in any outbreak of food poisoning. Common sense and an intelligent understanding, as well as an accurate analysis is very important. Thus symptomatology, epidemiology, pathology, and laboratory diagnosis all play an important role in characterizing any type of food poisoning.

Infections to Be Differentiated from Bacterial Food Poisoning

Viruses.—Infectious hepatitis may be food-borne. The information is very meager in regard to transmission of the disease in foods although fecal-oral routes have been suspected especially since persons are known to be fecal carriers.

The incubation period may range from 10 to 40 days. The symptoms are usually headache, general malaise, fatigue, nausea, chills, vomiting, and jaundice in some cases.

No therapeutic measures can be used. An attempt to recognize the infectious agent and differentiate it from bacterial food poisoning is recommended but the laboratory procedure is difficult and inconclusive.

Viruses Associated with Foods.—Many authorities believe that hepatitis, poliomyelitis, coxsackie, herpes simplex, mumps, influenza, and perhaps other viruses are present in the alimentary tract of healthy individuals. One group affects the nose, throat, and lungs and is known either as the ARD-acute respiratory disease group or the ADC or adenoidopharyngo-conjunctival group. Some of the viruses are noted for their destructive effect on monkey-kidney tissue. These tissue cultures have revealed a new group of viruses present in numerous healthy children.

Another group of viruses are called ECHO or enteric cytopathogenic human orphan viruses, (not associated with orphan children). They are viruses of unknown classification and unknown reactions. They are commonly present in the intestinal tract.

Rickettsiae.—Q Fever was described in 1937 as being present in packing house workers in Queensland, Australia. *Rickettsia burnetii* and *Coxiella burnetii* have been involved in foods.

Rickettsiae have been isolated from raw milk by guinea pig inoculations. Fortunately pasteurization of milk is effective in destroying the Rickettsiae. Rickettsiae can be transmitted by ticks. It has been reported that calves are very susceptible.

Symptoms in Man.—Common symptoms are sudden severe fever, chills, headache, bodyaches and pains, coughing, and bloody sputum. The symptoms are often diagnosed as a typical pneumonia The symptoms last about one to three weeks accompanied by a long convalescence especially with older persons. The fatality rate is usually very low.

Characteristics of Rickettsiae.—They are intracellular parasites of arthropods such as lice and ticks. They are transmitted by bites or in the excreta of the vectors.

Biologically, they have features common to bacteria and viruses. They are non-filtrable, gram-negative, and appear as coccobacillary bodies in the nucleus of the host cells. They are intracellular parasites and they will not grow in a synthetic culture medium. They do not form spores, are non-motile and readily destroyed by heat, dehydration, and antiseptics.

Characteristics of Aerobic and Anaerobic Bacterial Toxins

Aerobes

1. The toxin is fairly easily destroyed by heat.
2. The toxin cannot always be demonstrated.
3. The mortality is relatively low in food poisoning caused by aerobic food poisoning bacteria.
4. The toxin is preformed and liberated into the food although there are exceptions as in the case of Salmonella organisms.
5. The causative organisms are all non-spore forming.

Anaerobes

1. The toxin is extremely potent; a minute amount may be fatal to man.
2. The toxin is preformed and then liberated into the food.
3. The toxin can be more easily destroyed by heat than the toxin produced by aerobic organisms.
4. The organisms produce resistant spores which may survive the temperatures employed in the canning process if it is not done carefully.

In the past all kinds of food poisoning were called "ptomaine poisoning." Our present day knowledge of bacteriology has produced much more detailed knowledge. Bacterial food poisoning results from certain kinds of micro-organisms that may be present in the food which grow and produce an exotoxin which is harmful to man. A more elaborate explanation of food poisoning will be discussed under public health and sanitation.

Chemical Food Poisoning

Food Poisoning Due to Toxic Plants

a. Inedible mushrooms produce a poisonous substance called "muscarine" and "phallin."
   Symptoms are: Nausea, vomiting, thirst, and later convulsions.
b. Ergot—produced by the fungus, *Claviceps purpurea.* Ergotism results from eating bread made of rye on which the fungus has grown.
   Symptoms are: Itching, muscle cramps, gangrene, and convulsions.
c. Oxalic acid found in rhubarb leaves; poisoning results from using the leaves as cooked greens.
d. Milk sickness or trembles follows consumption of milk of cows that have grazed on white snake root.
   Symptoms are: Vomiting, constipation, profound weakness, and later alkalosis.
e. Mussel (shellfish) poison probably elicited by a certain protozoan (flagellate) on which the mussels feed.
   Symptoms are: Muscle weakness and paralysis, including respiratory paralysis.

Food Poisoning Due to Chemical Substances

Chemical Agent	Source
Arsenic	Deliberately added to food.
Antimony	Food prepared in poor quality gray enamel pans.
Cadmium	Acid foods cooked in cadmium plated utensils.
Zinc	Acid foods cooked in galvanized utensils.
Lead	Same as arsenic.
Sodium fluoride	Cockroach powder, spilled into foods or mistaken for baking powder or powdered milk.
Germicides, herbicides, fungicides, pesticides	Accidentally added to food.
Antibiotics	Antibiotic medication.

Table 29 shows the results of poor food handling.

TABLE 29

FOOD HANDLING AND PUBLIC HEALTH[1]

(a) Unsanitized glasses, dishes, and silverware. Exposure of food to coughing, sneezing, spitting:
    Common cold
    Diphtheria
    Encephalitis
    Measles
    Mumps
    Pneumonia
    Poliomyelitis
    Scarlet fever
    Septic sore throat
    Tuberculosis
    Whooping cough

(b) Use of common cup, towels, and toilet articles by employees:
    Common cold
    Influenza
    Septic sore throat
    Syphilis
    Tuberculosis
    Typhoid fever

(c) Failure of employees to wash hands thoroughly after each visit to toilet:
    Dysentery, bacillary
    Dysentery, amoebic
    Food infection
        and poisoning
    Paratyphoid fever

(d) Employment of people who are carriers:
    Dysentery, bacillary
    Dysentery, amoebic
    Paratyphoid fever
    Tuberculosis
    Typhoid fever

(e) Improper washing, preparation, and refrigeration of foods:
    Botulism
    Dysentery, bacillary
    Dysentery, amoebic
    Food infection and poisoning
    Paratyphoid fever
    Typhoid fever

(f) Employment of personnel in preparation of foods with sores and boils on hands or arms:
    Food infection and poisoning

(g) Use of ungraded milk and milk products:
    Diphtheria
    Dysentery, bacillary
    Paratyphoid fever
    Scarlet fever
    Septic sore throat
    Tuberculosis
    Typhoid fever
    Undulant fever (Brucellosis)

(h) Use of uncertified oysters:
    Paratyphoid fever
    Typhoid fever
    Infectious hepatitis

(i) Use of contaminated drinking water and home-made drinks:
    Dysentery, bacillary
    Dysentery, amoebic
    Paratyphoid fever
    Typhoid fever

(j) Lack of screening, exposure of food to flies:
    Dysentery, bacillary
    Dysentery, amoebic
    Typhoid fever
    Paratyphoid fever

(k) Improper storage of food, lack of rat control:
Paratyphoid fever
Typhus fever
Infectious jaundice
Food infection and poisoning

(l) Plumbing and water supply incorrectly connected:
Dysentery, amoebic
Dysentery, bacillary
Paratyphoid fever
Typhoid fever

¹ From Food Handler's Training Program, Texas State Board of Health.
² Carrier: A person who, without symptoms of a communicable disease, harbors and disseminates the specific micro-organisms.
Infected person: A person in whose tissues the etiological agent of a communicable disease is lodged and produces symptoms.

Table 30 summarizes methods of detection, diagnosis, and prevention for food poisoning epidemics.

TABLE 30

DETECTION AND DIAGNOSIS OF BACTERIAL FOOD POISONING

A. Primarily Clinical
  1. Secure complete list of cases involved.
  2. Obtain details and complete history in each individual case, if possible.
  3. Ascertain vehicle of infection by appropriate laboratory techniques.
  4. Study the history of implicated food.
  5. Obtain evidence as to the manner in which the food was contaminated.
B. Laboratory Examination
  1. If possible, obtain samples of infected food consumed.
  2. Examine blood, liver, spleen, and intestinal contents of fatal cases.
  3. Examine feces and blood of suspected carriers.
  4. If the bacteriological findings are negative, then an examination for the presence of harmful chemicals should be made.
C. Epidemiology of Foods
  1. Prepare a spot map of the area involved.
  2. Complete bacteriological examination of the milk supply in the area.
  3. Bacteriological examination of the water supply, especially shallow wells and wells not properly protected from surface water.
  4. Record of age groups of persons, also incidence and number of cases involved.

Precautions in Order to Prevent Food Poisoning and Infections

Summary of precautionary steps:

1. Proper attitude of food handler in regard to essential rules of sanitation with respect to personal cleanliness, and of the utensils, lastly the preparation of food.
2. A known carrier of enteric pathogens should not be allowed to handle or prepare food for human consumption.
3. Any person suffering from an upper respiratory infection should keep away from food service.
4. Foods should be kept at suitable temperatures in order to assure a minimum of bacterial multiplication.
5. Protect all foods from insects, rodents, and vermin.

TABLE 51

CLASSIFICATION OF ILLNESS ATTRIBUTABLE TO FOODS

Type of Illness	Causative agent	Food Usually Involved	Incubation Period	Symptoms
A. Bacterial Food Infections				
Shigellosis Bacillary Dysentery	Members of the genus *Shigella*	Moist prepared foods, milk and other dairy products, contaminated with excreta	Usually 2–3 days	Diarrhea, bloody stools, fever in severe cases
Cholera	*Vibrio Comma*	Fecally contaminated food and water	2–5 days	Nausea, vomiting, diarrhea, and abdominal cramps
Brucellosis, Undulant Fever or Bang's Disease	*Brucella abortus, B. melitensis,* or *B. Suis*	Raw milk or dairy products contaminated with raw milk, animal contact (meat)	3–21 days sometimes several months	Chills, sweats, weakness, malaise, headache, fever, muscle and joint pains, and loss of weight
Diphtheria	*Corynebacterium diphtheriae*	Milk contaminated from human sources	3–7 days	Insidious onset, inflammation of throat and nose
Hemolytic streptococci, scarlet fever and septic sore throat	Beta hemolytic streptococci	Food contaminated with nasal or oral discharges and milk from cows having udder infections	1–7 days	Fever, sore throat, sometimes rash
Streptococcal food infections	*Enterococcus coccus fecalis* *Strepto-*	Food contaminated with excreta or human carrier	2–18 days	Nausea, vomiting, pains, and diarrhea
Salmonellosis a. Typhoid Fever	*Salmonella typhi*	Any food contaminated with excreta from human case or carrier	Usually 7–21 days	Malaise, lack of appetite, headache, fever
b. Paratyphoid A.	*Salmonella paratyphi A.*	Same as for typhoid fever	1–10 days	Same as for typhoid fever

c. Other Types

	Salmonella typhimurium Salmonella enteritis Salmonella cholera suis Salmonella newport	Meat, poultry salads, and egg products	12–72 hours	Abdominal pain, diarrhea, chills, fever, vomiting, and prostration
Tuberculosis	Mycobacterium tuberculosis, human and bovine types A and B	Raw contaminated milk and other dairy products	Variable	Depends on part of body affected
Tularemia	Pasteurella tularensis	Wild game animals	3–10 days	Sudden onset, headache, chills, body pains, fever, vomiting, swollen lymph glands, and loss of appetite
Trichinosis	Trichinella spiralis	Raw pork or similar products	36–72 hours	

B. Bacterial Food Intoxications

Staphylococcal intoxication	Staphylococcus producing Enterotoxin	Meats, food rich in carbohydrates, especially salads and warmed over foods	2–11 hours	Nausea, vomiting, diarrhea, and abdominal cramps
Botulism	Exotoxin Clostridium botulinum and C. parabotulinum	Home processed foods and contaminated canned foods with pH over 4.5	12 hours to 6 days	Dizziness, double vision, muscular weakness, difficulty in swallowing, speech and respiration
Clostridium perfringens (welchii)	Cl. welchii Type A. Exotoxin Alpha type	Cold and reheated meats, water, milk, salt rising bread. Found in intestinal tract of man and animals	8–22 hours (variable)	Acute abdominal pains, diarrhea, nausea, and vomiting rare

NOTE: *Clostridium perfringens* and *Bacillus cereus* may cause symptoms identical to *Streptococcus fecalis*, providing they are present in the food product in large numbers.

TABLE 32

DIVISION BY SPECIFIC ETIOLOGY OF THE TOTAL OF CONFIRMED AND UNCONFIRMED OUTBREAKS OF FOODBORNE ILLNESS—1968 AND 1969[1]

Etiology	1968				1969			
	Total Outbreaks		Total Patients		Total Outbreaks		Total Patients	
	Number	Percent	Number	Percent	Number	Percent	Number	Percent
Bacterial	220	63.8	14,617	83.2	243	65.5	25,911	90.7
B.cereus	4	1.2	12	.1	3	0.8	14	[2]
Brucella	9	2.6	10	.1	10	2.7	17	0.1
C. botulinum	56	16.2	5,966	34.0	65	17.5	18,527	64.9
C. perfringens	6	1.7	1,234	7.0	5	1.3	398	1.4
E. coli	42	12.2	1,287	7.3	49	13.2	1,892	6.6
Shigella	6	1.7	407	2.3	10	2.7	1,444	5.1
Staphylococcus	82	23.8	4,419	25.2	94	25.3	3,481	12.2
Streptococcus	15	4.3	1,282	7.3	4	1.1	37	0.1
Vibrio parahemolyticus					2	0.5	71	0.2
Multiple etiologies					1	0.3	30	0.1
Parasitic:								
Giardia lambia								
Trichinella spiralis	9	2.6	82	.5				
Viral								
Hepatitis	6	1.7	238	1.4	9	2.4	116	0.4
Chemical								
Chinese restaurant syndrome (Monosodium glutamate)	5	1.4	15	0.1	2	0.5	6	[2]
Mushroom	17	4.9	98	0.6	4	1.1	9	[2]
Other chemical	3	0.9	76	.7	21	5.7	157	0.5
Miscellaneous								
Unknown	85	24.6	2,441	13.9	80	21.6	2,310	8.1
Total	345	100.0	17,567	100.0	371	100.0	28,563	100.0

[1]Data are estimates only, because of inadequate reporting of food poisoning outbreaks. Taken from NCDC Morbidity and Mortality Report USPHS, Atlanta, Ga.
[2]Values less than 0.05 have been omitted.

6. Do not eat cream-filled pastries and custards in public eating places unless they are refrigerated.
7. Avoid all home canned low acid foods unless they have been processed under steam pressure.
8. Never eat canned foods that have an "off-flavor" unless they are first boiled for at least 12 to 15 minutes.
9. Wash thoroughly all fresh fruit and vegetables before eating.

Tables 31 and 32 summarize the sources and incidence of food poisoning epidemics in the United States.

TABLE 32A

VEHICLES ASSOCIATED WITH FOODBORNE ILLNESS OF SPECIFIC ETIOLOGY—1969[1]

Etiology	Turkey[2]	Chicken[2]	Beef[2]	Pork[2]	Other Meat[2]	Egg	Milk	Cheese	Other Dairy Products	Shellfish	Other Fish	Vegetables and Fruit	Mushrooms	Bakery Products	Chinese Food	Water
Bacterial																
B. cereus										1				1		
C. botulinum												6	1			
C. perfringens[3]	16	4	34	3			1	4		1		7				
E. coli	1		1							1						2
Salmonella[4]	11	7	6	2		3		1			1	4		5		1
Shigella												2				4
Staphylococcus[5]	12	7	16	31		3	1	1		5	2	8		9	1	
Streptococcus			2	1						1						
Vibrio parahemolyticus										2						
Multiple etiologies				1												
Parasitic																
Giardia lamblia																1
Trichinella spiralis				11												
Viral																
Hepatitis[5]	1		2							1						5
Chemical																
Chinese restaurant syndrome (Monosodium glutamate)															2	
Mushroom													4			
Other chemical[7]			1	3						2	2	8			1	
Unknown[8]	6	5	10	11					2	4	2	6		6	2	2
Total	47	23	72	63		6	2	6	2	18	7	41	5	21	6	15

[1] Includes suspected as well as proved vehicles. Data are estimates only, because of inadequate reporting of food poisoning outbreaks. Taken from NCDC Morbidity and Mortality Report, USPHS, Atlanta, Ga.
[2] Includes some outbreaks due to meat and/or gravy and/or dressing.
[3] Includes 2 outbreaks with 2 vehicles. 1 outbreak with 3 vehicles and 1 outbreak with 4 vehicles.
[4] Includes 4 outbreaks with 2 vehicles.
[5] Includes 4 outbreaks with 2 vehicles, and 3 outbreaks with 3 vehicles.
[6] Includes 1 outbreak with 3 vehicles.
[7] Includes 1 outbreak with 2 vehicles.
[8] Includes 3 outbreaks with 2 vehicles.

TABLE 32B

PLACE OF ACQUISITION OF FOODBORNE ILLNESS OF SPECIFIC ETIOLOGY—1969[1]

Etiology	Restaurant	Delicatessen	Cafeteria	Home	Picnic	School	Church	Camp	Other	Total
Bacterial										
B. cereus	2			1					1	3
C. botulinum	1			8				1		10
C. perfringens	30	1	3	8		17			5	65
E. coli	3		1			1				5
Salmonella	7			26		3	3	2	8	49
Shigella	1			4		2	1		2	10
Staphylococcus	26		1	39	3	5	2	2	16	94
Streptococcus	2			2						4
V. parahemolyticus								2		2
Multiple etiologies				1						1
Parasitic										
Giardia lambia				1						1
Trichinella spiralis	2			9						11
Viral										
Hepatitis				7		1		1		9
Chemical										
Chinese restaurant syndrome (Monosodium glutamate)	1			1						2
Mushroom				4						4
Other chemical	5			12		1			3	21
Unknown	24	1	1	34		8	2	3	8	80
Total 1969	104	1	6	157	3	38	8	11	43	371
Number of persons ill—1969	2,922	6	982	1,373	681	19,842	527	416	1,814	28,563

[1] Data are estimates only, because of inadequate reporting of food poisoning outbreaks. Taken from NCDC Morbidity and Mortality Report, USPHS, Atlanta, Ga.

TABLE 33

FOOD-BORNE DISEASES

Disease	Etiologic Agent	Foods Usually Involved
1. Botulism	*Cl. botulinum* toxins	Canned and bottled food improperly processed
2. Staphylococcus	Staphylococci enterotoxin	Custard pastries, cooked ham, hollandaise sauce
3. Salmonellosis	A variety of members of the *Salmonella* group	"Hand-made" salads, sliced cooked meats, "warmed over" foods
4. Typhoid fever	Typhoid bacillus	Contaminated food, water, milk, shellfish
5. Dysentery, Bacillary	Various species of genus *Shigella*	Contaminated food, water, by contact with excreta
6. Dysentery, Amoebic	*Endamoeba histolytica*	Cold moist foods, contaminated drinking water
7. Tularemia	*Pasteurella tularensis*	Wild rabbits (by handling)
8. Brucellosis	*Brucella melitensis, Brucella abortus, Brucella suis*	Ingestion of infected milk and dairy products. Direct contact with infected animals or animal products
9. Q fever	*Coxiella burnetii*	Milk, contact, or exposure to infected livestock
10. Trichinosis	*Trichinella spiralis*	Insufficiently cooked pork or pork products

Average Time of Onset	Symptoms	Preventive Procedure
1. 1–2 days	Difficulty in swallowing and speech, double vision	Careful canning procedure. Cooking to detoxify toxins.
2. 3–6 hours	Nausea, vomiting, abdominal cramps	Prompt refrigeration of foods; pasteurization of custard-filled pastries.
3. 6–18 hours	Diarrhea, abdominal cramps, vomiting	Strict attention to cleanliness of hands of food handlers. Protection of foods during processing and storage. Refrigeration of food.
4. 7–14 days	Fever	Pasteurization of milk, safe water supply; approved source of shellfish; isolation of carrier from food handling.
5. 1–7 days	Diarrhea, fever	Protection of water supply; handwashing.
6. Several days to 4 weeks	Diarrhea	Handwashing. Prevention of cross connections.
7. 1–10 days	Sudden chills and fever	Avoid handling of rabbits or use protective gloves.
8. 6–30 days	Undulating fever; pains in joints and muscles	Pasteurization of milk and dairy products; care in handling meat and meat products.
9. 2–3 weeks	Sudden chills, headaches, severe sweats, malaise	Pasteurization of milk.
10. 2–28 days	Nausea, diarrhea, soreness in muscles, fever	Thorough cooking of pork and pork products. Antigen testings of hogs. Prevent feeding of raw garbage to hogs. Freezing of pork.

BIBLIOGRAPHY

Dack, G. M. 1956. Food Poisoning, 3rd ed. University of Chicago Press, Chicago, Ill.

Hauge, S. 1951. Staphylococci in milk, 1951. Nord Vet. Med. *3*, 931–956.

Hauge, S. 1955. Food poisoning caused by spore forming bacilli. J. Appl. Microbiol. *18*, 591–595.

Esselen, W. B., and Levine, A. S. 1941. Bacterial Food Poisoning and Its Control. Bull. *493*. Dept. of Food Technol., University of Mass., Amherst.

Esty, J. R., and Myer, K. F. 1922. The heat resistance of the spores of *B. botulinus* and allied anaerobes. J. Infectious Diseases, *31*, 650–663.

Glasser, J. 1895. Toxins formed in meat and sugar syrups by bacilli. Centbl. f. Bakt. Abt. *11*, 879–889.

Jay, J. M. 1970. Modern Food Microbiology. Van Nostrand Reinhold Co., New York

Jensen, L. B. 1954. Microbiology of Meats, 3rd ed. The Garrard Press, Champaign, Ill.

Lewis, K. H., and Angelotti, R. 1964. Examination of foods for enteropathogenic and indicator bacteria. U.S. Dept. of Health, Education, and Welfare, Washington, D.C.

Skerman, V. B. D. 1967. A guide to the Identification of the Genera of Bacteria, 2nd ed. The Williams and Wilkins Co., Baltimore.

Tanner, F. W. 1933. Food Borne Infections and Intoxications. Twin City Printing Co., Champaign, Ill.

United States Public Health Service. 1950. Ordinance and Code Regulating Eating and Drinking Establishments. U.S. Public Health Service Pub. No. 27.

Weiser, H. H., Winter, A. R., and Lewis, M. N. 1954. The control of bacteria in chicken salad. Food Research *19*, 465–471.

Wilson, E., Foter, M. J., and Lewis, K. H. 1957. Public health aspects of food poisoning. J. Milk and Food Technol. *20*, 65–71.

CHAPTER 21

Microbiology of Water

Sources of Water Supply

When water falls upon the land it either flows into streams, lakes and reservoirs, soaks into the ground, is absorbed by plants, or is evaporated. Water supplies are called surface supplies when they are taken from streams, lakes, or reservoirs, and ground supplies when they are taken from wells or springs.

Large municipalities make use of surface sources to secure an adequate supply of water, whereas smaller communities, private estates, and industrial plants ordinarily use underground sources. It is almost impossible to find a source of either surface or underground water that will meet the modern requirements for a public water supply without some form of treatment.

The requirements for a public water supply are:

1. That it shall contain no organisms which cause disease.
2. That it be sparkling clear and colorless.
3. That it be good tasting, free from odors, and preferably cool.
4. That it be neither scale-forming nor corrosive.
5. That it be reasonably soft.
6. That it be free from objectionable gas, such as hydrogen sulfide, and objectionable minerals, such as iron and manganese.
7. That it be plentiful and low in cost.

Consumption and Uses of Water

Water is one of our most precious natural resources. Without sufficient quantity, life as we know it would be impossible. Water is used in ever increasing amounts by industry. Moreover, it is one of the cheapest utilities used in the home, perhaps we as individuals are unappreciative of the small cost of the water we drink and use. Considering that treated water, bacteriologically and chemically pure, costs about 5 cents per ton, literally, it is cheaper than dirt.

An excerpt from "Conservation for Tomorrow's America" echoes an appropriate watchword, "water." Moreover, how often do we hear this sentence, "I want a drink." The Water Division of Natural Resources reminds us of a timely statement, "Water, water, everywhere, but not a drop to waste."

Our very existence is measured in raindrops since rain is the ultimate source of our water supply.

Next to air, water is the most abundant compound used by all life. It has been stated that water covers about three-quarters of the earth's surface. Because the composition and availability are important factors in obtaining a good potable water supply, the sea where most of the water is found is not a good source although in special situations it has been and will increasingly be used in the future.

Industrial Uses of Water

Water for industry is used in large volumes. Perhaps a few statistics will reveal the important uses of water by industry. The water required in various industrial processes is shown in the following table.

TABLE 34

GALLONS OF WATER REQUIRED PER UNIT OF FINISHED PRODUCT

Product	Gallons
Aluminum	960 per lb. ingot
Brewing	470 per bbl.
By-product coke	3,600 per ton coal
Coal washing	200 per ton
Cotton fiber to fabric	37 per lb. of goods
Cotton cloth processing	15 per lb. of goods
Distilling	300–600 per bu. of washed grain
Oil refining	770 per 42 gal. bbl.
Papermaking	30 per lb. of paper
Steel, finished	65,000 per ton
Tanning	800 per 100 lb. hide

The production of electric power by steam requires 80 gal. per kilowatt hour or nearly 1,000 times as much water by weight as coal. The State of Ohio uses more than 15 billion kilowatt hours of electricity per year. The water required is equal to 1,200 billion gallons. This would fill a reservoir one mile wide and 100 miles long to a depth of 57 feet.

Water Requirements of Growing Plants

Growing a United States corn crop requires 860 billion gallons of water as a vehicle to carry nutrients into the plants. A single corn stalk may transpire 1 to $1^1/_2$ gal. daily when the ear is forming, and a total of as much as 30 gal. during the season. Ideal distribution is indicated in the old dictum; "A dry June, a wet July, and a dripping August make a good corn crop." Growth of extra bushels per acre with hybrid seed means more water taken from the soil and transpired to the atmosphere.

Uses of Water in the Food Industry

The uses of water in the food industry may be grouped as follows:

a. Cleaning, washing, or spraying the food product.
b. Immersion of food in hot water or steam during the blanching process. Also cooking or pasteurizing the food in a water medium.
c. Use of water as a cooking medium of various products.
d. Wash water with or without detergents or other compounds used in the general cleaning of food processing equipment.

AMOUNTS OF WATER USED IN PROCESSING OF A FEW SELECTED FOOD PRODUCTS

Product	Gallons
Corn canning	1100 per ton of corn in husks
Corn syrup	30–40 per bu. corn
Dairying	5 per gal. milk
Meat packing	6,000 per ton on the hoof
Tomato canning	60 gal. per bushel

For example it takes from 30,000 to 60,000 lbs. of water to produce 1 lb. of beef.

Water Purification

Since water is such an important utility in our everyday life, its composition and public health qualities are extremely important. Perhaps some attention should be given as to how water varies in composition and the manner in which it is contaminated by micro-organisms harmful to man.

Water is approximately as pure as distilled water when it leaves the clouds. When it reaches the earth's surface, suspended foreign material in the air has been picked up by the water. The amount and kind of material picked up will vary considerably. The most important factor is the contamination of the water with airborne micro-organisms. As a rule the air is not free of these organisms so their presence in rainfall is not unusual.

When the water reaches the soil, it becomes grossly contaminated with large numbers of micro-organisms always present in the soil. The soil contains millions of organisms per gram under environmental conditions favorable for microbial existence. The water carries large amounts of suspended soil particles with innumerable micro-organisms. River water, after a hard rain, becomes muddy due to soil suspensions washed into the river and the microbial content is extremely high as compared to the river water prior to the rainfall.

FIG. 34. MILLIPORE FILTER

Used to identify selected kinds of micro-organisms in water supplies.

However, not all the rainfall runs off as surface water. Large amounts enter the soil to replenish the ground water supply. As the water penetrates through the soil layers, much of the suspended soil matter and organisms are removed. For instance, water leaving a tile drain is usually crystal clear thus showing the filtering effect of the soil. The microbial content of this kind of water is very low. Again as the water penetrates through the soil it picks up soluble minerals, such as calcium, magnesium, and iron salts. These chemicals contribute to the hardness of the water.

The water may also come in contact with decayed organic matter in the soil, resulting in undesirable flavors and odors.   Man-made pollutions should not be ignored, such as industrial wastes of various kinds dumped into a surface water supply and domestic raw sewage from municipalities which do not have adequate facilities to treat their sewage supply.   One can readily see how easy it is for water to be contaminated with all kinds of micro-organisms.   Obviously the harmful or disease producing organisms must be removed or destroyed in a water supply if it is to be made safe for human consumption.   One laboratory method of identifying the kinds of micro-organisms present utilizes a millipore filter (see Fig. 34).

Ground Water Supplies

Ground water is usually considered as being well water although it may include water from wells, springs, and infiltration galleries.   Public supplies in this country are usually taken from wells.   Well water supplies have certain advantages over surface supplies:

1.   They are usually clearer.
2.   They contain fewer bacteria.
3.   If taken from a single well they usually have a uniform mineral content.
4.   They usually have a more nearly constant and lower temperature during the summer.

The temperature of ground water, coming from a depth of 50 feet, is the same as the average temperature of the region under which it lies. Water from a depth of less than 50 feet will be a little colder in the winter and a little warmer in summer.   Water from a depth greater than 50 feet has a temperature higher than the average temperature of the region under which it lies.   The temperature increases on an average of one degree for each 60 feet of depth below 50 feet.

Some of the disadvantages of ground water are:

1.   Its scarcity for large consumers.
2.   Its uncertainty.
3.   Calcium and magnesium compounds are present in larger quantities than in surface waters found in the same localities.
4.   Iron and manganese are present in many well supplies.
5.   Hydrogen sulfide is often present.
6.   The cost of pumping well water is usually greater than the cost of pumping surface water.
7.   The mineral content from two wells may be entirely different even though located in the same plot of ground.

Surface Supplies.—Surface water, whether from streams, lakes, or reservoirs, usually is contaminated and therefore unsafe and unsatisfactory for human consumption until properly treated. Municipalities sometimes discharge partially treated sewage into a water course that is used as a public water supply. This is perhaps the most dangerous source of contamination. Soil washings may carry mud, leaves, decayed vegetation, and human and animal refuse into the supply, thus rendering it turbid or unclean in appearance. The turbidity, or muddiness, and mineral content of water in flowing streams vary from day to day. Following heavy rains it may be extremely muddy and low in mineral content, whereas during dry seasons it may be relatively clear and more highly mineralized. Surface supplies may be muddy or clear, soft or hard, depending on the season. The immensity of the problem of mud removal from water taken from surface sources may be realized when we find that many of the large communities remove from 100 to 1,000 or more tons of mud from a single day's supply of water before pumping it to the consumer. Human feces and urine may cause typhoid fever, dysentery, and other enteric diseases. Organic wastes furnish food for micro-organisms, which include vegetable growths such as algae and the lower forms of animal life. They may impart to the water disagreeable tastes and odors.

The waste liquors from manufacturing plants, mines, and quarries are often discharged into streams. These wastes may be objectionable because many of them are acid in nature, in which case they render the water either unfit for use or too corrosive for distribution through the ordinary iron pipe distributing systems. Industrial wastes also may contain excessive quantities of organic material, which after decomposition causes the water to be unpalatable. Substances such as phenols from coke-oven plants are sometimes discharged into streams and lakes and are especially objectionable if chlorine is used in the treatment of the water supply. Chlorophenols are produced which impart to the water a disagreeable medicinal taste which is extremely difficult to remove.

Farm Ponds

The water requirements in rural areas and especially for large dairy farms, vegetable crop irrigation, and domestic consumption are comparable in demand to municipal uses of potable water.

In many cases, underground water supplies such as springs and wells have not been adequate to supply sufficient water for all purposes. The farm pond idea has come into prominence in meeting

FIG. 35.   A TYPICAL FARM POND

In many areas, artificially created ponds such as this supply a major portion of the water needed in stock raising and other agricultural requirements.

the demand for water.   Where the topography of the land is suitable for the construction of farm ponds they have been built at a minimum of expense.   Fig. 35 shows a typical farm pond.   The farm pond can be constructed of any size ranging from $1/4$ acre, to several acres in size, thus it is possible to store millions of gallons of water for domestic use, recreation, and fish culture.

The major problem is primarily to remove the sediment and purify the water for domestic use.   The author has been working on the microbiology of farm ponds for several years.   Many publications are available covering the details of the uses of farm pond waters.

The use of contaminated water presents a serious health problem. Many pathogenic organisms are water-borne.   These micro-organisms may cause disease in man or animals or both.   Fortunately many farm pond operators treat the water adequately to make it safe for human consumption.

The contaminated water also carries many food spoilage organisms which alter the quality of milk, dairy products, and other foods, when the water is used in various ways in food processing.

It is inappropriate to discuss the biology and treatment of farm pond water supplies because of the many concepts involved.   However, in summary, farm ponds are the answer in many cases for adequate rural water supplies.   Practical methods are now available for treating farm pond water both from the chemical and public health standpoints, thus making this source of water supply adequate for all purposes in rural homes and on the farm.

The Natural Purification of Water

There is a popular notion that streams purify themselves in 20 miles of flow. Although there are natural processes that tend to lessen impurities this notion is questionable.

Bacteria and algae consume and thrive on organic materials. Smaller micro-organisms eat bacteria and algae, larger micro-organisms live on the smaller ones, and fish and higher forms of animal life in turn consume the larger micro-organisms. Unless the velocity of flow is too great, mud and suspended matter naturally settle out of suspension and organic matter is rendered harmless by oxidation, which is accomplished much more quickly and effectively if the stream flows over rough beds, riffles, and spillways. Sunlight has some germicidal effect due to its ultraviolet rays, but it penetrates only a little below the water surface and is not constant in its action because at night, and on some days, the sun does not shine at all.

Although nature tends to purify water by physical, chemical, and biological processes or a combination of forces, it is not sufficient to assure a safe drinking water supply.

The following factors play an important role in the purification of water.

Temperature: As a rule during the summer months pathogens die off more rapidly than in the winter time.

Dilution: In a fast flowing stream the dilution of organic matter and micro-organisms is a significant factor in purification of water. The microbial content of a fast-flowing stream is usually very low as compared to a quiet stream.

Sedimentation.—If water in reservoirs or lakes is allowed to stand, much of the suspended organic matter will settle out. Hence, many organisms are removed in this way. Authorities in water purification recognize the importance of this process, and have accelerated the procedure by adding certain chemicals to the water which hasten the settling of suspended solids. Such a procedure may remove 80 to 90 per cent of the bacteria from the clear water.

Filtration.—Water percolating through the top soil layers tends to remove large amounts of organic matter and organisms. The rate of water filtration will depend upon the type of soil. Sand and gravel offer the most efficient type of filtering material while clay soil offers the least efficient, because the clay particles are so small that water passes through them very slowly. Natural filtration will remove from 95 to 99 per cent of the organisms from polluted water.

Modern treatment plants have modified the filtering process in order to accelerate the treatment of water on a large volume basis although the fundamental principle of natural filtration remains the same.

These natural processes, therefore, are not positive, and it is unsafe to generalize regarding the number of miles of flow necessary to accomplish self-purification. One river, for example, which received sewage for years, did not even become clear or lose its sewage odor until it had flowed some seventy or eighty miles. It was not bacterially safe even after many more miles of flow. Water in reservoirs after thirty or more days' storage may become practically free from turbidity and bacteria. However, this condition may be entirely changed in a few hours by the so-called overturning of the reservoir. This occurs when the surface water becomes chilled or warmed to a temperature of 39.2°F (3.8°C). At this temperature water has its greatest density. Heavy water, of course, cannot stay at the surface and convection currents are set up that may become sufficiently active to cause a complete overturn of the reservoir, resulting in much turbidity being diffused throughout the entire contents of the reservoir.

Storage.—Purification by storage involves storing water in basins or reservoirs for long periods of time. For example, storm water must be stored in reservoirs in order to have an adequate supply during the low flow periods. For such storage a dam is usually constructed across a valley to form an impounding reservoir. This affords an opportunity for the subsidence of silt and clay, reduction in color, and for the death of bacteria. Considerable time is required for these results to be accomplished by storage alone, and even then bacteria and finely divided particles of clay are not entirely removed. The sizes of the basins or reservoirs required make this method very expensive. The tendency toward stagnation and the multiplication of low forms of animal and vegetable growth make it undesirable. Even though many days of storage are provided, other methods of treatment usually are required to insure a satisfactory product.

Aeration.—Many water supplies do not need to be aerated. Surface supplies, however, sometimes have offensive tastes and odors. Aeration may remove them if they are due to dissolved gases resulting from the decomposition of organic matter. If, however, they are due to dissolved organic matter, aeration will not be very effective.

Ground supplies usually contain carbon dioxide, and sometimes hydrogen sulfide, iron, and manganese. Aeration reduces the carbon dioxide and hydrogen sulfide and, in most cases, oxidizes the iron, causing it to precipitate as insoluble ferric compounds which can be removed readily by filtration. Manganese, especially if it is present in appreciable quantities, is not so easily removed as iron. Aeration and filtration usually are not adequate. Iron and manganese can be precipitated from aerated water very effectively by the addition of lime. Manganese requires more lime for its precipitation than iron. A pH of 9.4 is usually adequate for the precipitation of manganese. The reduction of carbon dioxide by aeration decreases the cost of softening water if lime is used as the reagent. One objection to the aeration of oxygen-free ground water is that it becomes oxygenated and under some circumstances may be more corrosive. Aeration is also expensive.

Physical Methods of Water Purification

Slow Sand Filtration.—Slow sand filters are beds of sand 30 to 40 in. deep, contained in concrete basins, each about one acre in extent. They date from about 1830, are commonly regarded as the English type of filters, and are used extensively abroad. Very few slow sand filters have been built in this country since the introduction of the American or rapid type of sand filter about 1890 to 1900. Chemicals are used with the rapid type to assist clarification before filtration, thus increasing the filtration rate from about one to two million gallons per acre per 24 hours to about one hundred and twenty-five million gallons per acre per 24 hours.

The operation of some of the slow sand filters in the United States has been supplemented by features characteristic of the rapid sand type, principally preliminary coagulation and disinfection.

The slow sand filter is adapted to the treatment of water having a turbidity not exceeding about 30 parts per million and of low color. For high turbidities and high color, coagulation generally is a necessary or desirable adjunct. With such conditions the rapid sand filter is more economical. Chief disadvantages of slow sand filters are:

1. The large area required for construction of filters.
2. Their successful operation is limited to clear water with low color.
3. The first cost is relatively high.

Rapid Sand Filtration.—To obtain a high rate of filtration through sand filters (100 to 200 million gallons per acre per day), it is usually necessary to treat the water ahead of the filters. This preparatory treatment includes: (1) aeration to free the water from dissolved gases and to oxidize iron and organic matter if present; (2) coagulation; and (3) settling.

The addition of the coagulant to the water, followed by a short period of agitation, results in the formation of a precipitate which entangles the mud, bacteria, and suspended matter into clumps, readily removed by settling. The settled water then passes to the filter which removes the finely divided suspended matter that does not settle in the settling tanks.

Chemical Treatment of Water

Hardness of water means its soap-consuming power. The underlying principle is based upon the ability of the soap to form an insoluble precipitate with the calcium and magnesium salts contained in the water. In laboratory testing when these compounds are removed by precipitation with standard soap solution, a permanent lather or foam is formed and serves as the end point in calculating the hardness. It is expressed in grains per gallon or parts per million of calcium carbonate. Water can contain temporary or permanent hardness or both.

However, the types of hardness may greatly influence the cleaning procedure as suggested in the following statements.

Temporary or carbonate hardness is that part of the total hardness which can be removed by boiling. It is due to the bicarbonates of calcium or magnesium present in the water. This type of hardness gives an alkaline reaction when titrated with an acid. Due to the slight solubility of calcium and magnesium carbonates formed when a solution of the bicarbonate is boiled, not quite all of the temporary hardness is removed.

Permanent or noncarbonate hardness is not removed by boiling and is due to sulfates and chlorides of calcium and magnesium. If the temporary hardness is removed by boiling, the permanent hardness, i.e., calcium and magnesium, remaining in solution, can be determined by adding standard "soda reagent" (equal parts of NaOH and Na_2CO_3) which precipitates the magnesium as hydroxide and the calcium as carbonate. The amount of standard soda reagent remaining represents the amount consumed as calcium and magnesium when the reagent is added in excess and titrated with a standard acid.

The true total hardness of a water supply may be determined by neutralizing the water sample with H_2SO_4, which converts all the temporary into permanent hardness. By determining the permanent hardness the true total hardness of the water is obtained.

Calcium and magnesium bicarbonates in the water are responsible for the temporary hardness while the sulfates and salts other than bicarbonates contribute to the permanent hardness.

The two types of hardness can be distinguished by the fact that the bicarbonates tend to settle out when the water is heated or boiled while the sulfates do not precipitate out. However, magnesium carbonates are only partly precipitated upon heating so this may lead to some misconception of the terms "temporary" and "permanent" hardness.

One can appreciate that water can have several complex combinations. These affect its use as wash water in the presence of detergents or the direct use of water in the food and beverage industry by altering the flavor of the products due to the presence of certain salts.

In softening water, a chemical reaction takes place which in one case removes the chemical constituents in the form of dissolved mineral compounds, or converts the compounds to a form in which scale is removed. In hard water, the salts are present in solution, therefore, they cannot be removed by filtration. Obviously, a chemical reaction must take place in order to remove the harmful salts or convert them into harmless forms.

In treating hard water, lime-soda-ash softening is used most widely. The basic principle is based on the low solubility of calcium carbonate ($CaCO_3$) and magnesium hydroxide ($Mg(OH)_2$). If sufficient quantities of lime and soda are added to hard water and then stirred, an insoluble compound is eventually formed which settles out upon standing. The supernatant water is soft. In order to hasten the reaction of lime and soda ash, a compound of aluminum sulfate is added to facilitate the precipitation of $CaCO_3$ and $Mg(OH)_2$. Otherwise, the calcium carbonate and magnesium hydroxide settle out very slowly.

Rapid sand filters are used to remove and prevent suspended salts from forming scale deposits.

Obviously, soft water is highly desirable due to its inherent cleaning properties. As water increases in hardness, especially permanent hardness, the soap consumption and waste is greater. Likewise, an alteration of the chemical composition of any detergent takes place and cuts down the efficiency of the product. Hence, the calcium and magnesium sulfates and chlorides which are soluble in the wash water tend to form insoluble carbonates, phosphates, and silicates, while the soluble sodium compounds form the basis of any cleaner being used.

On the other hand, acid cleaners tend to increase the solubility of calcium and magnesium sulfates. In this way water stone deposits have been very largely prevented by precipitation from a hard water. An acid cleaner tends to be corrosive. This objection has been overcome by the use of corrosion inhibitors.

Temporary or Carbonate Hardness.—This is due to calcium and magnesium carbonates with sufficient carbon dioxide present to form the acid carbonates or bicarbonates which are soluble. In the usual case magnesium bicarbonate accounts for about 60 per cent of the hardness in water.

$$H_2O + CO_2 \rightarrow H_2CO_3$$
$$H_2CO_3 + CaCO_3 \rightarrow Ca(HCO_3)_2$$
$$H_2CO_3 + MgCO_3 \rightarrow Mg(HCO_3)_2$$

This type of hardness when it is the calcium salt is removed by precipitation with exactly the required quantity of lime.

$$Ca(HCO_3)_2 + Ca(OH)_2 \rightarrow \underline{2CaCO_3} + 2H_2O$$

Calcium carbonate is extremely insoluble; it settles as a sediment and can thus be removed.

If a solution of bicarbonates is heated as in a boiler, carbon dioxide is driven off and calcium carbonate precipitates as scale.

$$Ca(HCO_3)_2 \rightarrow \underline{CaCO_3} + CO_2 + H_2O$$

Magnesium bicarbonate requires more lime to precipitate it because magnesium carbonate is somewhat soluble while magnesium hydroxide is very insoluble.

$$Mg(HCO_3)_2 + Ca(OH)_2 \rightarrow MgCO_3 + \underline{CaCO_3} + 2H_2O$$
$$MgCO_3 + Ca(OH)_2 \rightarrow \underline{Mg(OH)_2} + \underline{CaCO_3}$$

Adding, $$Mg(HCO_3)_2 + 2Ca(OH)_2 \rightarrow \underline{Mg(OH)_2} + \underline{2CaCO_3} + 2H_2O$$

Aluminum sulfate or alum is usually added which, in the presence of basic substances, e.g., sodium carbonate, will form insoluble aluminum hydroxide, a flocculent precipitate which causes the calcium carbonate and magnesium hydroxide to settle more quickly.

$$Al_2(SO_4)_3 + 6Na_2CO_3 + 3H_2O \rightarrow \underline{2Al(OH)_3} + 3Na_2SO_4 + 6NaHCO_3$$

or, using lime

$$Al_2(SO_4)_3 + 3Ca(OH)_2 \rightarrow \underline{2Al(OH)_3} + 3CaSO_4$$

In the latter case, the slightly soluble calcium sulfate would remain as permanent hardness. It can be removed as shown on page 345.

The settling of any precipitate, especially a flocculent precipitate has the incidental but very valuable effect of sweeping down and thus removing nearly all micro-organisms originally present in the water. Hence, removing hardness purifies the water biologically as well.

Permanent Hardness.—This consists of non-carbonate salts of calcium and magnesium such as the sulfates and chlorides. It is called *permanent* hardness because it cannot be removed by simple boiling. Calcium salts are removed with soda ash, i.e., sodium carbonate.

$$CaSO_4 + Na_2CO_3 \rightarrow \underline{CaCO_3} + Na_2SO_4$$

Non-carbonate magnesium salts are treated with lime and soda ash.

$$MgSO_4 + Ca(OH)_2 \rightarrow \underline{Mg(OH)_2} + CaSO_4$$
$$CaSO_4 + Na_2CO_3 \rightarrow \underline{CaCO_3} + Na_2SO_4$$

Adding, $MgSO_4 + Ca(OH)_2 + Na_2CO_3 \rightarrow \underline{Mg(OH)_2} + \underline{CaCO_3} + Na_2SO_4$

The effect of lime-treated water upon survival of bacteria was studied by Riehl, Weiser, and Rheins (1952) when a high pH was maintained. The same fundamental principle is applied in the destruction of bacteria during sanitization of dairy and other food handling equipment. It is just as important to destroy harmful organisms in a drinking water supply as in various kinds of foods. Although the maintenance of a high pH in foods is not practicable in order to control the undesirable bacteria, a low pH, or high acidity, either biological acidity or the addition of different organic acids has been used for a long time as a means of preserving certain foods. The authors confined their work to water treatment with the following objectives: To determine (1) the survival of selected bacteria when added to various water samples; (2) the effect of pH on the survival of the organisms; (3) the influence of the composition of the test waters—distilled, hard, soft, and turbid; and (4) the influence of temperatures such as 37° to 41°F (3° to 5°C), 60°F (15.5°C), and 77°F (25°C).

Escherichia coli, Salmonella typhi, and *Salmonella montivideo* do not survive for prolonged periods in water when high pH levels are maintained by the addition of excess lime in a pH range from 11.0 to 11.5, a temperature of 59°F (15°C), and a holding period of slightly longer than 4 hours. This method was effective in destroying many of the test organisms. Freshly isolated strains of the test bacteria were more resistant than the same species propagated for several months on culture media.

Municipal and Industrial Waste Treatment Processes

At the present time sewage treatment is based largely on natural and biological purification processes. However, the biological methods are designed to provide optimum conditions so that these natural processes can operate at an accelerated rate. There are two principal methods in use: primary and secondary treatment. The former consists of those processes which mechanically remove solids from the liquid wastes. This procedure involves screening, grit settling, plain settling and the precipitation of colloidal particles by the addition of chemicals. The solids remaining are known as sludge and are acted upon by bacteria which reduce the sludge to an inert humus-like residue. The liquid portion of the sewage may be discharged into a stream, providing there is sufficient flow of water in the stream to dilute the effluent so that it will not be a nuisance. In other words, there must be sufficient dissolved oxygen in the water to oxidize any suspended solids in the effluent. A more satisfactory method is to discharge the liquid onto a filter bed, thus allowing desirable oxidizing bacteria to digest the suspended solids. The remaining liquid is sparkling clear when it passes through the filter bed. This is the most efficient method but it may not be economical.

In many instances, primary treatment may be sufficient to handle the industrial wastes providing the stream flow is large enough to dilute the wastes. Thus the normal biological action that takes place in the stream may be sufficient to handle the extra load of wastes discharged into the water. It is often necessary that the secondary treatment be used to supplement the primary treatment. This is especially true during a drought where the stream is not able to absorb the pollution load.

In many instances primary treatment may be sufficient to handle the industrial wastes providing the stream flow is large enough to dilute the wastes. Thus the normal biological action that takes place in the stream may be sufficient to handle the extra load of wastes discharged into the water. It is often necessary that the secondary treatment be used to supplement the primary treatment. This is especially true during a drought where the stream is not able to absorb the pollution load.

There are many types of both primary and secondary treatment processes in use at the present time. Regardless of the type they should include the following objectives for efficient and safe operation.

1. A screen of sufficient size, to remove the larger floating or suspended solids.
2. A grit chamber to remove the inert materials, thus allowing them to settle out and ultimately be removed.
3. A sedimentation tank, where the lighter organic and inorganic solids are allowed to settle and thus be removed as sludge and scum.
4. A sludge digestion tank and drying bed. The sludge is removed from the sedimentation tank and placed in a sludge digester where bacterial action takes place.

The biological action is due to anaerobic bacteria. The digested sludge from the digesters is placed on drying beds and allowed to dry. In some cases, the dried sludge is used as a land fill or as a fertilizer when properly supplemented by other plant food. Some plants expose the sludge on vacuum filters for drying and then burn the sludge. There are several variations in the primary treatment processes. The chemical treatment of incoming raw sewage by coagulation and flocculation to assure a more rapid and complete precipitation of suspended solids is receiving considerable attention at the present time. Chemical treatment is often used as an intermediate step between primary and secondary treatments.

Secondary treatment of raw sewage is used only after some form of primary treatment. Biological action is necessary to destroy the organic material in solution. The trickling filter and the activated sludge method are the two principal processes used at the present time.

The trickling filter consists of a bed of coarse stone, provided with an underdrain, over which the sewage is sprayed and allowed to percolate down through the bed. Biological life accumulates on the surface of the stones, and this mixed microflora called "Schmutsdecke," meaning ground, cover oxidizes the organic materials to produce an effluent which, having undergone primary treatment, has had removed from it about 85 per cent of the pollution load of the original raw sewage.

The activated sludge process works on the same biological principle, except the mixed microflora are cultivated in the sludge. Tanks are constructed of sufficient capacity to allow the sewage to flow through at a slow rate. Large volumes of air are blown in at the bottom of the tank thus providing stirring and oxygen. The incoming raw sewage is inoculated with a complex biological life by returning at least one-fifth of the sludge already removed from sewage previously treated. A thorough mixing of biological life with the raw sewage along with sufficient air provides purification in much the same manner as a trickling filter. The activated sludge in some mysterious way accelerates the settling of the solids in the raw sewage, thus saving approximately two-thirds of the time required for the natural settling of the solids in the primary treatment.

The Problem of Industrial Waste and Domestic Sewage

In general, there are several well-known methods of water purification; namely, prolonged storage; filtration through slow sand filters; coagulation and filtering through rapid sand filters; combined water softening and iron removal, coagulation, and filtration through rapid sand filters; water softening; iron and manganese removal; and disinfection. In addition to these, there are a number of special treatment processes and modifications. Very often it is necessary that a combination of treatments be used in order to obtain the desired results.

During the past few years, a marked increase in industrial activity has resulted in many of the industrial wastes being dumped into the municipal sewage system. The outcome of this practice, in many cases, is an upset of the normal biological activity in municipal sewage. Obviously, the character or composition of industrial wastes will determine the biological action of the ordinary sewage when these wastes are dumped into it.

No attempt will be made to discuss all types of industrial wastes, but some attention to those wastes normally associated with the food industry will be considered.

Milk products factory wastes are common wastes in municipal sewage because nearly all cities and towns have milk plants. Since dairy products undergo an acid fermentation, the wastes are usually acid in character. The dilution factor is very important in determining the effect on normal sewage. If too much milk waste enters the sewage, it becomes acid; and this factor may interrupt the normal biological activity of the sewage.

One of the basic principles of sewage treatment is to create a suitable environment for micro-organisms to act effectively upon the sewage. Usually, municipal sewage without any industrial wastes will undergo normal processes. The composition of many industrial wastes are quite different. Hence, the normal activity of desirable micro-organisms is checked.

The first step in sewage purification is the separation of the liquid from the solids. This can be done by settling and then the liquid is sprayed into the air to incorporate atmospheric oxygen. Aerobic bacteria oxidize the suspended solids to a liquefiable state and the material is then filtered through layers of gravel where the oxidation process is most active. The final effluent can be safely disposed of in a stream. This procedure is frequently called the primary treatment. The solids can be placed in large digesting tanks where anaerobic bacteria attack the solids and break them down to gases, liquids, and inert solids. The gases constitute a valuable by-product in the digestion of sewage solids. The combustible methane gas is used as fuel in combustion engines for the development of electrical power and heat for plant operation. The inert solids are burned as useful fuel or combined with plant food and sold as commercial fertilizer, the liquid passes through gravel filters where aerobic oxidation stabilizes the effluent which then is discharged into the stream.

In many cases, the industrial wastes must be pre-treated before they enter the municipal sewage system. At the present time a great deal of attention is given to the pre-treatment and this is considered as an integral part of sewage treatment. Each waste must be treated by the most economical and practical method. Many factors enter into this phase of treatment and no attempt will be made to discuss the various methods in detail.

Recently, Federal and State laws have been established which prohibit the discharge of municipal raw sewage and industrial wastes of any kind into a surface water supply without some preliminary treatment to render it less objectionable for a good quality water supply.

Many food processing plants have their own treatment plant to take care of their food wastes. This is especially true in the canning industry. The use of lagoons, covering large areas of land, has been very successful. The biological changes involved have been effective in transforming the wastes into stable products with little odor and a maximum reduction in the volume of wastes.

Food processing plants use large volumes of water, therefore it is essential that the water be free of pathogens and other organisms that may cause spoilage in processed foods. In the case where water is used for cooling purposes or for washing the food, the water should be chemically treated to render it free of harmful organisms.

Food wastes from processing plants vary widely in composition, some of the constituents are easily oxidized while others are more complex and may be difficult to decompose by microbial action.

Fresh surface water supplies may contain up to 10 p.p.m. of free oxygen. Obviously the presence of organic wastes results in action by micro-organisms until the free oxygen is used up. The term biochemical oxygen demand (BOD) is used to indicate the quantity of oxygen required to completely oxidize the organic wastes present. When the BOD rises above 4 p.p.m. aquatic life ceases to exist. Then anaerobic conditions (without free oxygen) begin to operate, resulting in hydrolysis, putrefaction, and fermentation. Under anaerobic conditions the end products are not completely oxidized, giving rise to offensive odors. Such waters are not suitable for food processing in any form.

It takes about 50 tons of pure oxygen a day to process the sewage in a city with a population around 500,000. This is about 250 tons of air or about 4 million cu. ft. Every molecule of oxygen goes through the bacterial cell. When industries such as oil cracking plants and plastic industries discharge their wastes into sewage, carbonic acid,

TABLE 35

SUMMARY OF FISH KILLED OVER A 10-MONTH PERIOD BY WATER POLLUTION AS REPORTED BY THE FIELD PERSONNEL OF THE OHIO DIVISION OF WILDLIFE

Species of Fish	No. of Fish Killed
Small-mouthed Bass	417
Large-mouthed Bass	216
Rock Bass	107
Muskellunge	1
Grass Pike	16
Bluegills	240
Green Sunfish	591
White and Black Crappies	614
Channel Catfish	54
Bullheads	1,809
Carp	6,483
Suckers	129,091
Quillback	1
Gizzard Shad	242
Darters	7
Creek Chubs	432
Crayfish	3,865
Minnows and fry	385,990
Unidentified	1,384
Total	531,560

TABLE 36

NUMBER OF INDUSTRIAL PLANTS IN OHIO PRODUCING WASTES ASSUMED INIMICAL TO FISH

Food processing	2,134
Paper and allied products	207
Chemical and allied products	558
By-products of coal and oil refining	78
Rubber products	141
Leather and tanning	99
Prime metal industries	516
Metal fabrication	1,376
Machinery, manufacturing	1,542
Electrical devices	284
Transportation equipment	232
Miscellaneous	806
Total	7,973

phenols, and other compounds that are poisonous to bacteria prevent the organisms from oxidizing or stabilizing the sewage.

If every home had a garbage disposal unit, it would be necessary to double the facilities of sewage disposal systems. Moreover, the ever increasing use of detergents in the home laundry, as well as public ones, may cause the biological system in the sewage plant to function abnormally. This problem is very new and will require some fundamental research. Studies by Malaney, Sheets, and Ayers

(1960) have shown the effect of different concentrations of detergents on the biological processes normally associated with sewage treatment. Table 35 indicates the importance of stream pollution to Ohio fish life, and Table 36 shows how numerous are the sources of pollution in a typical industrial eastern state.

BIBLIOGRAPHY

Gainey, P. L., and Lord, T. H. 1952. Microbiology of Water and Sewage. Prentice-Hall, New York.

Hoover, C. P. 1951. Water Supply and Treatment. National Lime Assoc., Washington, D. C.

Malaney, G. W., Sheets, W. D., and Ayers, J. 1960. Effect of anionic surface agents on waste water treatment units. J. Water Pollution Control Federation, Washington, D. C.

Matz, S. A. 1965. Water in Foods. Avi Publ. Co., Westport, Conn.

Phelps, E. B. 1944. Stream Sanitation. John Wiley & Sons, New York.

Prescott, S. C., Winslow, C. A., and McCrady, M. H. 1946. Water Bacteriology, 6th ed. John Wiley & Sons, New York.

Riehl, M. L., Weiser, H. H., and Rheins, B. T. 1952. Effect of lime treated water upon survival of bacteria. J. Am. Water Works Assoc. *44*, No. 5, 466–470.

Laboratory Manual of Methods[1]

I. INTRODUCTION

The manual describes methods which have been found useful for the bacteriological examination of foods on the basis of the authors' firsthand laboratory experience. From the techniques reviewed in Part One, as well as developmental and evaluative studies conducted by the Public Health Service, methods have been selected that may be employed successfully to examine foods, either routinely, or when implicated in disease outbreaks. The choices may seem arbitrary, especially where several feasible methods are available, but they represent the best judgment of the group in 1964. Future work may well demonstrate the superiority of other techniques; meanwhile, the manual serves as a practical guide for our own work, for the instruction of bacteriologists who enroll in training courses, and for the guidance of other laboratories that periodically request advice about the bacteriological examination of foods.

Attention has been directed primarily toward the development of methods for the detection and enumeration of pathogenic and indicator bacterial species in foods. Two procedural lines of investigation are presented: (a) Direct plating methods applicable to foods implicated in food-borne disease outbreaks in which the causal organism may be expected in relatively large numbers, and (b) enrichment methods suitable for indicating the sanitary quality of foods, in which pathogenic species may be present in small numbers.

Though *Proteus, Pseudomonas, Vibrio,* and *Bacillus* species, in addition to other minor groups, have occasionally been reported to cause food poisoning, the methods presented in this manual are directed primarily toward the determination of etiological agents of the common types of food-borne disease outbreaks and to the enumeration of indicator organisms. In the interest of simplicity, commercially available reagents, apparatus, and dehydrated culture media have been prescribed whenever possible. For the most part, comparable products are available from several manufacturers, and brand names are mentioned only for purposes of identification. The use of a particular trade name does not indicate any preference for this item over comparable products from other sources. Complete formulae are given only on media that are not now available commercially.

Each method is divided into two main sections: apparatus, materials, and culture media; and procedure. In the interest of brevity, duplication of directions has been avoided whenever possible; thus the laboratory worker is directed to refer to appropriate preceding methods for instructions, where the same information applies to methods described later in the manual. For example, the

---

[1]Reprinted with permission of authors from: Lewis, K. H., and Angelotti, R., 1964. Examination of Foods for Enteropathogenic and Indicator Bacteria. U. S. Dept. of Health, Education and Welfare, Washington, D. C.

basic tools, glassware, and apparatus to prepare dilutions of food, plate them in agar, and count the resulting colonies is initially presented in IV—Agar Plate Colony Count. In all subsequent methods in which identical materials are required, the reader is instructed to obtain the designated materials as listed in section IV.

The manual is presented in such a fashion as to provide reasonable assistance to those who are not professional bacteriologists but are required to perform bacteriological analyses of foods as part of their responsibilities. To insure efficient utilization of manpower and materials and to obtain reliably valid results, these methods should, however, be applied only by laboratory personnel familiar with bacteriological techniques under the supervision and direction of an experienced, formally trained microbiologist.

In the interest of protecting the laboratory staff, appropriate safety precautions should be observed. The hazard of contracting infections from foods being examined bacteriologically in the laboratory is not great when good techniques are used consistently. It is, however, prudent that foods be handled in the laboratory in a manner consistent with acceptable practice for handling infectious material. Special attention should be given to observing safety precautions, frequently omitted in sanitation laboratories to avoid infection and spread of contamination. Enteric pathogenic bacteria and coagulase-positive staphylococci are not uncommon in foods, and, because of their presence, as well as the occasional presence of other pathogenic forms, the following precautions should be observed:

(1) Avoid smoking or eating while working in the laboratory. The worker's hands may become contaminated in removing screw caps from bottles, shaking dilution bottles, and other manipulations, and handling a pipe or cigarette may be a possible means of transmitting contamination to the mouth.

(2) Contamination of the upper end of a pipette with the finger may be a source of infection.

(3) Wash the hands and rinse them with disinfectant, if they become contaminated, and keep the hands dry.

(4) Use covered mechanical blenders to avoid aerosol contamination.

(5) Place all discarded pipettes, bent glass rods, and other implements in disinfectant solution.

(6) All discarded plates, tubes, bottles, and other contaminated materials should be especially marked for autoclaving before glassware is washed.

(7) As soon as laboratory work is completed, wipe table top with disinfectant and wash hands thoroughly and rinse with disinfectant before drying.

II. PREPARATION OF FOOD HOMOGENATE

A. Apparatus and Materials:

1. Mechanical blender, Waring Blendor, 2-speed standard model, with low speed operating at 8,000 rpm, or equivalent equipment.

2. Glass or metal jars of 1,000 ml. capacity, with covers for above blender. One jar for each food specimen sampled.

3. Balance, with weights, 500 gm. capacity, sensitivity 30 mg.

4. Beakers 250 ml. low form, covered with aluminum foil before sterilization (for weighing sample). One beaker for each food specimen weighed.

5. Widemouthed jars (1-qt. capacity) or Pyrex flask (1-liter capacity) for

450 ml. of sterile, phosphate-buffered dilution water. One jar or flask of dilution water for each food specimen to be examined.

6. Instruments for preparing samples: knives, forks, forceps, scissors, tablespoons, spatulas, or tongue depressors (Sterilized previous to use—either by autoclaving or hot air).

7. Phosphate-buffered dilution water—formula:

   a. Stock phosphate-buffer solution:

Monobasic potassium phosphate, KH_2PO_4 ....34.0 gm.
Distilled water ....500.0 ml.
1 N NaOH soln. added to give pH 7.2*
Distilled water to make ....1,000.0 ml.

   b. Final phosphate-buffered dilution water:

Stock phosphate-buffer soln. ....1.25 ml.
Distilled water to make ....1,000.0 ml.

   c. Fill dilution bottle with predetermined volume so that after autoclaving volume remaining will be 99 ml. ± 2 ml.

   d. Final reaction after sterilization to be pH 7.0 ± 0.1.

B. Procedure:

1. Using aseptic technique, weigh 50 gm. of the food sample into a tared 250-ml. beaker.
2. Transfer the weighed sample to a sterile blended jar and use part of the 450 ml. of phosphate-buffered dilution water to rinse any adhering food from the beaker into the blender jar.
3. Add the remainder of the 450 ml. of dilution water to the blender jar and blend for 2 min. at low speed (8,000 rpm).
4. This 1:10 dilution is now ready to use in preparing a series of decimal dilutions such as 10^{-1} to 10^{-6}.

III. MICROSCOPIC EXAMINATION

A. Gram Stain Reagents (Hucker Modification)

1. Ammonium oxalate crystal violet (primary stain);

Soln. A.: Crystal violet (90% dye content*) ....2.0 gm.
        Ethyl alcohol (95%) ....20.0 ml.
Soln. B: Ammonium oxalate ....0.8 gm.
        Distilled water ....80.0 ml.
        Mix soln. A and soln. B

2. Iodine solution (mordant):

Iodine crystals ....1.0 gm.
Potassium iodide ....2.0 gm.
Distilled water ....300.0 ml.

3. Ethyl alcohol (95%) (Decolorizer)

4. Safranin (Counterstain)

Safranin 0 (2.5% solution in 95% ethyl alcohol) ....10.0 ml.
Distilled water ....100.0 ml.

B. Apparatus and Materials:

1. Glass slide 25 x 72 mm., etched portion for labeling
One slide for each blended food sample (10^{-1} diln.).

---

*NOTE   About 175 ml. 1 N NaOH are usually required to give pH 7.2.

2. Wire loops, 4 mm. platinum-iridium or nichrome, B & S gauge, No. 26.
3. Gram stain reagents (see A above).
4. Microscope with oil objective lens (98X) and 10X ocular.
5. Immersion oil.
6. Blended food sample (10^{-1} diln.).

C. Procedure—Gram Stain:
   1. Prepare a smear of the blended food sample (10^{-1} diln.).
   2. Air dry smear and fix by quickly passing 3 times through a Bunsen flame.
   3. Defat by immersing slide for 1 to 2 min. in xylene.
   4. Drain and dry.
   5. Stain smear 1 min. with crystal violet soln.
   6. Wash in tap water.
   7. Immerse in iodine soln. for 1 min.
   8. Wash in tap water and blot dry.
   9. Decolorize for 30 sec. in 95% ethyl alcohol.
   10. Blot dry.
   11. Counterstain 10 sec. with safranin.
   12. Wash in tap water and blot dry.
   13. Use a microscope equipped with an oil immersion objective (98X) and a 10X ocular and adjust the lighting systems for optimum illumination of the smear.
   14. Examine at least 10 fields noting types of organisms present and their relative numbers without actually counting the bacteria present.

IV. AGAR PLATE COLONY COUNT

A. Apparatus, Materials, and Culture Media:
   1. Thirteen culture dishes (100 x 15 mm.), glass or plastic.
   2. Pipettes, APHA milk diln. specifications;
      a. 1.1-ml. with 0.1-ml., and 1-ml. graduations (3 pipettes).
      b. 11-ml. with 1-ml. graduations (2 pipettes).
   3. Dilution blanks, phosphate-buffered distilled water, 99 ml. ± 2 ml. (See item II, A, 7).
   4. Water bath for tempering agar, 45° ± 1° C.
   5. Incubator 35° ± 1° C.
   6. Wax labeling pencil.
   7. Colony counter, Quebec, dark field model.
   8. Tally register.
   9. Standard Methods agar (approximately 200 ml. for each food specimen examined).

B. Procedure:
   1. Using separate sterile pipettes, prepare decimal dilutions of 10^{-2} to 10^{-6} of the 1:10 dilution of food-homogenate prepared in II above. Mix throughly by shaking.

   NOTE: The same series of dilutions is used to inoculate other culture media for the detection of various groups of microorganisms as described in the following sections of this manual.

   2. Pipette carefully 1 ml. of each dilution into each of appropriately marked duplicate culture dishes, being careful to agitate each dilution bottle to resuspend material that may have settled out.

3. Pour plates with 10 to 12 ml. of Standard Methods agar melted and tempered to 45° C.
4. Immediately mix dilution and the agar medium by rotating or by rotating and tilting dishes.
5. Pour an agar control plate.
6. Allow plates to solidify.*
7. Invert dishes and incubate them at 35° C for 48 hr.
8. Following incubation, count all colonies on plates containing 30 to 300 colonies, and record results.
9. Compute the colony count per gram of food and record this figure.

V. COLIFORM BACTERIA

A. Plate-Count Method (Suitable for analyzing foods in which large numbers of coliform bacteria may be expected):
1. Apparatus, materials and culture media:
   a. Same as Agar-Plate Colony Count (IV, A, 1 through 8).
   b. Inoculating needle, nichrome or platinum—iridium wire, B & S gauge No. 26.
   c. Violet Red Bile Agar (VRB)—Approximately 200 ml. for each food specimen examined.
   d. Brilliant Green Lactose Bile Broth 2%—Dispense in 10-ml. volumes in 150 x 15 mm. tubes with aluminum caps and containing Durham fermentation tubes. Sterilize by autoclaving at 121° C for 15 min. Six tubes of broth for each countable plate.
2. Procedure:
   a. Pipette carefully 1 ml. of each dilution of the food homogenate prepared in II above to each of appropriately marked, duplicate culture dishes.
   b. Pour each plate with 10 to 15 ml. of Violet Red Bile Agar.
   c. Thoroughly mix inoculum and agar immediately after pouring plates and allow to solidify.
   d. Pour an overlay of 3 to 4 ml. of the VRB agar on the first layer of each plate, including an agar control.
   e. Invert plates and incubate at 35° C for 18 to 24 hr.
   f. Following incubation, remove plates from incubator and observe macroscopically for type of growth and colony size.
   g. Using the Quebec Colony Counter, count dark red colonies having an estimated diameter of 0.5 mm. or more (colony size will be affected by the number of colonies per plate). Record results.
   h. Calculate number of coliform organisms per gram of food.
   i. Select six typical colonies from the countable plates and inoculate each into a tube of Brilliant Green Lactose Bile Broth 2%.
   j. Incubate Brilliant Green Lactose Bile Broth 2% at 35° C for 24 and 48 hr.
   k. Remove tubes of Brilliant Green Lactose Bile Broth 2% from incubator after 24 hr. of incubation and examine for presence of gas in fermentation tubes. Return all negative tubes at 35° C incubator for another 24-hr. incubation and record results. Gas within 24 to 48 hr. of incuba-

---

*NOTE: Agar does not solidify as quickly in plastic dishes as in glass.

tion is interpreted as confirming presence of organisms of the coliform group.*

B. Most Probable Number Method (recommended for use in the routine surveillance of foods for sanitary quality in which small numbers of coliform bacteria may be expected):

1. Apparatus, materials, and culture media:
   a. Same as Agar Plate Colony Count (IV, A, steps 3,4,5, and 6).
   b. 1.1-ml. pipettes marked in 0.1- and 1.0-ml. graduations—1 pipette for dilution.
   c. Inoculating needle, nichrome or platinum-iridium wire B & S gauge No. 26.
   d. Lauryl Sulfate Tryptose Broth: Dispense in 10-ml. volumes in 150 x 15 mm. tubes with aluminum caps containing Durham fermentation tubes. Sterilize by autoclaving at 121° C for 15 min. Five tubes of broth for each decimal dilution.
   e. Endo Agar.
   f. Eosin Methylene Blue Agar.

2. Procedure:
   a. Pipette aseptically 1 ml. of each of the decimal dilutions of food-homogenate prepared in II above to each of 5 separate tubes of Lauryl Sulfate Tryptose Broth.
   b. Incubate inoculated tubes at 35° C for 24 and 48 hr.
   c. Following 24-hr. incubation, examine tubes for gas production and record. Return tubes not displaying gas to incubator for additional 24-hr. incubation.
   d. Following 48-hr. incubation, observe tubes for gas production and record.
   e. Select the highest dilution in which all 5 tubes are positive for gas production and the next 2 higher dilutions. If this is not possible, because none of the dilutions yielded 5 positive tubes or because further dilutions beyond the one yielding 5 positive tubes were not made, select the last 3 diln. and record the number of positive tubes in each dilution. For example, if the last 3 positive dilutions were 1:100, 1:1,000 and 1:10,000 and the number of positive tubes in each diln were 5, 3, and 1, respectively, the results are recorded as 1:100 diln. = 5, the 1:1,000 diln. = 3, and the 1:10,000 diln. = 1.
   f. Confirm that tubes of Lauryl Tryptose Sulfate broth selected in (e) above are positive for coliform organisms by inoculating a loopful of growth from each to tubes of Brilliant Green Lactose Bile Broth 2% or by streaking Endo or Eosin Methylene Blue Agar plates. Incubate confirmatory tubes for 24 and 48 hr. at 35° C observe for gas production. Observe solid confirmatory media for typical coliform colonies after 24 and 48 hr. of incubation at 35° C.
   g. Record the number of tubes in each dilution that were confirmed as positive for coliform organisms.
   h. To obtain the MPN proceed as follows: if all tubes in the last 3 positive dilutions (1:100, 1:1,000, and 1:10,000, example in (e) above) yielded

---

*NOTE: Most foods contain fermentable carbohydrates, which are carried over to the coliform medium employed for enumeration. For this reason, confirmation of coliform organisms is usually necessary.

TABLE A.1

MOST PROBABLE NUMBERS PER 100 ML. OF SAMPLE, PLANTING 3, 4, OR 5 PORTIONS IN EACH OF 3 DILUTIONS IN DECIMAL SERIES

Number of positive tubes			Combinations of tubes planted		
10 ml	1 ml	0.1 ml	3-10 / 3-1 / 3-0.1	4-10 / 4-1 / 4-0.1	5-10 / 5-1 / 5-0.1
0	0	0			
0	0	1	3.0	2.3	1.8
0	0	2	6.0	4.5	3.6
0	0	3	9.0	6.8	5.4
0	0	4		9.0	7.2
0	0	5			9.0
0	1	0	3.0	2.3	1.8
0	1	1	6.1	4.6	3.6
0	1	2	9.2	6.8	5.5
0	1	3	12	9.1	7.3
0	1	4		11	9.1
0	1	5			11
0	2	0	6.2	4.6	3.7
0	2	1	9.3	6.9	5.5
0	2	2	12	9.2	7.4
0	2	3	16	12	9.2
0	2	4		14	11
0	2	5			13
0	3	0	9.4	7.0	5.6
0	3	1	13	9.3	7.4
0	3	2	16	12	9.3
0	3	3	19	14	11
0	3	4		16	13
0	3	5			15
0	4	0		9.4	7.5
0	4	1		12	9.4
0	4	2		14	11
0	4	3		17	13
0	4	4		19	15
0	4	5			17
0	5	0			9.4
0	5	1			12
0	5	2			14
0	5	3			17
0	5	4			19
0	5	5			22

Number of positive tubes			Combinations of tubes planted		
10 ml	1 ml	0.1 ml	3-10 / 3-1 / 3-0.1	4-10 / 4-1 / 4-0.1	5-10 / 5-1 / 5-0.1
1	0	0	3.6	2.6	2.0
1	0	1	7.2	5.1	4.0
1	0	2	11	7.8	6.0
1	0	3	15	10	8.0
1	0	4		13	10
1	0	5			12
1	1	0	7.3	5.2	4.0
1	1	1	11	7.9	6.1
1	1	2	15	11	8.1
1	1	3	19	13	10
1	1	4		16	12
1	1	5			14
1	2	0	11	8.0	6.1
1	2	1	15	11	8.2
1	2	2	20	13	10
1	2	3	24	16	12
1	2	4		19	15
1	2	5			17
1	3	0	16	11	8.3
1	3	1	20	14	10
1	3	2	24	16	13
1	3	3	29	19	15
1	3	4		22	17
1	3	5			19
1	4	0		14	11
1	4	1		17	13
1	4	2		20	15
1	4	3		23	17
1	4	4		26	19
1	4	5			22
1	5	0			13
1	5	1			15
1	5	2			17
1	5	3			19
1	5	4			22
1	5	5			24

Number of positive tubes			Combinations of tubes planted		
10 ml	1 ml	0.1 ml	3-10 / 3-1 / 3-0.1	4-10 / 4-1 / 4-0.1	5-10 / 5-1 / 5-0.1
2	0	0	9.1	6.0	4.5
2	0	1	14	9.1	6.8
2	0	2	20	12	9.1
2	0	3	26	16	12
2	0	4		19	14
2	0	5			16
2	1	0	15	9.3	6.8
2	1	1	20	13	9.2
2	1	2	27	16	12
2	1	3	34	20	14
2	1	4		23	17
2	1	5			19
2	2	0	21	13	9.3
2	2	1	28	16	12
2	2	2	35	20	14
2	2	3	42	24	17
2	2	4		28	19
2	2	5			22
2	3	0	29	17	12
2	3	1	36	20	14
2	3	2	44	24	17
2	3	3	53	28	20
2	3	4		32	22
2	3	5			25
2	4	0		21	15
2	4	1		25	17
2	4	2		29	20
2	4	3		33	23
2	4	4		37	25
2	4	5			28
2	5	0			17
2	5	1			20
2	5	2			23
2	5	3			26
2	5	4			29
2	5	5			32

For smaller portions of sample than 10, 1, and 0.1 ml (or g), use the MPN in the table according to following formula:

$$\frac{\text{MPN from table}}{100} \times \text{dilution factor of middle tube} = \text{MPN/g}$$

TABLE A.1 (Continued)

MOST PROBABLE NUMBERS PER 100 ML. OF SAMPLE, PLANTING 3, 4, OR 5 PORTIONS IN EACH OF 3 DILUTIONS IN DECIMAL SERIES

Number of positive tubes			Combinations of tubes planted		
10 ml	1 ml	0.1 ml	3-10 / 3-1 / 3-0.1	4-10 / 4-1 / 4-0.1	5-10 / 5-1 / 5-0.1
3	0	0	23	11	7.8
3	0	1	39	16	11
3	0	2	64	20	13
3	0	3	95	26	16
3	0	4		31	20
3	0	5			23
3	1	0	43	16	11
3	1	1	75	21	14
3	1	2	120	26	17
3	1	3	160	32	20
3	1	4		38	23
3	1	5			27
3	2	0	93	21	14
3	2	1	150	27	17
3	2	2	210	33	20
3	2	3	290	40	24
3	2	4		47	27
3	2	5			31
3	3	0	240	28	17
3	3	1	460	34	21
3	3	2	1,100	41	24
3	3	3		48	28
3	3	4		56	31
3	3	5			35
3	4	0		35	21
3	4	1		43	24
3	4	2		50	28
3	4	3		59	32
3	4	4		67	36
3	4	5			40
3	5	0			25
3	5	1			29
3	5	2			32
3	5	3			37
3	5	4			41
3	5	5			45

Number of positive tubes			Combinations of tubes planted	
10 ml	1 ml	0.1 ml	4-10 / 4-1 / 4-0.1	5-10 / 5-1 / 5-0.1
4	0	0	23	13
4	0	1	34	17
4	0	2	50	21
4	0	3	71	25
4	0	4	95	30
4	0	5		36
4	1	0	36	17
4	1	1	55	21
4	1	2	81	26
4	1	3	110	31
4	1	4	140	36
4	1	5		42
4	2	0	62	22
4	2	1	94	26
4	2	2	130	32
4	2	3	170	38
4	2	4	210	44
4	2	5		50
4	3	0	110	27
4	3	1	160	33
4	3	2	220	39
4	3	3	280	45
4	3	4	360	52
4	3	5		59
4	4	0	240	34
4	4	1	390	40
4	4	2	700	47
4	4	3	1,400	54
4	4	4		62
4	4	5		69
4	5	0		41
4	5	1		48
4	5	2		56
4	5	3		64
4	5	4		72
4	5	5		81

Number of positive tubes			Combinations of tubes planted
10 ml	1 ml	0.1 ml	5-10 / 5-1 / 5-0.1
5	0	0	23
5	0	1	31
5	0	2	43
5	0	3	58
5	0	4	76
5	0	5	95
5	1	0	33
5	1	1	46
5	1	2	64
5	1	3	84
5	1	4	110
5	1	5	130
5	2	0	49
5	2	1	70
5	2	2	95
5	2	3	120
5	2	4	150
5	2	5	180
5	3	0	79
5	3	1	110
5	3	2	140
5	3	3	180
5	3	4	210
5	3	5	250
5	4	0	130
5	4	1	170
5	4	2	220
5	4	3	280
5	4	4	350
5	4	5	430
5	5	0	240
5	5	1	350
5	5	2	540
5	5	3	920
5	5	4	1,600

Adapted from: Hoskins, J. K., "Most Probable Numbers for Evaluation of Coli-Aerogenes Tests by Fermenation Tube Method," Public Health Reports, Vol. 49, 393–405 (1934).

confirmatory results for coliform organisms, then the confirmed number to be looked up in the MPN table appended to the end of this coliform organism section is 531. By observing the MPN table we see that 531 equals an MPN of 110 per 100 ml. of sample. To obtain the MPN of coliform organisms per gram of food, use the following formula:

$$\frac{\text{MPN from table}}{100} \times \text{diln. factor of middle tube} = \text{MPN/gm.}$$

In so doing we find that an MPN of 110 = 1,100 coliform organisms per gram of food as follows:

$$\frac{110}{100} \times 1,000 = \text{MPN of 1,100 coliform organisms per gm.}$$

C. Coliform Organisms of Fecal Origin:
1. Comment: As a rule, sufficient measurement of the sanitary quality of foods is accomplished by means of the coliform determination. In certain instances, however, it may be desirable to determine the probable origin of coliform bacteria isolated from food and to obtain an estimate of the proportion of the total coliform density representative of recent fecal contamination. Because of the definite association of *Escherichia coli* Type I and II with human fecal material, a procedure which favors the selection and growth of these organisms may be useful in examining certain categories of foods. The modified Eijkman test described below has been used with some success for isolating *E. coli* from oysters and precooked frozen foods. The great majority of fecal coliform organisms (*E. coli*), but only a few *A. aerogenes* or *E. freundii,* produce gas under the conditions of this test. Consequently, a positive result (gas production) with the Eijkman test constitutes, from a practical standpoint, an indication of the presence of recent fecal contamination. Though the test is not wholly specific for *E. coli,* it may be used as a rapid confirmatory procedure for indicating the presence of coliform organisms of probable fecal origin.
2. Apparatus, materials and culture media:
   a. Inoculating needle, nichrome or platinum-iridium wire, B & S gauge No. 26.
   b. Circulating water bath, thermostatically controlled to hold 44.5° ± 0.2° C.
   c. EC broth: Dispense 10-ml. volumes in 150 x 15 mm. tubes with aluminum caps containing Durham fermentation tubes. Sterilize by autoclaving at 121° C for 15 min. One tube of broth for each Lauryl Sulfate Tryptose broth tube positive for gas production.
3. Procedure:
   a. Select tubes of Lauryl Sulfate Tryptose broth that are positive for gas production from coliform bacteria determination described in V, B above.
   b. Inoculate a loopful of growth from each positive Lauryl Sulfate Tryptose broth tube to a tube of EC broth. Incubate inoculated EC broth tubes at 44.5° (± 0.2° C) and read for gas production at the end of 24 and 48 hr.

c. EC broth tubes displaying gas production may be considered as positive for fecal coliform organisms.*

VI. FECAL STREPTOCOCCI

A. Plate Count Method (suitable for analyzing foods in which large numbers of fecal streptococci may be expected):
1. Methods, materials and culture media:
   a. Same as Agar Plate Colony Count (IV, A, steps 1 through 8).
   b. KF *Streptococcus* agar—approximately 300 ml. for each food specimen examined.
2. Procedure:
   a. Pipette aseptically 1 ml. of each dilution of the food-homogenate, prepared in II above to each of appropriately marked duplicate culture dishes.
   b. Pour each plate with 10 to 15 ml. of KF *Streptococcus* agar.
   c. Thoroughly mix inoculum and agar immediately after pouring plates and allow to solidify. Pour an agar control plate on each bottle of agar.
   d. Invert plates and incubate 35° C for 48 hr.
   e. Remove plates from incubator and observe macroscopically for type of growth, colony size, and color.
   f. Select plates showing an estimated 30 to 300 colonies and, using a dissecting microscope, count dark red colonies or those having a red or pink center.
   g. Calculate number of organisms per gram of food by multiplying colony counts by dilution factor. Record results.
B. Most Probable Number Method (recommended for use in the routine surveillance of foods for sanitary quality in which small numbers of fecal streptococci may be expected):
1. Apparatus, materials and culture media:
   a. Same as Agar Plate Colony Count (IV, A, steps 3, 4, 5, and 6).
   b. 1.1 ml. pipettes with 0.1-ml. and 1-ml. graduations—one pipette for each dilution.
   c. KF *Streptococcus* broth.
      Dispense 10-ml. amounts into 150 x 15 mm. screw-capped or aluminum-capped tubes. Sterilize by autoclaving for 10 min. at 121° C. Five tubes of broth for each dilution.
2. Procedure:
   a. Pipette aseptically 1 ml. of each of the decimal dilutions of food-homog-

---

*NOTE: In routine analyses of foods, confirmation of EC-positive tubes for *E. coli* is not usually feasible because of the time and labor involved in performing the procedure. In special instances, however, where the extra effort is merited, the following procedure is satisfactory. Confirmation is accomplished by streaking a portion of each gaspositive EC broth tube to an Eosin Methylene Blue agar plate and incubating 24 hr. at 35° C. Typical coliform-type colonies (black or dark colored colonies with a metallic sheen when viewed by reflected light) are fished from the plates and tested for purity by restreaking on nutrient agar plates to obtain isolated colonies. Purification plates are incubated at 35° C for 24 hr. Individual colonies are selected and transferred to slants of nutrient agar. Growth occurring on slants after incubation at 35° C for 24 hr. is tested for its IMViC pattern according to the procedures outlined in "Standard Methods for the Examination of Water and Waste," 11th Ed., American Public Health Association 1960, pp. 517–520.

enate prepared in II above to each of 5 separate tubes of KF *Streptococcus* broth.
   b. Incubate inoculated tubes at 35° C for 48 hr.
   c. Following incubation, observe tubes for color change to yellow and for turbidity.
   d. Tubes that have developed yellow color are considered positive for fecal streptococci. Select the highest dilution at which all 5 tubes are yellow and the next 2 higher dilutions.
   e. Determine the MPN of fecal streptococci per gram following instructions under V, B, 2, e and h above (Coliform bacteria, Most Probable Number Method.)

VII.   STAPHYLOCOCCI

A. Plate Count Method (suitable for analyzing foods in which large numbers of staphylococci may be expected).
   1. Apparatus, materials and culture media:
      a. Same as Agar Plate Colony Count (IV, A, 1, 3 through 8).
      b. Pipettes, 1.1 ml. with 0.1-ml. and 1.0-ml. graduations—1 pipette for each dilution.
      c. Sterile glass spreader bar (Glass rod bent into hockey stick form and fire polished). Six spreader bars for each food specimen examined.
      d. Tellurite-Polymyxin-Egg Yolk Agar (TPEY)—Approximately 200 ml. for each food specimen examined:

   Tryptone ....10 gm.
   Yeast extract ....5 gm.
   d-Mannitol ....5 gm.
   Sodium chloride..20 gm.
   Lithium chloride..2 gm.
   1% soln. of Polymyxin B (Seitz filtered)..............................0.4 ml.
   1% soln. of potassium tellurite (sterilized at 121° C for 15 min.)..........10 ml.
   Agar ....18 gm.
   Egg yolk emulsion...100 ml.
   Distilled water..900 ml.

Place the first 5 ingredients in 900 ml. cold distilled water and dissolve completely by warming. Adjust to pH 7.2 to 7.3 and add the agar. Heat to boiling to dissolve the agar. Sterilize by autoclaving at 121° C for 15 min. Cool to 50 to 55° C in a water bath. Aseptically add the Polymyxin B and potassium tellurite solutions and egg yolk emulsion. Mix and pour 15 to 17 ml. per plate. Permit plates to dry thoroughly overnight. (Egg yolk emulsion is a 30% volume per volume mixture in physiological saline. Fresh eggs are soaked for 1 min. in a 1:1000 diln. of saturated mercuric chloride solution to sterilize the shells. The eggs are cracked and the yolks removed aseptically. Thirty milliliters of egg yolk is added to 70 ml. of sterile physiological saline in a Waring Blendor and homogenized for approximately 5 sec. at slow speed).
      e. Trypticase Soy Agar: Dispense in 5- to 7-ml. volumes in screwcapped, 150 x 15-mm. tubes and sterilize at 121° C for 15 min. Tilt tubes to make agar slants. Five slants for each countable plate.
      f. Trypticase Soy Broth: Dispense in 5-ml. volumes in 150 x 15-mm. screw-capped tubes and sterilize at 121° C for 15 min. One tube of broth is sufficient for approximately eight coagulase tests.

g. Coagulase Plasma (available commercially).

h. Agglutination tubes, 10 x 100 mm.—one tube for each coagulase test and one plasma control and one coagulase-positive control.

2. Procedure:

  a. Pipette aseptically 0.1 ml. of each dilution of the food-homogenate prepared in II above to the surface of each appropriately marked, duplicate plates of TPEY medium. In surface plating techniques 0.1 ml. of each dilution is plated. Because only 0.1 ml. is used 0.1 ml. of each dilution is always plated on the agar plate marked with the next higher dilution. (For example, 0.1 ml. of the 10^{-1} diln. onto the surface of the plate marked 10^{-2}.)

  b. Continue inoculating aliquots from all serial dilutions through 10^{-6}.

  c. Using a separate and sterile gas spreader bar for each dilution, smear the inoculum evenly and completely over the agar surface.

  d. Place all dilution plates in the incubator in the inverted position and incubate for 24 hr. at 35° C.

  e. Following incubation, observe plates for the development of jet black circular, convex colonies 1.0 to 1.5 mm. in diameter. Coagulase-positive staphylococci usually show one or more of the following reactions (a) zone of precipitation around colony (b) clear zone (halo) around colony and white precipitate beneath (c) no zone or halo around colony but precipitation beneath the colony. If the colonies are too small or reactions indistinct, reincubate plates for an additional 12 to 24 hr. at 35° C.

  f. Count the number of such colonies on plates with 30 to 300 colonies wherever possible and record as the presumptive number of coagulase-positive staphylococci per gram.

  g. From countable plates with well isolated colonies select and mark five colonies for coagulase testing.

  h. With the tip of a straight needle touch the selected colony and inoculate a slant of Trypticase Soy Agar. Incubate for 24 hr. at 35° C.

  i. With a loop remove the remainder of the colony and emulsify in 0.2 ml. of Trypticase Soy Broth in an agglutination tube. Add to the tube 0.5 ml. of coagulase plasma, mix and incubate in a 35° C water bath for 4 hr.

  j. Following incubation, observe plasma tubes for coagulation. Any degree of coagulation, even a fibrin strand, is considered positive.

  k. Note those tubes which are negative and obtain the 24-hr. Trypticase Soy Agar slant culture made from the original colony.

  l. Emulsify a loopful of growth from 24-hr slant culture in 0.2 ml. Trypticase Soy Broth and repeat coagulase test as in (i) and (j) above.

B. Most Probable Number Method (recommended for use in the routine surveillance of foods for sanitary quality in which small numbers of staphylococci may be expected):

1. Apparatus, materials and culture media:

  a. Same as Agar Plate Colony Count (IV, A, 3 through 6).

  b. 1.1-ml. pipettes marked in 0.1- and 1.0-ml. graduations—1 pipette for each dilution.

  c. Inoculating needle, nichrome or platinum-iridium wire B & S gauge No. 25.

  d. TPEY agar (See VII, A, 1, d above)—one plate for each broth tube inoculated.

e. Cooked Meat 10% Salt (NaCl) Broth.

The basal medium described above is available commercially in the dehydrated form and is used as the stock medium for preparing Cooked Meat 10% Salt (NaCl) Broth. Suspend 125 gm. of Cook Meat Medium in 1,000 ml. of cold distilled water. Add 95 gm. of sodium chloride, mix thoroughly and allow to stand for at least 15 min. or until all meat particles are saturated. Dispense the medium in 150 x 15 mm. screw-capped tubes. Attempt to maintain an approximate ratio in each tube of ⅓ meat particles and ⅔ supernatant broth for a total volume of approximately 10 ml. Sterilize at 121° C for 30 min. Five tubes of medium for each dilution.

f. Trypticase Soy Agar (See VII, A, 1, e above)

One slant tube of agar for each colony to be coagulase tested.

g. Trypticase Soy Broth (See VII, A, 1, f above)

Four tubes of broth.

2. Procedure:

a. Pipette aseptically 1 ml. of each of the decimal dilutions of food-homogenate prepared in II above to each of 5 separate tubes of Cooked Meat 10% Salt (NaCl) Broth. Take care to introduce the inoculum well down into the meat particles.

b. Incubate inoculated tubes at 35° C for 24 hr.

c. Following incubation, transfer a loopful of material from each inoculated tube to the surface of dried plates of TPEY agar to obtain isolated colonies. Incubate plates for 24 hr. at 35° C and select typical staphylococcal colonies (VII, A, 2, e above) for coagulase testing.

d. Test colonies for coagulase production (as described in VII, A, 2, h through k above).

e. Record the number of tubes in each dilution from which coagulase-positive staphylococci were isolated on TPEY agar.

f. Determine the MPN per gram of confirmed coagulase-positive staphylococci according to the instructions under V, B, 2, e and h above (Coliform bacteria, Most Probable Number Method).

VIII.   SALMONELLAE-SHIGELLAE

A. Enrichment method suitable for the isolation of salmonellae and shigellae from foods in which they are present in low concentrations:

1. Materials:

a. Sterile, 16-oz., screw-capped jars or sterile plastic bags similar to those used for the collection of milk samples. One container for each food specimen to be examined.

b. Sterile tongue depressors or similar instruments for filling containers with food specimens.

c. Balance, with weights, 500 gm. capacity, sensitivity 100 mg.

d. Mechanical blender capable of operation at approximately 8,000 rpm.

e. Inoculating loop, 5 to 6 mm., platinum-iridium or nichrome, B & S gauge, No. 24.

f. Culture dishes (100 x 15 mm.) glass or plastic.

g. Pipettes, 1-ml. capacity, with 0.01-ml. graduations and 5 and 10 ml. capacity with 0.1-ml. graduations and 0.2-ml. capacity with 0.01-ml. graduations.

h. Incubator 35° C to 37° C.

2. Culture media and reagents:
  a. Dehydrated products to be prepared as directed on bottle:
   (1) Brilliant Green agar (BG).

   NOTE: Sterilization of this medium is critical. A longer period tends to decrease its selectivity and insufficient sterilization results in inhibitory action against salmonellae.

   (2) Brilliant Green Sulfadiazine agar (BGS). Prepare a 1.6% soln. of sodium sulfadiazine in distilled water. Boil for 10 min. to sterilize. Add aseptically 5 ml. of this solution per liter of Brilliant Green agar just prior to pouring plates.
   (3) Triple Sugar Iron agar (TSI). Slant in such a manner to obtain a 1- to 1¼-in. butt.
   (4) Bismuth Sulfite agar (WB).
   (5) SS agar (Shigella-Salmonella agar).
   (6) MacConkey agar.
   (7) Lysine Iron agar. Slant tubes so as to obtain approximately a 1-in. butt and a 1½-in. slant.
   (8) Nutrient broth.
   (9) Lactose broth.
   (10) Simmons Citrate agar.
   (11) Urea agar (for 24-hr. test).
   (12) Tetrathionate enrichment broth.
       Cool the base broth and add 1 ml. of a 1:1000 aqueous solution of brilliant green to 100 ml. of broth and 2 ml. of iodine solution just prior to tubing. The iodine solution is prepared by dissolving 5 gm. of potassium iodide (CP) in 20 ml. of distilled water and adding 6 gram of iodine crystals (CP-resublimed). Comparative studies have shown that the iodine solution may be added when the medium is prepared if used within 8 days after preparation (Galton, et al., J. Infectious Diseases 91, 1–18, 1952).
  b. Tergitol No. 7—10% aqueous solution. Sterilize at 121° C for 20 min.
  c. Rapid urea test medium:

  Urea ....2.0 gm.
  Monopotassium phosphate, dihydrogen ....0.1 gm.
  Dibasic sodium phosphate ....0.1 gm.
  Sodium chloride ....0.5 gm.
  Ethyl alcohol ....1.0 ml.
  Distilled water ....99.0 ml.

  The reagent is adjusted to pH 7.0 with NaOH and 0.5 ml. of a 0.2% aqueous solution of phenol red added. Do not sterilize except by filtration. Sterility is not necessary, however, as the medium may be stored in the refrigerator for several weeks unsterilized without spoilage. If the medium becomes pink (alkaline to phenol red), it should be discarded. To perform test, dispense broth into 3- or 4-in. clean tubes in 0.2-ml. amounts. Inoculate with a generous amount of growth from the Triple Sugar Iron agar slant using a wire loop. Incubate for 30 min. at 37° C, then read. A change in color from the pale yellow of the fresh medium to an intense pink or fuchsia indicates the hydrolysis of urea or a positive test.

d. Rapid indol test solution:

Tryptone .... 2.0 gm.
Dibasic sodium phosphate (anhydrous) .... 0.2 gm.
Monopotassium phosphate (anhydrous), dihydrogen .... 0.1 gm.
Sodium chloride .... 0.8 gm.
Distilled water .... 100.9 ml.

The pH is adjusted to 7.0 to 7.2. The solution should be sterilized at 121° C for 20 min. It may be kept in the refrigerator in a flask and dispensed as needed with a sterile pipette. This solution should be diluted with an equal volume of normal saline before use. The tubes in which the tests are performed need not be sterile.

To perform test, dispense the diluted medium into 3- or 4- in. clean tubes in 0.2-ml. amounts. Inoculate a generous amount of growth from the Triple Sugar Iron agar (TSI) slant using a wire loop. Incubate 2 hr. at 37° C and add 0.2 to 0.3 ml. of Kovac's reagent. This reagent forms a layer over the surface of the broth culture. The liberation of indol is indicated by a color change of this layer from yellow to red.

Tryptone Broth (for 24 hr. test). Prepare a 1% soln. of tryptone, dispense in 2- to 3-ml. amounts in 4-in. tubes and sterilize at 121° C for 20 min.

e. Kovac's reagent:

Para-dimethylaminobenzaldehyde .... 5 gm.
Amyl alcohol .... 75 ml.
Concentrated hydrochloric acid .... 25 ml.

Mix the alcohol and aldehyde and heat in water bath or incubator at 50° to 60°C until the aldehyde is dissolved. When cool, add the hydrochloric acid slowly. Store in the dark in a brown bottle with a glass or rubber stopper.

f. Beef extract broth base for fermentation tests:

Beef extract .... 3 gm.
Peptone .... 5 gm.
Distilled water .... 950 ml.
Brom-cresol-purple (1.6% alcoholic soln.) .... 1 ml.
Agar .... 1 gm.
Sterilize in flask at 121° C for 20 min. .... 1 gm.

(1) Dissolve 10 gm. of the desired sugar in 50 ml. of distilled water and filter through a Seitz filter.
(2) Mix the broth base and carbohydrate solution aseptically and dispense in 2- to 3-ml. amounts into sterile 4-in. tubes containing inverted vials.
(3) Place the tubed media while still warm in the autoclave in flowing steam for 20 min. to fill the inverted vials.

g. Motility test medium (Edwards and Ewing, 1962, *Identification of Enterobacteriaceae*, 2nd ed., Burgess Publishing Co., Minneapolis, Minn.).

Beef extract .... 3 gm.
Peptone .... 10 gm.

Sodium chloride ....5 gm.
Agar ....4 gm.
Distilled water ....1,000 ml.

Adjust reaction to pH 7.4 and dispense in 13 x 100 mm. tubes, about 4 ml. per tube, and sterilize at 121° C for 15 min.
(1) Inoculate by stabbing into the top of the column of medium to a depth of about 5 mm.
(2) Incubate at 37° C for 1 or 2 days. If negative, follow with further incubation at 21 to 25° C for 5 days.

h. Potassium cyanide (KCN) medium (Edwards and Ewing, 1962, *Identification of Enterobacteriaceae*, 2nd ed., Burgess Publishing Co., Minneapolis, Minn.)

Peptone, Orthona special* ....10 gm.
Sodium chloride ....5 gm.
Monobasic potassium phosphate ....0.225 gm.
Dibasic sodium phosphate ....5.64 gm.
Distilled water ....1000 ml.
Adjust to pH 7.6

Sterilize the basal medium at 121° C for 15 min., then refrigerate until thoroughly chilled. To the cold medium add 15 ml. of 0.5% KCN soln. (0.5 gm. KCN dissolved in 100 ml. *cold* sterile distilled water). Then tube medium in approximately 1 ml. amounts in sterile tubes (13 x 100 mm.) and stopper *quickly* with corks sterilized by heating in paraffin. The medium can be stored safely for 2 weeks at 4° C. The final concentration of KCN in the medium is 1:13,300. 0.3% Bacto Proteose Peptone No. 3 may be substituted for Orthona Peptone. Inoculate the tubes with 1 small loopful of a 24 hr. broth culture grown at 37° C. Incubate 37° C and observe daily for 2 days. Positive results are indicated by growth in the presence of KCN.

i. Decarboxylase test media (Moeller, J., 1955, Acta Path. Microbiol. Scand. *36*, 158; Edwards and Ewing, 1962 *Identification of Enterobacteriaceae*, 2nd ed., Burgess Publishing Co., Minneapolis, Min.).

Basal medium
Peptone, Orthona special* ....5 gm.
Beef extract ....5 gm.
Brom-cresol-purple (1.6%) ....0.625 ml.
Cresol red (0.2%) ....2.5 ml.
Glucose ....0.5 gm.
Pyridoxal ....5 gm.
Distilled water ....1,000 ml.
Adjust pH to 6.0.

Divide basal medium into four equal portions. Tube one portion without the addition of an amino acid to be used for control purposes. To the second portion of basal medium add: 1% of L-lysine dihydrochloride. To the third portion of basal medium add: 1% of L-arginine monohydrochloride. To the fourth portion of basal medium add: 1% of L-ornithine dihydrochloride.

---

*Peptone Special "Orthona" Meat USPV from A/S Orthona, Kemish Fabrik, Copenhagen, Denmark.

If DL amino acids are used, they should be added in 2% concentrations, as the microorganisms apparently are active only against the L forms. The pH of the medium with ornithine added should be adjusted after its addition and prior to sterilization. Tube the amino acid media in 3- to 4-ml. amounts in small (13 x 100 mm.) screw-capped tubes and sterilize at 121° C for 10 min. A small amount of floccular precipitate may be seen in the ornithine medium, but this does not interfere with its use.

Inoculate lightly from a young agar slant or TSI culture. Then add a layer (4 to 5 mm. in thickness) of sterile mineral (paraffin) oil to each tube including the control tube. A control tube should be inoculated with each culture being studied. Incubate at 37° C and examine daily for 4 days. Positive reactions are indicated by a change in color of the indicator system from yellow to violet or reddish-violet. Most positive reactions will occur during the first 2 days, but the tubes must be observed for 4 days to detect the few delayed reactions.

j. Polyvalent *Salmonella* antiserum.
k. *Salmonella* "O" group antiserums: A, B, C_1, C_2, $E_{1, 2}$, F, G, H, and I.
l. Seven *Salmonella* "H" antiserum pools: I; II; III; IV; 1 ... complex; L ... complex; and en ... complex (Edwards, P. R., August 1962; *Serologic examination of Salmonella cultures for epidermiologic purposes.* DHEW, PHS, CDC, Atlanta, Georgia).
m. Shigellae polyvalent antiserum for Groups A, B, C, D, and Alkalescens-Dispar (A-D).

3. Procedure:
a. Sample collection and cultural examination:
(1) During collection of samples, strict precautions should be taken to avoid contamination. If foods are packaged, an effort should be made to obtain the sealed packages. For bulk foods, samples may be collected in sterile plastic bags used for collection of milk samples or in sterile, 16-oz., screw-capped refrigerator jars. At least 100 gm. of the sample should be obtained. Tongue depressors or other instruments used to fill the containers with each sample must be sterile.

Frozen foods should be kept frozen for transport to the laboratory. Other perishable foods that have not been frozen should be refrigerated during transport to the laboratory.
(2) Weigh out aseptically a 30-gm. sample food into a sterile 16-oz. screw-capped jar.
(3) Add 100 ml. of Tetrathionate Enrichment broth.
(4) Add 6 ml. (or the amount determined by preliminary titration) of a 10% soln. of Tergitol No. 7) to all meat samples and dehydrated products.
(5) Tighten lid and shake vigorously. Samples of dried products receive a second shaking after 1 hr.
(6) Incubate sample at 35° C overnight.

NOTE: If the sample is unground meat or other foods that need maceration, 30 gm. of the cut parts should be weighed in the sterile blender jars, the enrichment added as described above, the lid tightened securely, and the mixture blended for 1 to 2 min. After the foam from agitation has settled, Tergitol No. 7 is added and the mixture shaken. A higher recovery rate will be obtained if duplicate amounts are prepared in the enrichment for each sample. If *Proteus* is found to be a problem, sodium sulfathiazole added in the amount of 0.125 mg. per 100 ml. of tetrathionate enrichment will be helpful in suppressing their growth. For foods containing whole egg powder or dried egg white, inoculate a 20- to 30-gm. portion into 100 ml. of nutrient broth, add the desired amount of Tergitol, shake well, and incubate overnight. When shigellae are suspected, all types of food should be blended in amounts of 20 to 30 gm. per sample in 100 ml. of nutrient broth. A large loopful of the broth mixture should be streaked directly on an SS agar plate, then, using the same loop without obtaining a fresh inoculum, streaked to a MacConkey agar plate. Frozen foods should be held at refrigerator temperature long enough to allow partial thawing.

(7) After overnight incubation, a generous loopful of tetrathionate enrichment and of the nutrient broth should be streaked onto a. Brilliant Green agar plate containing 8 mg. of sodium sulfadiazine per 100 ml. of agar (BGS).

NOTE: When small numbers of salmonellae are present or the initial plates are negative, the tetrathionate and nutrient broths are incubated another 24 hr. The Tetrathionate is streaked to a BGS plate, the nutrient broth is subcultured into Tetrathionate broth which is also streaked to a BGS plate after 24 hr.

(8) Prepare a 1:1000 diln. from each enrichment broth in buffered distilled water and streak a loopful (5 to 6 mm. in diameter) of this dilution to a BGS plate and to a Bismuth Sulfite agar plate (WB).

(9) The BGS plates are incubated 22 to 24 hr. and the WB plates for 48 hr. at 35 to 37° C.

NOTE: The WB medium is used primarily to search for *Arizona* organisms as recommended by Edwards and Fife (Appl. Microbiol. *9*, 478–480, 1961). Some *Arizona* strains are slow lactose fermenters and can be detected on the BGS plates. However, others that have also been found in foods and in cases of food infection, ferment lactose rapidly and would be missed. Both *Arizona* strains and salmonellae produce similar typical black colonies on WB agar. Edwards has noted that *Arizona* and salmonellae have the common ability to produce both H_2S and lysine decarboxylase, not shared by other enteric bacteria. To determine this, he has developed a lysine-iron-agar to be inoculated from black colonies on WB agar. By this method, rapid lactose-fermenting *Arizona* strains may be detected.

(10) After incubation, pick suspicious colonies to differential media. On BGS agar, salmonellae colonies are usually transparent pink to deep fuschia. If the plate has a predominance of lactose-fermenting colonies, the salmonellae may be masked and appear as transparent brownish colonies with little change in the color of the medium. Characteristic colonies of enteric organisms as they appear on 4 different plating media are described in Table 1.

(11) Select suspected salmonellae colonies from BGS agar plates and pick portion of each colony to Triple Sugar Iron agar slants (TSI). In picking colonies from selective media, care should be taken to

touch only the center of the desired colony, since organisms which are inhibited may be viable but not visible as colonies. The TSI slants, prepared with about a 1-in. butt, are inoculated by stabbing the butt and streaking the slant.

(12) Suspicious colonies from WB agar are inoculated with a needle onto Lysine-Iron-agar by stabbing to the base of the butt and streaking the slant.

(13) Any colorless, transparent colonies or those with faint yellow centers and irregular edges on SS or MacConkey's agar should be picked to TSI agar as they may be shigellae (see Table 1).
The TSI and Lysine-Iron-agar slants are incubated overnight at 37° C, then separated according to reaction. The reactions of the various enteric groups on TSI and Lysine-Iron-agar are shown in Tables 2 and 3.

(14) Any cultures that appear contaminated on these media should be streaked on MacConkey's agar plates to purify.

b. Presumptive serological and biochemical confirmation:

(1) The TSI cultures with reactions characteristic of salmonellae are examined by the slide test with polyvalent salmonellae antiserum. Growth from the TSI slant is emulsified in a drop of saline on a glass slide, then mixed with a drop of the polyvalent serum. Those cultures that are positive by this test are inoculated into broth to screen for "H" antigens by the Spicer-Edwards simplified method. (Spicer, C. D., 1956, J. Clin. Pathol. 9, 378–379; Edwards, P. R., August, 1962, Serologic examination of *Salmonella* cultures for epidemiologic purposes. DHEW, PHS, CDC, Atlanta, Georgia). The same slide "spotting" method is used with growth from the TSI slants to determine the "O" group antigens.

(2) Positive reactions in the "O" group serums and/or the pooled "H" serums indicate a salmonellae serotype. Before forwarding to a *Salmonella* Typing Center for definitive serological identification, it is suggested that the following biochemical reactions be checked: urease, indole, and lysine decarboxylase production (if not checked previously) and growth in KCN. Typical salmonellae do not produce urease and indole or grow in KCN medium, but they do produce lysine decarboxylase. If these reactions are not characteristic, and *Salmonella* antigens have been demonstrated, the culture should be plated on MacConkey agar to obtain a pure culture.

(3) Certain serotypes may be differentiated by presumptive serology and further biochemical tests. For example, S. *pullorum* does not ferment dulcitol and is nonmotile.

(4) TSI cultures with reactions resembling shigellae should be examined by the slide test with polyvalent shigellae antiserums for Groups A, B, C, and D. The test may be performed by the same slide technique used to screen salmonellae. If positive, the following biochemical reactions should be checked: Urea (agar), indole, citrate utilization, motility (Semisolid agar), lysine, arginine and ornithine decarboxylase production and growth in KCN. In addition, if possible before referring the culture to a typing center, inoculation of the following carbohydrate broths is recommended: dextrose, mannitol, xylose, rhamnose, lactose, and sucrose.

(5) Cultures which are biochemically characteristic of a *Shigella* and fail to agglutinate in slide tests must be tested further. A suspension of the culture should be heated at 100° C for 30 min., cooled and retested with the *Shigella* grouping serums.

B. Enumeration of Salmonellae in Food Specimens:
  1. Materials:
    a. Mechanical blender capable of operating at approximately 8,000 rpm.
    b. Wide-mouth jars or Pyrex flasks containing approximately 400 ml. lactose broth.
    c. Blender jars for mechanical blender—3 to 5 jars for each food specimen examined.
    d. 1-ml. and 10-ml. capacity pipettes graduated in 0.1-ml. and 1-ml.—3 to 5 pipettes of each capacity for each food specimen examined.
    e. Incubator 37° C.
    f. Lactose broth (see VIII, A, 2, a, (9)) 400 ml. dispensed in jars or flasks and 10 ml. dispensed in tubes. Six tubes of broth and one jar or flask of broth for each food specimen examined.
    g. BG agar (see VIII, A, 2, a, (1)).
    h. TSI agar slants (see VIII, A, 2, a, (3)).
  2. Procedure:
    a. Place samples of 11.1 gm. of food specimen into each of 3 blender jars and cover with 99.9 ml. of lactose broth containing approximately 0.6% Tergitol No. 7. This test may also be performed as a 5-tube MPN if the additional accuracy is desirable.
    b. After standing for 1 hr., blend the samples for about 2 min.
    c. From each of the blended samples, pipette 10 ml., 1.0 ml. and 0.1 ml. each into a tube containing 10.0 ml. of lactose broth which will provide 10-gm., 1-gm., and 0.1-gm. portions of sample.
    d. All specimens are then incubated for 48 hr. at 37° C. After incubation, place 1 ml. from each broth tube into 10 ml. of Tetrathionate Enrichment medium, and incubate the latter for 24 hr. A loopful of the tetrathionate broth is then streaked onto BG agar.
    e. After 24 hr. of incubation, suspicious colonies are picked to TSI agar slants. Subsequent to incubation of these slants, the bacteria are confirmed as salmonellae as described in VIII, A, 3, b, (1) through (3) above. Determine the MPN per gram of confirmed salmonellae according to the instructions under V, B, 2, e and h above (Coliform bacteria, Most Probable Number Method).

C. Alternate Method: Enumeration of Salmonellae and Shigellae. Most Probable Number Method recommended for use in the routine surveillance of foods for sanitary quality in which small numbers of salmonellae and shigellae may be expected.
  1. Apparatus, materials, and culture media:
    a. Same as preparation of food-homogenate (II, A, 1, 2, 3, 4, and 6).
    b. Wide-mouth jars (1-qt. capacity) or Pyrex flask (1-liter capacity) for 540 ml. of sterile lactose broth.
    c. Pipettes 1.1-ml. capacity graduated in 0.1-ml. and 1.0-ml., 5-ml. and 10-ml. capacity graduated to 1.0 ml. and 0.1 ml. One of each type pipette for each food specimen examined.
    d. Inoculating needles and loops, nichrome or platinum-iridium wire, B & S gauge, No. 24.

TABLE A.2

APPEARANCE OF COLONIES OF ENTERIC ORGANISMS ON SELECTIVE PLATING MEDIA

Group of organisms	Bismuth Sulfite Agar (W.B.)	SS Agar and MacConkey Agar	Brilliant Green Agar (B.G.)
Salmonella typhi	Fully developed colonies are convex 1 to 3 mm; black with lustrous surface; form a shallow, soft, black pit in medium below colony, immature or overcrowded colonies range from clear, light green, punctiform colonies 1 mm in diameter with black centers by transmitted light. Light green colonies have a darker green center.	After 24 hours colonies usually colorless, transparent, but may have light tan, light pinkish or yellow appearance or tan center; 1 to 5 mm in diameter.	Transparent pink colonies. Grow rather sparsely, if at all.
Salmonella	Colonies similar to above but tending toward a dark rich brown rather than black; usually very lustrous. Colonies usually much larger than S. typhi, frequently dark brownish centers and lighter edge.	Colonies sometimes larger than above; otherwise similar. Sometimes show black centers on SS.	Transparent pink to deep fuchsia colonies. Occasionally will be brownish, showing little change in color of medium. If plate is heavily contaminated with coliform organisms, Salmonella may be masked and appear as transparent green colonies. Close observation by transmitted light will reveal the brownish appearance of these colonies.
Arizona	Colonies similar to Salmonella	Slow lactose fermenting types similar to Salmonella; rapid lactose-fermenting types will resemble coliform colonies.	As on SS, slow lactose fermenters resemble salmonellae; rapid lactose fermenters are yellowish green similar to coliforms.
Shigella	Most strains do not grow on this medium, although occasional strains of S. flexneri and S. boydii may grow. They appear light to dark green, smooth, flat and glistening.	Colonies usually colorless, transparent; may be smaller than Salmonella. Shigella sonnei may grow especially large with yellow centers and irregular edges.	No significant growth.
Coliaerogenes	Greatly inhibited; strains that grow show green to black colonies without pitting of medium, may be similar to immature typhoid colonies; yellowish and brick-red colonies are probably members of this group.	Largely inhibited on SS; may develop as large opaque colonies with varying shades of pink or red color throughout. Large mucoid colonies may have pink centers with white or yellow peripheries. Some E. coli 0:111 related strains may show transparent colonies on SS. On MacConkey, colonies may be surrounded by a precipitate of bile salts in the medium.	Large opaque yellowish green colonies inhibited to some extent on BGS.
Proteus	Similar to coliform group. Usually bright to brownish green with darker centers. Flat.	Usually small, transparent, water-clear colonies; may have "fuzzy" or veil-like edge. Sometimes show black centers.	Greatly inhibited.

TABLE A.2 (Continued)

APPEARANCE OF COLONIES OF ENTERIC ORGANISMS ON SELECTIVE PLATING MEDIA

Bethesda -------------	Some appear as light green colonies with dark green centers flat with entire edges. Some produce greenish brown colonies with dark centers.	Clear transparent colonies similar to *Salmonella*. Occasionally black centered on SS.	Usually similar to *Salmonella*.
Pseudomonas ---------	Greenish brown colonies sometimes with darker centers. Similar to paracolons.	Transparent grayish colonies usually rough with irregular edges.	Deep pink to purplish colonies, usually "fuzzy" edges on BG. On BGS usually inhibited. Many develop as pinpoint colonies in 36 to 48 hours.

    e. Lactose broth (See VIII A, 2, a, (9) above) 540 ml. in a flask—1 flask for each specimen examined. Fifteen tubes of broth containing 10 ml. per tube for each food specimen examined.

    f. Selenite—Cystine broth. L-cystine is prepared by dissolving 1.0 gm. in 10 to 20 ml. of N NaOH and making up to 100 ml. with distilled water. Add 1.0 ml. of this 1% solution to 1 liter of medium, mix and distribute in 1.0- to 2.0-ml. volumes in small tubes (10 x 10 mm.). Expose to flowing steam for 20 min. Do not autoclave.

    g. Brilliant Green Sulfadiazine agar plates (BGS) (See VIII, A, 2, a, (2) above).

    h. *Salmonella-Shigella* agar (SS) (See VIII, A, 2, a, (5) above).

    i. Salmonellae and shigellae typing era (See VIII, A, 2, j, and m above).

2. Procedure:

    a. Prepare an initial 1:10 diln. of food by adding 60 gm. of sample to 540 ml. of lactose broth in a mechanical blender cup and homogenizing as described above (II, Preparation of Food Homogenate).

    b. From the initial 1:10 diln. of food homogenate, remove five 100-ml. aliquots and place in sterile bottles. Also remove five 10-ml. aliquots, five 1-ml. aliquots, and five 0.1-ml. aliquots. Add each of these last 3 sets of aliquots to separate tubes of lactose broth containing 10 ml. per tube. This results in a total of 20 samples as follows: 5 bottles containing 10 gm. of food each; 5 tubes containing 1 gm. of food each; 5 tubes containing 0.1 gm. of food each; and 5 tubes containing 0.01 gm. of food each.

    c. Incubate inoculated bottles and tubes for 24 hr. at 35° C.

    d. Following incubation, transfer by means of a loop, material from bottles and tubes of lactose broth to small tubes containing 1.0 ml. of selenite-cystine broth.

    e. Incubate selenite-cystine tubes for 6 or 7 hr. at 35° C.

    f. Streak each tube of Selenite-Cystine broth on Brilliant Green Sulfadiazine agar to detect salmonellae; streak SS agar to detect shigellae and *S. typhi.*

    g. Reincubate tubes of Selenite-Cystine broth for full 24 hr., reexamine for growth which may not have been evident after the initial incubation, and streak positive tubes to plates of BGS agar and SS agar.

    h. Incubate Brilliant Green Sulfadiazine and SS agar plates at 35° C for 24 hr. and select suspected salmonellae- and shigellae-type colonies for biochemical and serological identification as described in VIII, A, 3, a, (11) and VIII, A, 3, b, (1) through (5).

    i. Determine the MPN per gram of confirmed salmonellae or shigellae according to instructions under V, B, 2, e and h above (Coliform bacteria, Most Probable Number).

IX. CLOSTRIDIUM PERFRINGENS

A. Plate Count Method:

  1. Methods, materials and culture media:

    a. Same as Agar Plate Colony Count (IV, A, 1 through 8)

    b. Case-Anaero jar—Case Laboratories, Inc., 515 North Halsted Street, Chicago 22, Ill.

    c. Biological gas mixture for use in Case-Anaero jar—10% CO_2 with 90%

TABLE A.3

REACTION IN TRIPLE SUGAR IRON AGAR

Triple Sugar Iron Agar			Suggested Designation	Probable Group
Slant	Butt	H₂S		
Purplish or N.C.	Alk or N.C.	—	Alk	*Pseudomonas*-like
Alk or N.C.	Alk or N.C.	—	Alk	*Alcaligenes*-like
Acid	Acid & Gas	—	AslG —	Possibly pathogenic strains of *Coli* or *Klebsiella*
Acid	Acid	—	Asl —	Enterococci and occasionally *S. typhi, E. coli,* and the dispar type *Escherichia* may give this reaction. Gram stain.
Alk (Spreading growth)	Acid & Gas	+	spAG +	Probable *Proteus*, confirm with urea test
Acid	Acid & Gas	+	AslG +	*Proteus* — discard
Alk	Acid	— or +	A — or A +	*Shigella, S. typhi, Proteus,* or *Providence* and occasionally other anaerogenic *Salmonellae*
Alk	Acid & Gas	+ or —	AG + or AG —	*Salmonella, Proteus,* some Arizona, and some *Citrobacter* (formerly *E. freundii* or Bethesda Group).

Note: Alk slant indicates   — lactose and sucrose not fermented
Acid slant indicates   — lactose or sucrose fermented
Alk butt indicates   — dextrose not fermented
Acid butt indicates   — dextrose fermented
N.C.   — No Change
Alk   — Alkaline

TABLE A.4

REACTIONS OF CERTAIN ENTERIC GROUPS ON LYSINE IRON AGAR

Lysine Iron Agar				Group
Slant	Butt	H₂S	Gas	
Alkaline	Alkaline	+	Rare	*Salmonella* and Arizona
Red	Acid	—	—	*Proteus* and *Providence*
Alkaline	Alkaline	—	Variable	*Klebsiella, gerogenes* and *Hafnia*
Alkaline	Acid	+	+	*Citrobacter* (*E. freundii*)
Alkaline	Acid or Neutral	—	Variable	*Escherichia* and A — D group
Alkaline	Acid	—	—	*Shigella*

N_2. This mixture of purified gases is obtainable from The Matheson Company, Inc.

d. Powdered zinc.

e. Nitrite test reagents.

Reagent A. Dissolve 8 gm. sulphanilic acid in 1 liter of 5 N acetic acid (1 part glacial acetic acid to 2.5 parts of water).

Reagent B. Dissolve 5 gm. α-naphthylamine in 1 liter of 5 N acetic acid.

f. Spore Stain (Batholomew and Mittmer's "cold" method):

(1) Fix air-dried smear by passing through a flame 20 times.

(2) Stain 10 min. with saturated, aqueous malachite green (Approx. 7.6%) without heat.

(3) Rinse with tap water for about 10 sec.

(4) Stain 15 sec. in 0.25% aqueous safranin.

(5) Rinse with tap water and blot dry.

g. Sulfite Polymyxin-Sulfadiazine Agar (SPS—formula Basal Medium:

Tryptone	15.0 gm.
Agar	15.0 gm.
Yeast extract	10.0 gm.
Iron citrate	0.5 gm.
Distilled water	1,000.0 ml.

Adjust to pH 7.0 and sterilize at 121° C for 15 min. To each liter of sterile medium, the following Seitz filtered solns. are added aseptically; 5.0 ml. of freshly prepared 10% soln. of sodium sulfite ($Na_2SO_3 \cdot 7 H_2O$), 10 ml. of a 0.1% soln. of Polymyxin B sulfate and 10 ml. of a solution of sodium sulfadiazine containing 12 mg. per milliliter.

h. Motility-Nitrate Medium:

Beef extract	3.0 gm.
Peptone	5.0 gm.
Potassium nitrate	1.0 gm.
Agar	3.0 gm.
Distilled water	1,000.0 ml.

Adjust pH to 7.0, dispense in 10-ml. volumes in 150 x 15 mm. screw-capped tubes and sterilize at 121° C for 15 min.

i. Sporulation Broth:

Trypticase	20.0 gm.
Vitamin-free casamino acids	20.0 gm.
Sodium thioglycollate	1.0 gm.
Distilled water	1,000.0 ml.

Dispense in 10-ml. volumes in 150 x 15 mm. screw-capped tubes. Sterilize at 121° C for 15 min. Just prior to use, add to each tube of medium 1 ml. of a Seitz filtered stock solution of thiamine hydrochloride containing 10 μg per milliliter. The final concentration of thiamine hydrochloride in each tube is 1.0 μg per milliliter.

j. Fluid Thioglycollate Medium. Tube in 10-ml. volumes in 150 x 15 mm. screw-capped tubes. Sterlize in the autoclave at 121° C for 15 min. and cool quickly. Just before use, heat in flowing steam for 10 min. to drive off dissolved oxygen and cool rapidly in tap water. Final reaction of medium is pH 7.1.

2. Procedure:
   a. Pipette aseptically 1 ml. of each dilution of the food homogenate prepared in II above to each of appropriately marked, duplicate culture dishes.
   b. Pour 15 to 20 ml. of SPS agar into each plate, rotate to mix inoculum and agar and allow to solidify.
   c. Invert plates and place in Case-Anaero jar. Evacuate Anaero jar to 25 in. of vacuum and replace vacuum with the CO_2-N_2 gas mixture. Again evacuate to 25 in. of vacuum and fill with gas mixture once more. Place jar in a 35° C incubator and allow to incubate for 24 hr.
   d. Following incubation, remove plates from anaerobic jar and observe macroscopically for evidence of growth and black colony production.
   e. Select plates showing an estimated 30 to 300 black colonies; and, using the Quebec colony counter with a piece of white tissue paper over counting area, count colonies and calculate number of organisms per gram of food.
   f. Select a representative number of colonies from the countable plates (30 to 300 colonies) and from these stab inoculate Nitrate-Motility medium and Fluid Thioglycollate medium and make smears for Gram stains.
   g. Incubate Nitrate-Motility medium in a 37° C water bath overnight and Fluid Thioglycollate medium for 4 hr. in the 37° C water bath.
   h. Examine Gram-stained smears microscopically for presence of large Gram-positive bacilli with blunt ends.
   i. At the end of the 4-hr. incubation period, inoculate sporulation medium (10 ml.) with 1 ml. of growth from the Fluid Thioglycollate medium culture and incubate at 35° C for 18 to 24 hr.
   j. Examine tubes of Nitrate-Motility medium by transmitted light for type of growth along stab. Nonmotile organisms produce growth only in and along the line of stab. Motile organisms produce a diffuse growth out into the medium away from the stab. Make a smear for Gram stain from growth in tube.
   k. Test Nitrate-Motility medium for presence of nitrate by adding 5 drops of reagent A and 5 drops of reagent B. The production of a pink or red color denotes the presence of nitrites. If no color develops, mix reagents with upper third of medium by jabbing down into medium with sterile loop. If no color develops after this action, add a few grains of zinc metal and allow to stand for a few minutes. A negative test after the addition of zinc indicates that nitrates have been completely reduced. A positive test after the addition of zinc indicates that the organism is incapable of reducing nitrates.
   l. Make a smear of material in sporulation medium, air dry and heat fix. Stain for 10 min. with malachite green, wash with water, stain with water, stain with aqueous safranin for 15 sec., rinse, blot, dry, and examine microscopically. Spores will be stained green, vegetative cells red.
   m. Pipette 2 ml. of sporulation broth into a sterile test tube and heat in 80° C water bath for 10 min. Remove to ice bath and when cool add 1 ml. to a tube of fluid thioglycollate medium. Incubate in a 37° C water bath for 18 to 24 hr.

    n. Examine Fluid Thioglycollate medium for evidence of growth, and observe microscopically for typical Gram-positive rods.

    o. If growth is present, record that sporulation broth contained spores.

    p. If no growth is seen, reincubate for 24 hr. and examine once again. If no growth is evident after the second 24-hr. incubation, record that sporulation broth did not contain spores.

B. Enrichment method (Quantitative enrichment techniques have not been reported upon to date. The following procedure is offered as a proven means of detecting small numbers of *C. perfringens* in food; however, its application as an enumerative multiple-tube dilution test for obtaining an MPN value is untried).

  1. Methods, materials, and culture media:

    a. Same as Agar-Plate Colony Count (IV, A, 1, 2, 4, 5, and 6).

    b. Same as *Clostridium perfringens* plate count method (IX, A, 1, b through i).

    c. Sterile instruments for cutting or sampling food specimens knives, forceps, scissors, spatulas, tongue depressors, etc.

    d. Water bath, $46° \pm 0.5°$ C.

    e. Fluid Thioglycollate Medium (IX, A, 1, j) dispense in 25-ml. aliquots in 250 x 25 mm. Pyrex screw-capped tubes and sterilize at 121° C for 15 min. Two tubes of broth for each food specimen examined.

    f. McClung-Toabe Egg Yolk agar—formula:

Proteose peptone	40 gm.
$Na_2HPO_4 \cdot 7 H_2O$	5 gm.
$KH_2 PO_4$	1 gm.
NaCl	2 gm.
$MgSO_4$	0.1 gm.
Glucose	2 gm.
Agar	25 gm.
Distilled water	1,000 ml.

Adjust to pH 7.6 and sterilize in the autoclave at 121° C for 20 min. Add 10 ml. of sterile egg yolk suspension to each 90 ml. of sterile, cooled (50° C) medium. Pour 15 ml. per plate and dry plates overnight in the incubator before using.

    g. Egg yolk suspension:

Scrub and sterilize shells by immersing fresh eggs in concentrated Hg-Cl_2 solution. Aseptically remove yolks from eggs and place in sterile graduated cylinder. Add an equal volume of sterile saline, mix well. Add 10 ml. of egg yolk suspension to each 90 ml. of sterile, cooled (50° C) medium.

  2. Procedure:

    a. Aseptically place duplicate 25-gm. amounts of food into each of 2 tubes containing 25 ml. of Fluid Thioglycollate broth. Do not fully tighten screw-caps.

    b. Incubate the inoculated broth tubes in the 46° C water bath for 4 to 6 hr. The level of water in the bath should extend above the level of fluid in the tube by at least 1 in.

NOTE: Extended incubation (12 to 24 hr.) at 46° C usually results in a reduction of numbers of *C. perfringens* and overgrowth by concomitant flora capable of growing at 46° C.

    c. Following incubation, examine tubes for growth. Rapid growth of
C. perfringens occurs at 46° C and is accompanied by profuse gas production. Using a loop, remove a portion of turbid broth and streak to
the dry surface of McClung-Toabe Egg Yolk plates to obtain well-isolated colonies.

    d. Incubate inoculated egg yolk plates anaerobically in Case-Anaero jars
at 35° C for 24 hr. See IX, A, 1, b and c and IX, A, 2, c).

    e. Observe plates after incubation for presence of circular, slightly raised
colonies surrounded by a zone of precipitated egg indicative of lecithi-
nase production.

    f. Pick representative lecithinase-positive colonies to motility-nitrate
medium and proceed to confirm as *C. perfringens* as described in IX, A,
2, f through p.

X. CLOSTRIDIUM BOTULINUM

A. Detection of Toxin in Food:

  1. Methods, materials, and reagents:

    a. Standard toxin diluent (Phosphate buffer, 0.1 M, pH 6.5 with 0.2%
gelatin). Gelatin and buffer solutions must be prepared separately
to prevent flocculation.

      (1) Gelatin solution (0.4%) add 2.0 gm. of gelatin to 500 ml. distilled
water and dissolve by heating.

      (2) Buffer solution—mix 200 ml. of 0.2 M Na_2HPO_4 solution with 300
ml. of 0.2 M KH_2PO_4 solution. Determine pH of the buffer mixture
and adjust to pH 6.5, if necessary, by dropwise addition of dilute
HCl or NaOH solutions.

      (3) Sterilize solutions (1) and (2) separately at 121° C for 15 min. As
needed, mix aseptically equal volumes of the gelatin and buffer
solutions to obtain the standard toxin diluent.

    b. Mortar and pestle—small size, one for each food specimen examined.

    c. Sterile sand (approximately 20 gm. for each food specimen examined).

    d. Crushed ice.

    e. Mice (approximately 20 gm. weight).

    f. Sterile physiological saline solution (0.85% NaCl)—100 ml.

    g. Antitoxin for *C. botulinum* toxins A, B, and E.

    h. Refrigerator.

    i. Pipettes, 1.0- and 10-ml. capacities.

    j. Refrigerated centrifuge.

  2. Procedures:

    a. Extraction of toxin from food:

      (1) Suspected sample is aseptically macerated with sterile, chilled
sand and as small a quantity of toxin diluent as is practicable in a
sterile mortar immersed in ice-water mixture. If possible, the volume of extracting fluid should be no greater than the volume of
sample. Overnight storage in the cold of the macerated sample
diluent mixture is recommended for optimum extraction of toxin.
This is not practical, however, where speed of diagnosis is important.

      (2) The macerated sample —diluent mixture is centrifuged thoroughly
in the cold (refrigerated centrifuge or centrifuge installed in a cold

room) and the clear supernatant is drawn off aseptically. The extract is then diluted 1:10 (1 part extract to 9 parts toxin diluent) for injection and held in the cold until used.

(3) If type E toxin is suspected, much of the toxic material may be present in the form of "protoxin" and the extract must be treated with proteolytic enzyme in order to manifest toxicity. To accomplish activation, a 1.0% soln. of crude trypsin (Difco 1:250 or equivalent) is added to the extract to give a final trypsin concentration of 0.1%. The mixture is then incubated for 60–75 min. at 37° C. before assays are made. Activation of both the undiluted centrifugal food extract and a 1:10 extract in gelatin-phosphate buffer have been used with success.

b. Mouse protection test:

(1) Three to four hours before injection of toxic extract, mice of about 20 gm. weight are divided into groups of at least 2 mice each. There should be 1 group for each toxin type, plus 2 control groups. Each experimental group is "protected" by injection intraperitoneally with no more than 0.2 ml. of undiluted known antitoxin to *C. botulinum* toxin of types A, B, and E. The two control groups receive the same volume of sterile physiological saline solution in place of antitoxin.

NOTE: Most human cases of botulism are caused by ingestion of Types A, B, or E toxins. Botulism in animals is usually caused by Types C and D. Consequently, when investigating a human case of botulism, it is advisable to test for at least Types A, B, and E toxins. If antisera to Types C and D are available, these may be included.

(2) About 3 or 4 hr. later, the protected groups and one control group are "challenged" by intraperitoneal injection with 0.5 ml. of the 1:10 dilution of food extract supernate. The second control group is challenged with 0.5 ml. of the same supernatant dilution which has been heated at 100° C for 10 min. to destroy the toxin. These serve to indicate the presence of heat stable non-botulinal poisons. If speed is essential, antitoxin and the supernatant dilution can be mixed and injected together.

(3) Animals are observed for 96 hr. following injection. Symptoms of paralysis, respiratory difficulty, and finally death indicate botulinus toxicity. Symptoms may appear in hours. Severe symptoms in mice without subsequent death may indicate a low level of toxin.

(4) Presence of botulinal toxin is determined by deaths in the unprotected group which received unheated toxic supernatant and by survival of the unprotected mice which received heated toxin. The type of toxin is indicated by survival of one of the protected groups. For example, if the group of mice injected with Type A antitoxin survives and the two groups injected with Type B and Type E antitoxins die, then the type toxin produced in the original food was Type A.

B. Isolation and Cultivation From Food:

1. Methods, materials, culture media:

a. Pipettes, 1-ml. capacity.

b. Culture dishes (100 x 15 mm.) glass.

(1) Glazed porcelain covers for Petri dishes—obtainable from Fisher Scientific Company, Pittsburgh, Pennsylvania.

(2) Brewer aluminum Petri dish covers with absorbent discs—obtainable from Fisher Scientific Company, Pittsburgh, Pennsylvania.

c. Water bath, 60° C.

d. Water bath, 80° C.

e. Inoculating loop, nichrome or platinum-iridium wire B & S gauge No. 26.

f. Case-Anaero jar (See IX, A, 1, b and c above).

g. Cooked meat enrichment medium:

(1) Add 1.25 gm. of commercially available, dehydrated cooked meat medium to each of a series of 150 x 15 mm. screw-capped tubes.

(2) Prepare a solution containing 0.2% soluble starch and 0.5% glucose in distilled water.

(3) Add 10 ml. of the solution to each tube of medium and allow to stand until meat particles are thoroughly wetted.

(4) Sterilize in the autoclave at 121° C for 30 min.

h. Blood agar (Trypticase Soy agar base). Dispense into flasks and sterilize at 121° C for 15 min. Cool to about 45° C and add 5% sterile defibrinated blood. Pour into plates.

i. Reinforced *Clostridium* medium (RCM, Oxoid). This medium is an excellent medium for cultivation of clostridia and can be obtained in the prepared form from Consolidated Laboratories, Inc., Chicago Heights, Ill.

2. Procedure:

a. Heat nine tubes of cooked meat enrichment medium in boiling water to drive off oxygen, and cool rapidly in a water bath.

b. Place 3 tubes of the medium in a 60° C water bath and 3 in an 80° C water bath and allow to equilibrate to bath temperature. Three tubes are left unheated.

c. Inoculate approximately 1 gm. (or 1 ml.) of the suspected sample into each of the 9 tubes below the surface of the cooked meat layer and heat as follows: Those tubes that were preheated to 60° C before inoculation are returned to the 60° C water bath and heated at this temperature for 15 min.; those tubes that were preheated at 80° C before inoculation are returned to 80° C water bath and heated at 80° C for 30 min. After heat-treatment, cool tubes rapidly in running tap water.

d. Incubate inoculated tubes at 30° C until vigorous growth is visible, as evidenced by gas production, turbidity, and in some instances partial hydrolysis of the meat particles.* Cultures should be incubated for at least 10 days before they are considered negative for growth. Toxin is usually detectable within 48 to 96 hr. and as a rule is in the highest concentration after the period of active growth and gas production.

e. Following incubation, inoculate the surface of blood agar and/or RCM agar plates with culture material from the tubes of cooked meat medium. Attempt to obtain well-isolated colonies.**

f. Incubate plates at 30° C in a Case-Anaero jar, under an atmosphere of

---

*NOTE: If pure-culture isolates are desired, streak plates should be made at this time, according to instructions in steps (e), (f), and (g) below. If not, proceed immediately to step (h).

90% N_2 and 10% CO_2. Colonies usually appear within 1 to 3 days, depending upon the strain and medium employed. Though growth may be more rapid at 35° C for most strains, some Type E strains will not multiply at this temperature. For this reason, 30° C is recommended.

g. Pick isolated colonies from plates and inoculate tubes of cooked meat medium. If desired, these isolates may be tested for toxicity as already described.

h. Test cooked meat medium tubes inoculated with food sample for toxicity, as described under Mouse Protection Test (X, A, 2, b) above. If heated cultures (60° C for 15 min. and 80° C for 30 min.) are negative for toxin, test unheated cultures for toxicity. As a rule, if *C. botulinum* spores were present in the food, the heated tubes inoculated with this food will show toxicity as a result of germination and reproduction. If spores were not present, however (highly improbable), the heat treatments would be sufficient to destroy vegetative cells of *C. botulinum* and these tubes would be negative for toxin by the mouse test. For this reason, unheated tubes are also employed. Providing the vegetative cells of *C. botulinum* are not overgrown by concomitant bacteria, the unheated cultures usually develop toxicity.

NOTE: *C. botulinum* displays a tendency to yield a "spreading" type of growth on agar plates. To reduce spreading, the following techniques have been used successfully: (a) Increase the agar concentration of solid media to 6%; (b) thoroughly dry plates before inoculation (not reliable if much condensation develops in anaerobic jars); (c) use of absorbent type Petri dish covers as described in (X, B, 1, b) above.

Index